Biology Mo... Series

Skills in Biology

Third Edition

The Biozone Writing Team

Tracey Greenwood

Lissa Bainbridge-Smith

Kent Pryor

Richard Allan

Published by:
BIOZONE International Ltd
109 Cambridge Road, Hamilton 3216, New Zealand

Printed by REPLIKA PRESS PVT LTD using paper produced from renewable and waste materials

Distribution Offices:
United Kingdom & Europe
Biozone Learning Media (UK) Ltd, UK
Telephone: +44 1283 530 366
Fax: +44 1283 530 961
Email: sales@biozone.co.uk
Website: www.biozone.co.uk

Australia
Biozone Learning Media Australia, Australia
Telephone: +61 7-5535-4896
Fax: +61 7-5508-2432
Email: sales@biozone.com.au
Website: www.biozone.com.au

USA, Canada, and ROW
Biozone International Ltd, New Zealand
Telephone: +64 7-856 8104
Fax: +64 7-856 9243
FREE phone: 1-855-246-4555 (USA-Canada only)
FREE fax: 1-855-935-3555 (USA-Canada only)
Email: sales@biozone.co.nz
Website: www.thebiozone.com

ISBN: 978-1-877462-96-2
Previous Editions 2006, 2007
Third Edition 2011
Third printing

Front cover photographs:
Girl with microscope. Image ©2005 JupiterImages Corporation www.clipart.com
Plant research. © istock photos, www.istockphoto.com

Biology Modular Workbook Series

The BIOZONE *Biology Modular Workbook Series* has been developed to meet the demands of customers with the requirement for a flexible modular resource. Each workbook provides a collection of visually interesting and accessible activities, catering for students with a wide range of abilities and background. The workbooks are divided into a series of chapters, each comprising an introductory section with detailed learning objectives and useful resources, and a series of write-on activities ranging from paper practicals and data handling exercises, to questions requiring short essay style answers. Page tabs identifying "**Related activities**" and "**Weblinks**" help students to find related material within the workbook and locate weblinks that will enhance their understanding of the activity. During the development of this series, we have taken the opportunity to develop new content, while retaining the basic philosophy of a student-friendly resource that bridges the gap between textbook and study guide. Its highly visual presentation engages students, increasing their motivation and empowering them to take control of their learning.

Skills in Biology

This title in the *Biology Modular Workbook Series* provides students with guidelines for planning and executing biological investigations in both the laboratory and the field. The chapters correspond to five areas relating to student skills: the design of experimental work, the analysis of experimental work, practical skills in field work, biological classification, and laboratory techniques. These areas are explained through a series of one, two, or three page activities, each of which explores a specific topic area (e.g. data transformation). *Skills in Biology* is a student-centered resource. Students completing the activities, in concert with their other classroom and practical work, will consolidate existing knowledge and develop and practise the skills that they will use throughout their courses in biology. This workbook may be used in the classroom or at home as a supplement to a standard textbook. Some activities are introductory in nature, while others may be used to consolidate and test concepts already covered by other means (e.g. microscopy). Biozone has a commitment to produce a cost-effective, high quality resource which acts as a student's companion throughout their biology study. Please do not photocopy from this workbook; we cannot afford to provide single copies of workbooks to schools and continue to develop, update, and improve the material they contain.

Acknowledgements and Photo Credits

Royalty free images, purchased by Biozone International Ltd, are used throughout this workbook and have been obtained from the following sources: Corel Corporation from various titles in their Professional Photos CD-ROM collection; IMSI (International Microcomputer Software Inc.) images from IMSI's MasterClips® and MasterPhotosTM Collection, 1895 Francisco Blvd. East, San Rafael, CA 94901-5506, USA; ©1996 Digital Stock, Medicine and Health Care collection; ©Hemera Technologies Inc., 1997-2001; © 2005 JupiterImages Corporation www.clipart.com; ©Click Art, ©T/Maker Company; ©1994., ©Digital Vision; Gazelle Technologies Inc.; PhotoDisc®, Inc. USA, www.photodisc.com.

The authors would also like to thank those who have contributed towards this edition: • Sam Banks for his photograph of wombat scat • Pasco for their use of images of sampling using probeware • Vernier for use of their image of a respiration chamber • Dave Ward, Sirtrack Ltd, for photographs and information on radio-tracking • Campus Photography, University of Waikato for photographs of equipment used for monitoring physical factors • Stephen Moore for his photos of aquatic invertebrates • C. Pilditch for photos of rocky shore animals • K. Pryor for the photo of the rocky shore • Adam Luckenbach • NC State University for the poster presentation.

We also acknowledge the photographers that have made their images available through Wikimedia Commons under Creative Commons Licences 2.0, 2.5. or 3.0: • Yohan euan 04 • US Fish and Wildlife Service • Laitche • CDC: Dr Lucille K. Georg • Mnolf • Graham Bould

Photos kindly provided by individuals or corporations have been identified by way of coded credits as follows: **BOB**: Barry O'Brien (Uni. of Waikato), **BF**: Brian Finerran (University of Canterbury), **BH**: Brendan Hicks (University of Waikato), **CDC**: Centers for Disease Control and Prevention, Atlanta, USA, **COD**: Colin O'Donnell (Dept of Conservation, NZ), **GU**: Graeme Ussher (University of Auckland), **EII**: Education Interactive Imaging, **EW**: Environment Waikato, **FRI**: Forest Research Institute, **GW**: Graham Walker, **HF**: Halema Flannagan, **JDG**: John Green (University of Waikato), **KL-Sirtrack**: Kevin Lay (Sirtrack Ltd), **PASCO**: Pasco Probeware, **PH**: Phil Herrity, **RA**: Richard Allan, **RCN**: Ralph Cocklin, **Sirtrack**: Sirtrack Ltd, **VM**: Villa Maria Wines, **VU**: Victoria University, NZ, **WMU**: Waikato Microscope Unit.

Contents

Asking Questions, Finding Answers

Analysis and Reporting

Field Studies

Classification of Organisms

Laboratory Techniques

CODES: △ **Upgraded** this edition ☆ New this edition **Activity** is marked: ▫ to be done; ✓ when completed

How to Use this Workbook

Skills in Biology is designed to provide biology students with a resource that will help them to acquire the practical and investigative skills necessary for studying biology. The ability to plan investigations, present and analyze data, and accurately report your findings are core skills in most biology curricula.

This workbook is suitable for all students of biology, and will support the five Es (below), reinforcing and extending the ideas introduced and developed by your teacher. It is **not a textbook**; its aim is to complement your standard text. *Skills in Biology* provides the following useful resources in each chapter:

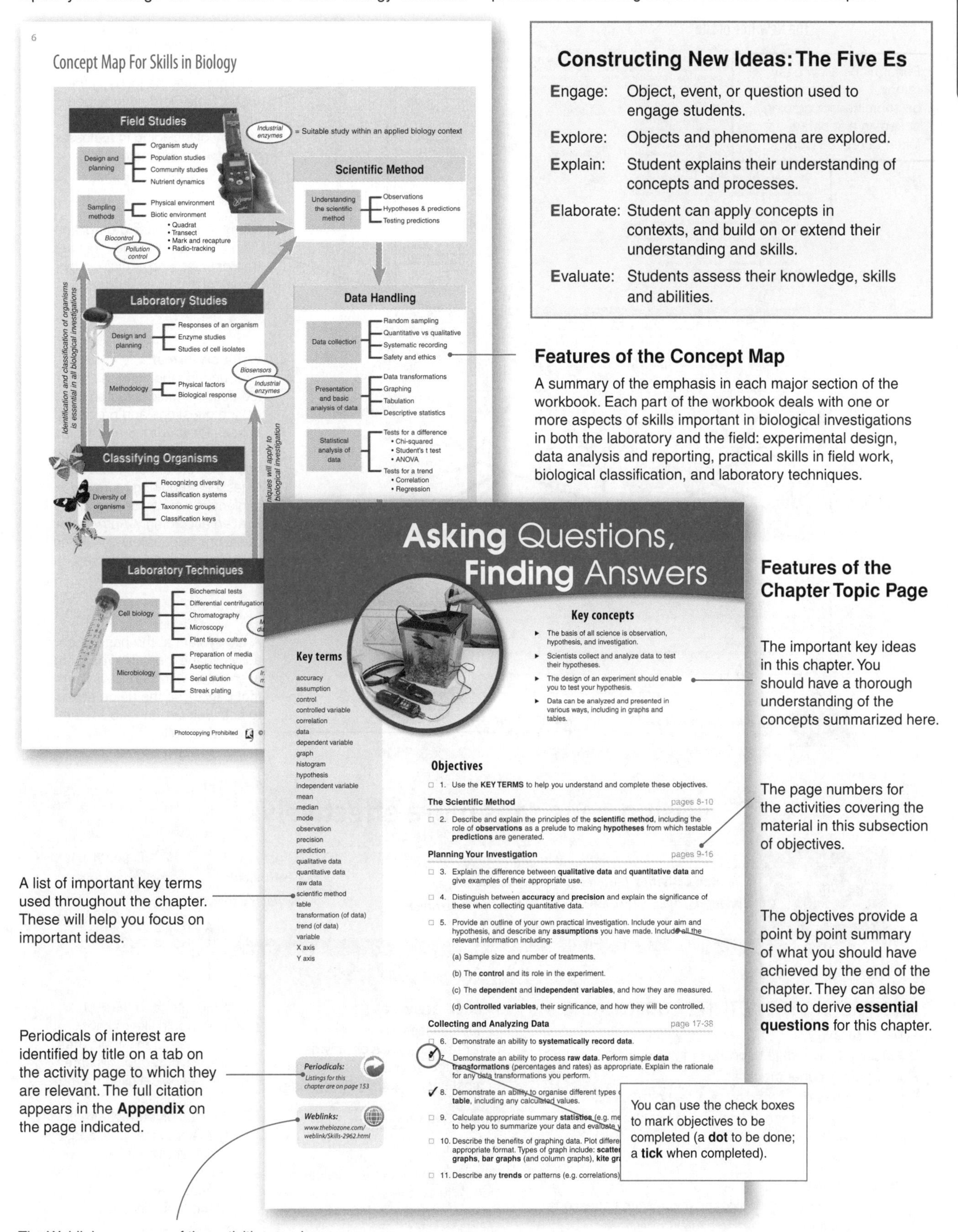

Constructing New Ideas: The Five Es

Engage: Object, event, or question used to engage students.

Explore: Objects and phenomena are explored.

Explain: Student explains their understanding of concepts and processes.

Elaborate: Student can apply concepts in contexts, and build on or extend their understanding and skills.

Evaluate: Students assess their knowledge, skills and abilities.

Features of the Concept Map

A summary of the emphasis in each major section of the workbook. Each part of the workbook deals with one or more aspects of skills important in biological investigations in both the laboratory and the field: experimental design, data analysis and reporting, practical skills in field work, biological classification, and laboratory techniques.

Features of the Chapter Topic Page

The important key ideas in this chapter. You should have a thorough understanding of the concepts summarized here.

The page numbers for the activities covering the material in this subsection of objectives.

The objectives provide a point by point summary of what you should have achieved by the end of the chapter. They can also be used to derive **essential questions** for this chapter.

You can use the check boxes to mark objectives to be completed (a **dot** to be done; a **tick** when completed).

A list of important key terms used throughout the chapter. These will help you focus on important ideas.

Periodicals of interest are identified by title on a tab on the activity page to which they are relevant. The full citation appears in the **Appendix** on the page indicated.

The Weblinks on many of the activities can be accessed through the web links page at: *www.thebiozone.com/weblink/Skills-2962.html*
See page 3 for more details.

Using the Activities

The activities make up most of the content of this book. Your teacher may use the activity pages to introduce a topic for the first time, or you may use them to revise ideas already covered by other means. They are excellent for use in the classroom, as homework exercises and topic revision, and for self-directed study and personal reference.

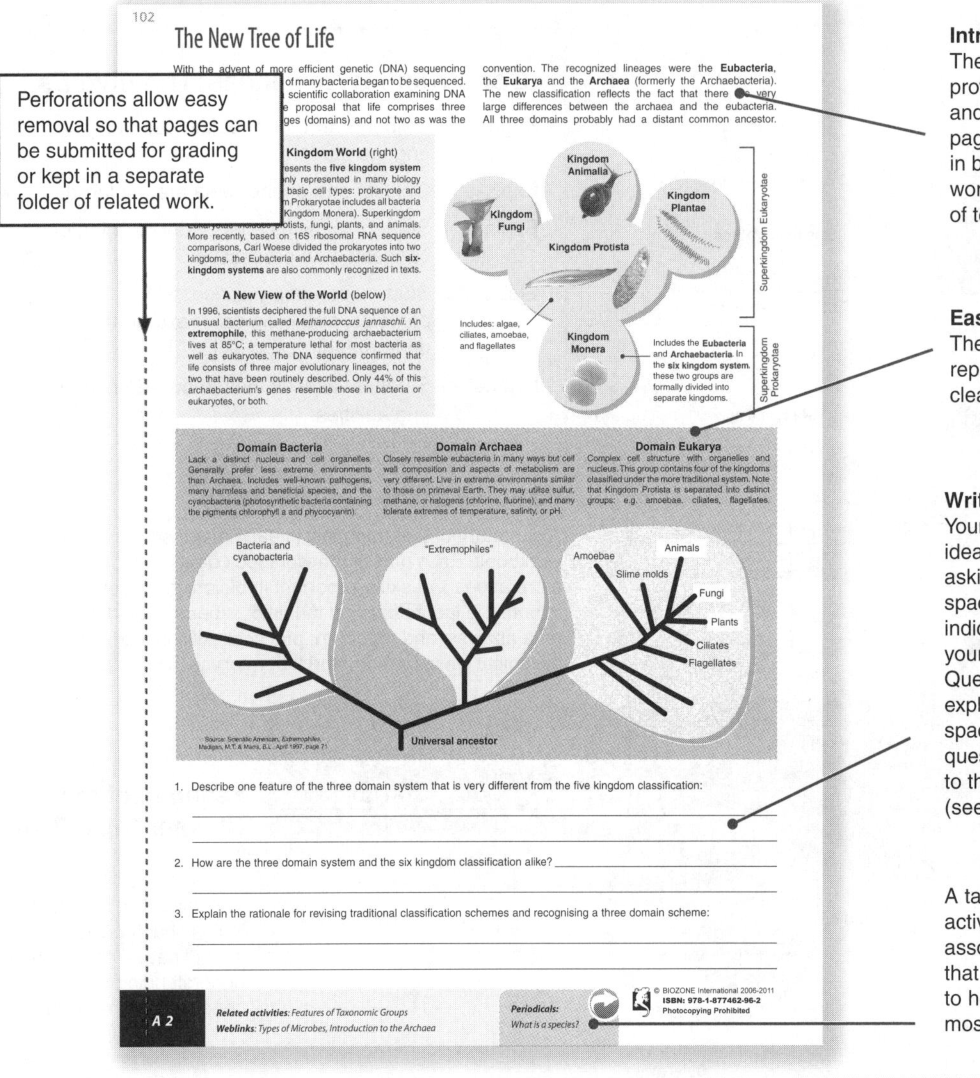

102

The New Tree of Life

With the advent of more efficient genetic (DNA) sequencing ... of many bacteria began to be sequenced. ... scientific collaboration examining DNA ... e proposal that life comprises three ... ges (domains) and not two as was the convention. The recognized lineages were the **Eubacteria**, the **Eukarya** and the **Archaea** (formerly the Archaebacteria). The new classification reflects the fact that there ... very large differences between the archaea and the eubacteria. All three domains probably had a distant common ancestor.

... Kingdom World (right)

... esents the **five kingdom system** ... nly represented in many biology ... basic cell types: prokaryote and ... m Prokaryotae includes all bacteria ... Kingdom Monera). Superkingdom ... otists, fungi, plants, and animals. More recently, based on 16S ribosomal RNA sequence comparisons, Carl Woese divided the prokaryotes into two kingdoms, the Eubacteria and Archaebacteria. Such **six-kingdom systems** are also commonly recognized in texts.

A New View of the World (below)

In 1996, scientists deciphered the full DNA sequence of an unusual bacterium called *Methanococcus jannaschii*. An **extremophile**, this methane-producing archaebacterium lives at 85°C; a temperature lethal for most bacteria as well as eukaryotes. The DNA sequence confirmed that life consists of three major evolutionary lineages, not the two that have been routinely described. Only 44% of this archaebacterium's genes resemble those in bacteria or eukaryotes, or both.

Domain Bacteria
Lack a distinct nucleus and cell organelles. Generally prefer less extreme environments than Archaea. Includes well-known pathogens, many harmless and beneficial species, and the cyanobacteria (photosynthetic bacteria containing the pigments chlorophyll a and phycocyanin).

Domain Archaea
Closely resemble eubacteria in many ways but cell wall composition and aspects of metabolism are very different. Live in extreme environments similar to those on primeval Earth. They may utilise sulfur, methane, or halogens (chlorine, fluorine), and many tolerate extremes of temperature, salinity, or pH.

Domain Eukarya
Complex cell structure with organelles and nucleus. This group contains four of the kingdoms classified under the more traditional system. Note that Kingdom Protista is separated into distinct groups: e.g. amoebae, ciliates, flagellates.

1. Describe one feature of the three domain system that is very different from the five kingdom classification:

2. How are the three domain system and the six kingdom classification alike? ____________

3. Explain the rationale for revising traditional classification schemes and recognising a three domain scheme:

A 2 | ***Related activities:*** *Features of Taxonomic Groups* ***Weblinks:*** *Types of Microbes, Introduction to the Archaea* | ***Periodicals:*** *What is a species?*

ISBN: 978-1-877462-96-2

Perforations allow easy removal so that pages can be submitted for grading or kept in a separate folder of related work.

Introductory paragraph: The introductory paragraph provides essential background and provides the focus of the page. Note words that appear in bold, as they are 'key words' worthy of including in a glossary of terms for the topic.

Easy to understand diagrams: The main ideas of the topic are represented and explained by clear, informative diagrams.

Write-on format: Your understanding of the main ideas of the topic is tested by asking questions and providing spaces for your answers. Where indicated by the space available, your answers should be concise. Questions requiring more explanation or discussion are spaced accordingly. Answer the questions adequately according to the questioning term used (see the introduction).

A tab system at the base of each activity page identifies resources associated with the activity on that page. Use the guide below to help you use the tab system most effectively.

Using page tabs more effectively

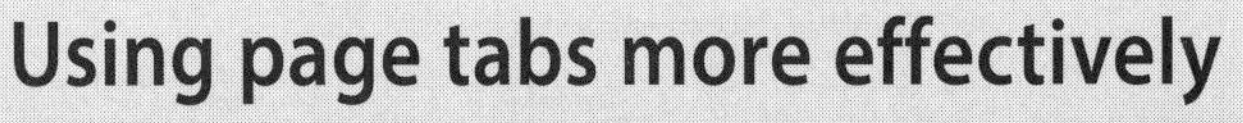

INTERPRETING THE ACTIVITY CODING SYSTEM

Type of Activity

D = includes some data handling or interpretation
P = includes a paper practical
R = *may* require extra reading (e.g. text or other activity)
A = includes application of knowledge to solve a problem
E = extension material

Level of Activity

1 = generally simpler, including mostly describe questions
2 = more challenging, including explain questions
3 = challenging content and/or questions, including discuss

Related activities

Other activities in the workbook cover related topics or may help answer the questions on the page. In most cases, extra information for activities that are coded R can be found on the pages indicated here.

Weblinks

This citation indicates a valuable video clip or animation that can be accessed from the Weblinks page specifically for this workbook. *www.thebiozone.com/weblink/Skills-2962.html*

Students (and teachers) who would like to know more about this topic area are encouraged to locate the periodical cited on the Periodicals tab. Articles of interest directly relevant to the topic content are cited. The full citation appears in the Appendix as indicated at the beginning of the topic chapter.

Using BIOZONE's Website

Access the **BIOLINKS** database of web sites directly from the homepage of our new website. Biolinks is organized into easy-to-use sub-sections relating to general areas of interest. It's a great way to quickly find out more on topics of interest.

Contact us with questions, feedback, ideas, and critical commentary. We welcome your input.

Use Google to search for websites of interest. The more precise your search words are, the better the list of results. Be specific, e.g. "Proteins in plasma membranes", rather than "Proteins".

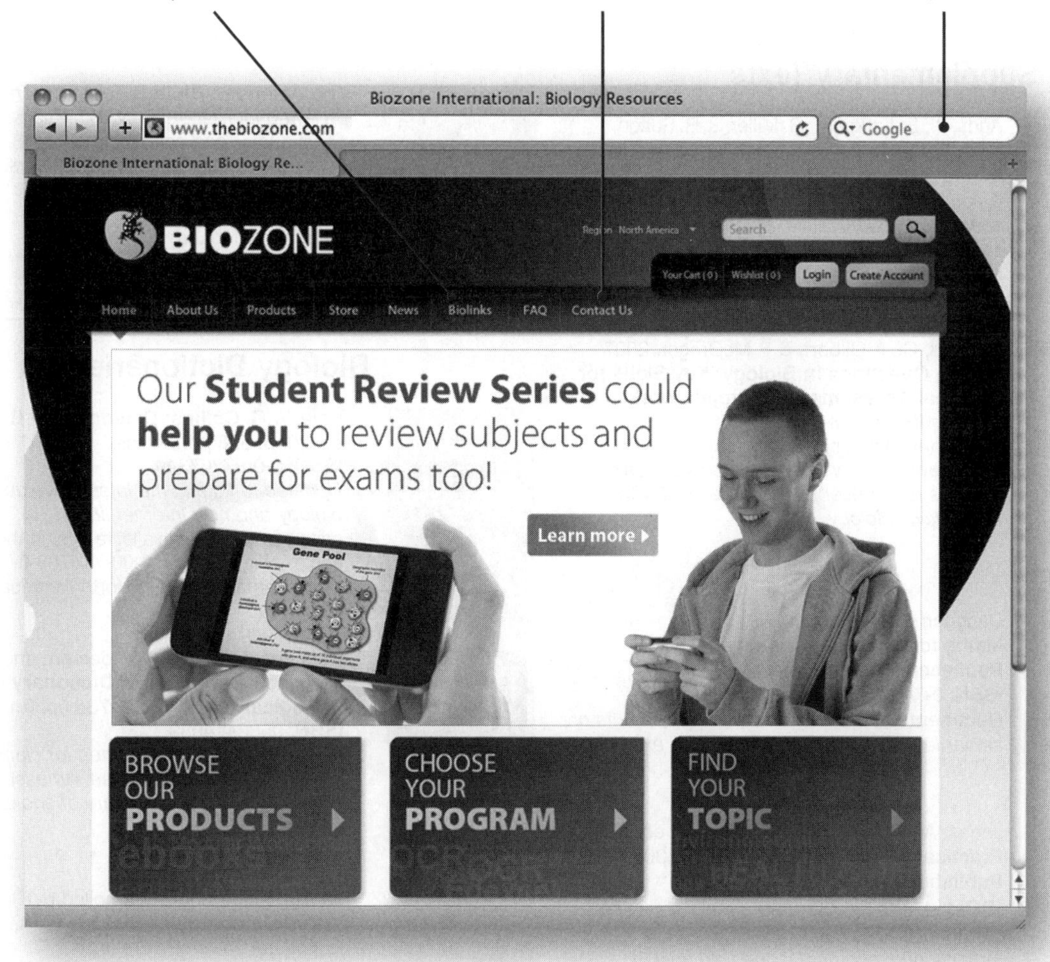

Weblinks: www.thebiozone.com/weblink/Skills-2962.html

BOOKMARK WEBLINKS BY TYPING IN THE ADDRESS: IT IS NOT ACCESSIBLE DIRECTLY FROM BIOZONE'S WEBSITE

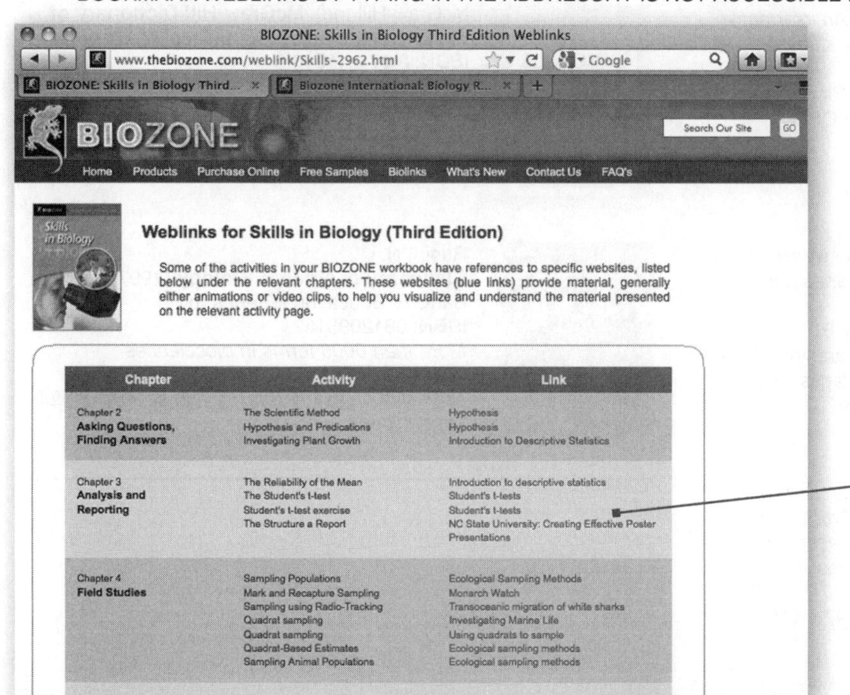

Throughout this workbook, some pages make reference to websites that have particular relevance to the activity by providing an explanatory animation or video clip. They are easy to use and a very useful supplement to the activity.

Web Link: Provides a link to an **external web site** with supporting information specifically for the activity. These are usually video clips or animations that explain a process or help students to visualize it.

Resources Information

A set text is a starting point for information, but there are many other resources available. A list of some of the resources available to support this topic is provided below. Access to the publishers of these resources can be made directly from BIOZONE's web site. Please note that listing any product in this workbook does not, in any way, denote BIOZONE's endorsement of that product and BIOZONE does not have any business affiliation with the publishers listed herein.

Supplementary Texts

Adds, J., E. Larkcom, R. Miller, & R. Sutton, 1999. **Tools, Techniques and Assessment in Biology**, 160 pp. **ISBN**: 0-17-448273-6
A course guide covering basic lab protocols, microscopy, quantitative lab and field techniques, advanced DNA techniques and tissue culture, data handling, and exam prep.

Barnard, C., F. Gilbert, & P. McGregor, 2007
Asking Questions in Biology: Key Skills for Practical Assessments & Project Work
256 pp. **ISBN**: 978-0132224352
Publisher: Benjamin Cummings
Comments: *Covers many aspects of design, analysis and presentation of practical work in senior level biology.*

Cadogan, A. and Ingram, M., 2002
Maths for Advanced Biology
Publisher: NelsonThornes
ISBN: 0-7487-6506-9
Comments: *Covers the maths requirements of senior level biology. Includes worked examples.*

Jones, A., R. Reed, & J. Weyers, 4th ed. 2007
Practical Skills in Biology, approx. 300 pp.
Publisher: Pearson
ISBN: 978-0-131775-09-3
Comments: *Provides information on all aspects of experimental and field design, implementation, and data analysis. A new edition is available in January 2012*

Periodicals, Magazines, and Journals

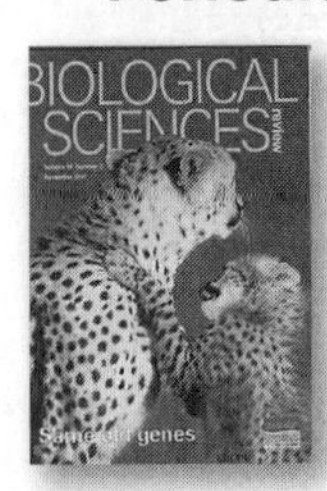

Biological Sciences Review: *An informative quarterly publication for biology students.* Enquiries:
Philip Allan Publishers, Market Place, Deddington, Oxfordshire OX 15 OSE
Tel: 01869 338652
Fax: 01869 338803
E-mail: sales@philipallan.co.uk

New Scientist: *Widely available weekly magazine with research summaries and features.* Enquiries:
Reed Business Information Ltd, 51 Wardour St. London WIV 4BN **Tel**: (UK and intl):+44 (0) 1444 475636 **E-mail**: ns.subs@qss-uk.com *or subscribe from their web site.*

Scientific American: *A monthly magazine containing specialist features. Articles range in level of reading difficulty and assumed knowledge.* Subscription enquiries: 415 Madison Ave. New York. NY10017-1111 **Tel**: (outside North America): 515-247-7631 **Tel**: (US& Canada): 800-333-1199

The American Biology Teacher: *The peer-reviewed journal of the NABT. Published nine times a year and containing information and activities relevant to biology teachers.* Contact: NABT, 12030 Sunrise Valley Drive, #110, Reston, VA 20191-3409
Web: www.nabt.org

Biology Dictionaries

Hale, W.G. **Collins: Dictionary of Biology** 4 ed. 2005, 528 pp. Collins.
ISBN: 0-00-720734-4.
Updated to take in the latest developments in biology and now internet-linked. (§ This latest edition is currently available only in the UK. The earlier edition, ISBN: 0-00-714709-0, is available though amazon.com in North America).

Henderson, I.F, W.D. Henderson, and E. Lawrence. **Henderson's Dictionary of Biological Terms**, 1999, 736 pp. Prentice Hall.
ISBN: 0582414989
An updated edition, rewritten for clarity, and reorganized for ease of use. An essential reference and the dictionary of choice for many.

Market House Books (compiled by).
Oxford Dictionary of Biology 5 ed., 2004, 698 pp. Oxford University Press.
ISBN: 0198609175. *Revised and updated, with many new entries. This edition contains biographical entries on key scientists and comprehensive coverage of terms in biology, biophysics, and biochemistry.*

McGraw-Hill (ed). **McGraw-Hill Dictionary of Bioscience**, 2 ed., 2002, 662 pp. McGraw-Hill.
ISBN: 0-07-141043-0
22 000 entries encompassing more than 20 areas of the life sciences. It includes synonyms, acronyms, abbreviations, and pronunciations for all terms. Accessible, yet comprehensive.

Rudin, N.
Dictionary of Modern Biology (1997), 504 pp. Barron's Educational Series Inc
ISBN: 0812095162.
More than 6000 terms in biosciences defined for college level students. Includes extensive cross referencing and several useful appendices.

Command Words

Questions come in a variety of forms. Whether you are studying for an exam or writing an essay, it is important to understand exactly what the question is asking. A question has two parts to it: one part of the question will provide you with information, the second part of the question will provide you with instructions as to how to answer the question. Following these instructions is most important. Often students in examinations know the material but fail to follow instructions and do not answer the question appropriately. Examiners often use certain key words to introduce questions. Look out for them and be clear as to what they mean. Below is a description of terms commonly used when asking questions in biology.

Commonly used Terms in Biology

The following terms are frequently used when asking questions in examinations and assessments. Students should have a clear understanding of each of the following terms and use this understanding to answer questions appropriately.

Account for: Provide a satisfactory explanation or reason for an observation.

Analyze: Interpret data to reach stated conclusions.

Annotate: Add **brief** notes to a diagram, drawing or graph.

Apply: Use an idea, equation, principle, theory, or law in a new situation.

Appreciate: To understand the meaning or relevance of a particular situation.

Calculate: Find an answer using mathematical methods. Show the working unless instructed not to.

Compare: Give an account of similarities and differences between two or more items, referring to both (or all) of them throughout. Comparisons can be given using a table. Comparisons generally ask for similarities more than differences (see contrast).

Construct: Represent or develop in graphical form.

Contrast: Show differences. Set in opposition.

Deduce: Reach a conclusion from information given.

Define: Give the precise meaning of a word or phrase as concisely as possible.

Derive: Manipulate a mathematical equation to give a new equation or result.

Describe: Give an account, including all the relevant information.

Design: Produce a plan, object, simulation or model.

Determine: Find the only possible answer.

Discuss: Give an account including, where possible, a range of arguments, assessments of the relative importance of various factors, or comparison of alternative hypotheses.

Distinguish: Give the difference(s) between two or more different items.

Draw: Represent by means of pencil lines. Add labels unless told not to do so.

Estimate: Find an approximate value for an unknown quantity, based on the information provided and application of scientific knowledge.

Evaluate: Assess the implications and limitations.

Explain: Give a clear account including causes, reasons, or mechanisms.

Identify: Find an answer from a number of possibilities.

Illustrate: Give concrete examples. Explain clearly by using comparisons or examples.

Interpret: Comment upon, give examples, describe relationships. Describe, then evaluate.

List: Give a sequence of names or other brief answers with no elaboration. Each one should be clearly distinguishable from the others.

Measure: Find a value for a quantity.

Outline: Give a brief account or summary. Include essential information only.

Predict: Give an expected result.

Solve: Obtain an answer using algebraic and/or numerical methods.

State: Give a specific name, value, or other answer. No supporting argument or calculation is necessary.

Suggest: Propose a hypothesis or other possible explanation.

Summarize: Give a brief, condensed account. Include conclusions and avoid unnecessary details.

In Conclusion

Students should familiarize themselves with this list of terms and, where necessary throughout the course, they should refer back to them when answering questions. The list of terms mentioned above is not exhaustive and students should compare this list with past examination papers and essays etc. and add any new terms (and their meaning) to the list above. The aim is to become familiar with interpreting the question and answering it appropriately.

Concept Map For Skills in Biology

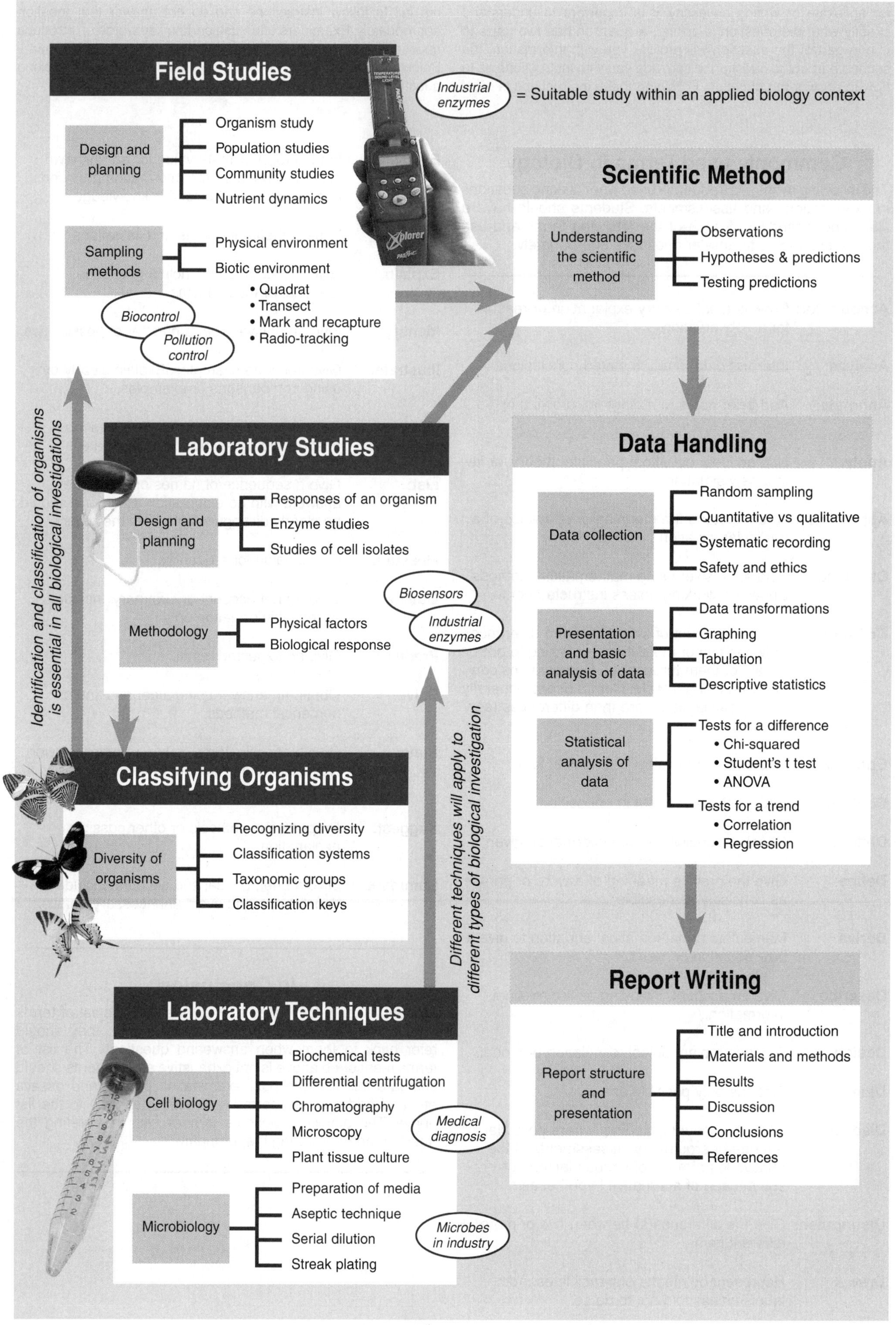

Asking Questions, Finding Answers

Key terms

accuracy
assumption
control
controlled variable
correlation
data
dependent variable
graph
histogram
hypothesis
independent variable
mean
median
mode
observation
precision
prediction
qualitative data
quantitative data
raw data
scientific method
table
transformation (of data)
trend (of data)
variable
X axis
Y axis

Periodicals:

Listings for this chapter are on page 153

Weblinks:

www.thebiozone.com/weblink/Skills-2962.html

Key concepts

- The basis of all science is observation, hypothesis, and investigation.
- Scientists collect and analyze data to test their hypotheses.
- The design of an experiment should enable you to test your hypothesis.
- Data can be analyzed and presented in various ways, including in graphs and tables.

Objectives

☐ 1. Use the **KEY TERMS** to help you understand and complete these objectives.

The Scientific Method — pages 8-10

☐ 2. Describe and explain the principles of **scientific methodology**, including the role of **observations** as a prelude to making **hypotheses** from which testable **predictions** are generated. Recognize that doing science is not a matter of following a linear set of rules but that collaboration and chance findings are important. What is important is that science is open-minded and rigorous.

Planning Your Investigation — pages 9-16

☐ 3. Explain the difference between **qualitative data** and **quantitative data** and give examples of their appropriate use.

☐ 4. Distinguish between **accuracy** and **precision** and explain the significance of these when collecting quantitative data.

☐ 5. Provide an outline of your own practical investigation. Include your aim and hypothesis, and describe any **assumptions** you have made. Include all the relevant information including:

(a) Sample size and number of treatments.

(b) The **control** and its role in the experiment.

(c) The **dependent** and **independent variables**, and how they are measured.

(d) **Controlled variables**, their significance, and how they will be controlled.

Collecting and Analyzing Data — page 17-38

☐ 6. Demonstrate an ability to **systematically record data**.

☐ 7. Demonstrate an ability to process **raw data**. Perform simple **data transformations** (percentages and rates) as appropriate. Explain the rationale for any data transformations you perform.

☐ 8. Demonstrate an ability to organise different types of data appropriately in a **table**, including any calculated values.

☐ 9. Calculate appropriate summary **statistics** (e.g. mean and standard deviation) to help you to summarize your data and evaluate your results.

☐ 10. Describe the benefits of graphing data. Plot different types of data in an appropriate format. Types of graph include: **scatter plots**, **line graphs**, **pie graphs**, **bar graphs** (and column graphs), **kite graphs**, and **histograms**.

☐ 11. Describe any **trends** or patterns (e.g. correlations) in your data.

The Scientific Method

Scientific knowledge grows through a process called the **scientific method**. This process involves observation and measurement, hypothesising and predicting, and planning and executing investigations designed to test formulated **hypotheses**. A scientific hypothesis is a tentative explanation for an observation, which is capable of being tested by experimentation. Hypotheses lead to **predictions** about the system involved and they are accepted or rejected on the basis of the investigation's findings. Acceptance of the hypothesis is not necessarily permanent: explanations may be rejected later in light of new findings.

One possible model of the scientific method is shown here but there are many others. In reality, the observation, testing, and use of data is fluid and may not proceed in a strict linear direction as the pool of data, techniques, and ideas develops and increases over time.

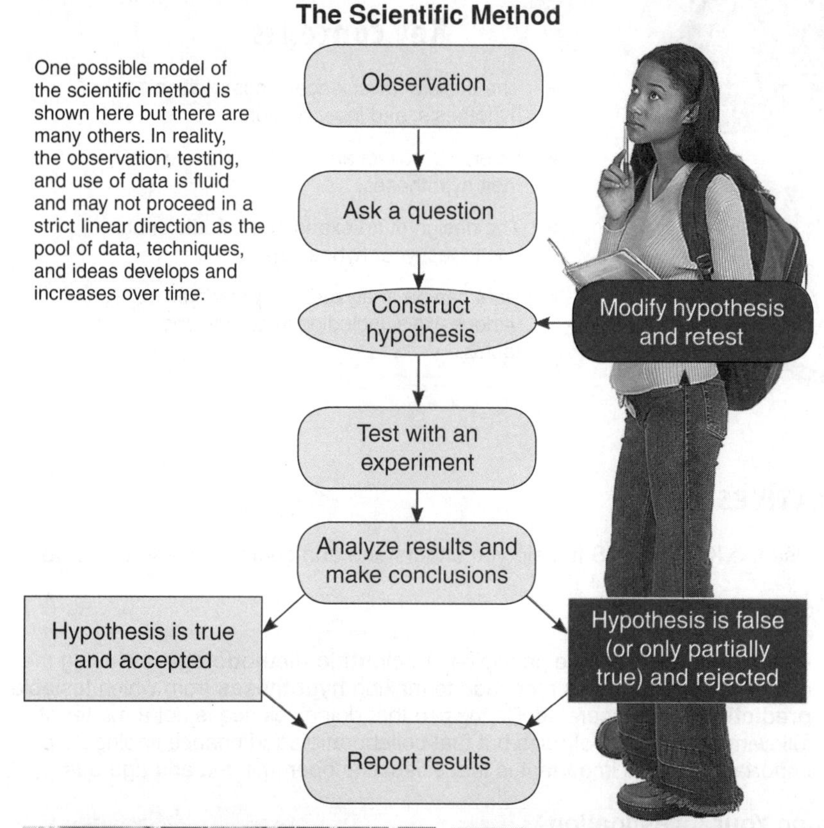

Forming a Hypothesis

Features of a sound hypothesis:

- It is based on observations and prior knowledge of the system.
- It offers an explanation for an observation.
- It refers to only one independent variable.
- It is written as a definite statement and not as a question.
- It is testable by experimentation.
- It leads to predictions about the system.

Testing a Hypothesis

Features of a sound method:

- It tests the validity of the hypothesis.
- It is repeatable.
- It includes a control which does not receive treatment.
- All variables are controlled where possible.
- The method includes a dependent and independent variable.
- Only the independent variable is changed (manipulated) between treatment groups.

Hypothesis involving manipulation

Used when the effect of manipulating a variable on a biological entity is being investigated. **Example:** The composition of applied fertiliser influences the rate of growth of plant A.

Hypothesis of choice

Used when investigating species preference, e.g. for a particular habitat type or microclimate. **Example:** Woodpeckers (species A) show a preference for tree type when nesting.

Hypothesis involving observation

Used when organisms are being studied in their natural environment and conditions cannot be changed. **Example:** Fern abundance is influenced by the degree to which the canopy is established.

1. Why might an accepted hypothesis be rejected at a later date? ______________________

____

2. Explain why a method must be repeatable: ______________________

____

____

3. In which situation(s) is it difficult, if not impossible, to control all the variables? ______________________

____

***Related activities:** Planning A Quantitative Investigation*
***Weblinks:** Hypothesis*

Periodicals:
The truth is out there

ISBN: 978-1-877462-96-2

Hypotheses and Predictions

A hypothesis offers a tentative explanation to questions generated by observations and leads to one or more **predictions** about the way a biological system will behave. Experiments are constructed to test these predictions. For every hypothesis, there is a corresponding **null hypothesis**; a hypothesis of no difference or no effect. Creating a null hypothesis enables a hypothesis to be tested in a meaningful way using statistical tests. If the results of an experiment are statistically significant, the null hypothesis can be rejected. If a hypothesis is accepted, anyone should be able to test the predictions with the same methods and get a similar result each time. Scientific hypotheses may be modified as more information becomes available.

Observations, Hypotheses, and Predictions

Observation is the basis for formulating hypotheses and making predictions. An observation may generate a number of plausible hypotheses, and each hypothesis will lead to one or more predictions, which can be tested by further investigation.

Observation 1: Some caterpillar species are brightly colored and appear to be conspicuous to predators such as insectivorous birds. Predators appear to avoid these species. These caterpillars are often found in groups, rather than as solitary animals.

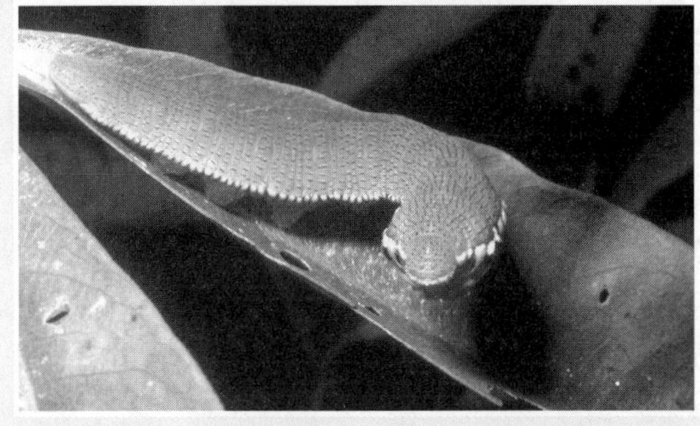

Observation 2: Some caterpillar species are cryptic in their appearance or behavior. Their camouflage is so convincing that, when alerted to danger, they are difficult to see against their background. Such caterpillars are usually found alone.

Assumptions

Any biological investigation requires you to make **assumptions** about the biological system you are working with. Assumptions are features of the system (and your investigation) that you assume to be true but do not (or cannot) test. Possible assumptions about the biological system described above include:

- Insectivorous birds have color vision.
- Caterpillars that look bright or cryptic to us, also appear that way to insectivorous birds.
- Insectivorous birds can learn about the palatability of prey by tasting them.

1. Study the example above illustrating the features of cryptic and conspicuous caterpillars, then answer the following:

   (a) Generate a hypothesis to explain the observation that some caterpillars are brightly colored and conspicuous while others are cryptic and blend into their surroundings:

   Hypothesis: ______________________________

   ____

   ____

   (b) State the null form of this hypothesis: ______________________________

   ____

   (c) Describe one of the **assumptions** being made in your hypothesis: ______________________________

   ____

   ____

   (d) Based on your hypothesis, generate a **prediction** about the behavior of insectivorous birds towards caterpillars:

   ____

   ____

ISBN: 978-1-877462-96-2

Related activities: *The Scientific Method, Designing Your Experiment*
Weblinks: *Hypothesis*

2. During the course of any investigation, new information may arise as a result of observations unrelated to the original hypothesis. This can lead to the generation of further hypotheses about the system. For each of the incidental observations described below, formulate a prediction, and an outline of an investigation to test it. *The observation described in each case was not related to the hypothesis the experiment was designed to test:*

(a) **Bacterial cultures**

Prediction:

Outline of the investigation:

Observation: During an experiment on bacterial growth, these girls noticed that the cultures grew at different rates when the dishes were left overnight in different parts of the laboratory.

(b) **Plant cloning**

Prediction:

Outline of the investigation:

Observation: During an experiment on plant cloning, a scientist noticed that the root length of plant clones varied depending on the concentration of a hormone added to the agar.

ISBN: 978-1-877462-96-2

A Guide to Research Projects

The following guide will assist you in preparing and executing your own research project. The main points associated with each stage in your project are outlined. Some of these are expanded in detail later in this topic. The right hand column provides a checklist. At the completion of each stage you may wish to consult with your teacher to check your progress.

Choosing a Topic

Your project should be interesting to you and within your capabilities to investigate. Consider:

- Resources (e.g. equipment) available to you.
- The time allocated to complete the project.
- Ethical considerations if animals are involved.

Background Research

You will need some background knowledge of your topic. Research your topic via:

- Textbooks and encyclopedias.
- Journals, periodicals, and magazines.
- Consultation with experts in the field.

Design and Organization

Your study design should enable you to test your hypothesis. Consider:

- How you will collect the data (survey, experiment, observation).
- Design constraints such as sample size, size of the sampling unit, controls, validity of data collected, precision, and accuracy.

Data Collection

This is a major part of your project and should be carefully planned. Where possible, collect quantitative data. Consider:

- The type of data collected, methods used to collect it, and when and how you will record it.
- Whether the data that you are collecting are applicable to the question(s) you are asking.
- The measuring device(s) you will use (suitability, ease of use, precision), the units you will use to express your data, and errors involved in your data collection.

Data Analysis

Decide how you will present results in the report.

- Tables to summarize raw data and show any transformations.
- Graphs to illustrate trends and highlight important features in the data.
- Statistical tests are analyses that may allow you to accept or reject your hypothesis.

Writing Your Report

Plan to have five principal sections in your report: introduction, methods, results, discussion, and references. Additional sections (abstract, conclusions, and appendices) are useful.

- Spend time making sense of your findings.
- Write clearly on the topic.
- Prepare a draft. Revise and proof read it.

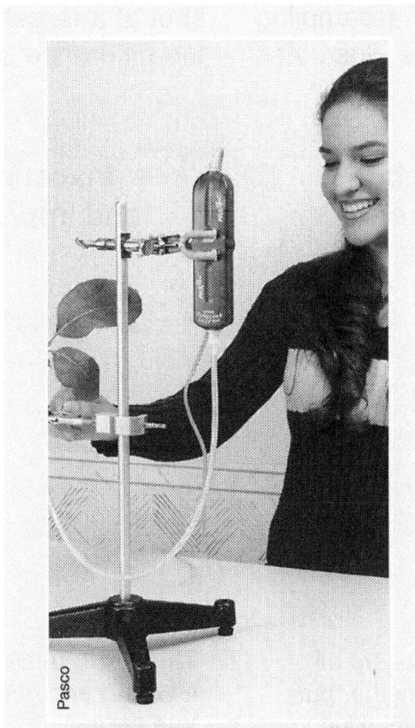

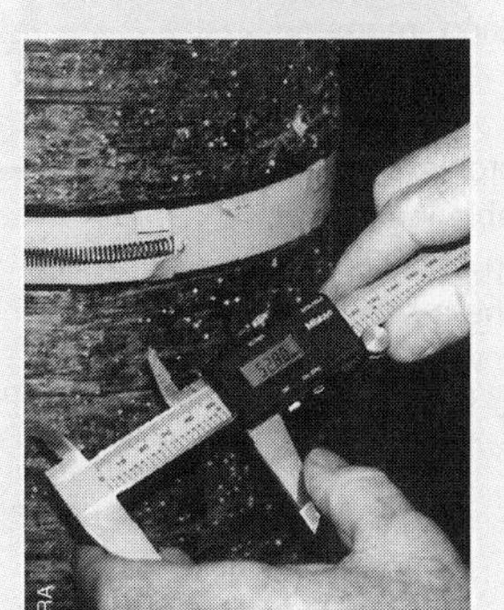

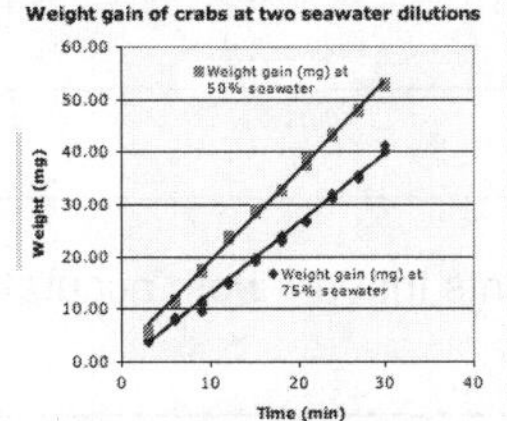

Fig. 1: Graph of weight gain of crabs in two diutions of seawater. n = 5 for both dilutions.

Project Plan Checklist

- ☐ Project is feasible given available resources.
- ☐ There is adequate time to complete the study (it is not too ambitious).
- ☐ Project ethics and animal welfare issues have been addressed.

Teacher's checkpoint: ....

- ☐ Topic has been researched in enough depth to satisfy the requirements of the project.
- ☐ An equipment list has been compiled and the availability of the necessary equipment has been assessed.

Teacher's checkpoint: ....

- ☐ The hypothesis has been clearly stated
- ☐ The best approach for the study (survey, experimental) has been identified.
- ☐ If there is a need for a pilot study, this has been identified.
- ☐ Design features (e.g. sample sizes and controls) meet the needs of the study.
- ☐ The study is robust enough not to fail completely if one stage goes wrong.

Teacher's checkpoint: ....

Project Execution Checklist

- ☐ The methods of data collection and the type of data collected are appropriate to the study and the questions being asked.
- ☐ The methods used for collecting and recording the data (including units of measurement) are consistent throughout.
- ☐ For safe keeping, there are copies of data and preliminary analyses (if present).

Teacher's checkpoint: ....

- ☐ Raw data has been summarized and any transformations necessary have been done.
- ☐ The way in which the data are presented is appropriate for the data involved and the information being conveyed.
- ☐ Any statistical tests are appropriate to the data and the hypothesis being tested.

Teacher's checkpoint: ....

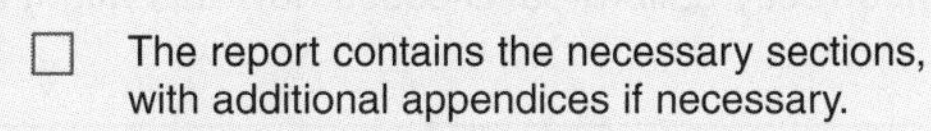

- ☐ The report contains the necessary sections, with additional appendices if necessary.
- ☐ Each section contains material appropriate to that section.
- ☐ The citations and reference list are correctly and consistently formatted.
- ☐ The draft has been proof read.

Teacher's checkpoint: ....

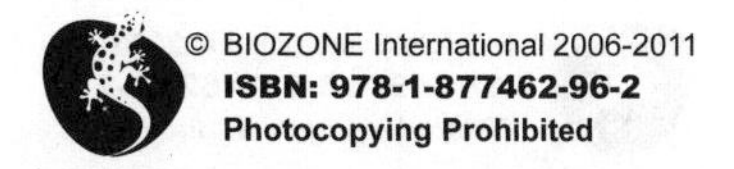

ISBN: 978-1-877462-96-2

Related activities: *Choosing Your Topic, Designing Your Experiment, Taking the Next Step*

Accuracy and Precision

The terms accuracy and precision are often confused, or used interchangeably, but their meanings are different. In any study, **accuracy** refers to how close a measured or derived value is to its true value. Simply put, it is the correctness of the measurement. It can sometimes be a feature of the sampling equipment or its calibration. **Precision** refers to the closeness of repeated measurements to each other, i.e. the ability to be exact. A balance with a fault in it could give very precise (i.e. repeatable) but inaccurate (untrue) results. Using the analogy of a target, repeated measurements are compared to arrows being shot at a target. This analogy can be useful when thinking about the difference between accuracy and precision.

Accurate but imprecise

The measurements are all close to the true value but quite spread apart.

Analogy: The arrows are all close to the bullseye.

Precise but inaccurate

The measurements are all clustered close together but not close to the true value.

Analogy: The arrows are all clustered close together but not near the bullseye.

Inaccurate and imprecise

The measurements are all far apart and not close to the true value.

Analogy: The arrows are spread around the target.

Accurate and precise

The measurements are all close to the true value and also clustered close together.

Analogy: The arrows are clustered close together near the bullseye.

The accuracy of a measurement refers to how close the measured (or derived) value is to the true value. The precision of a measurement relates to its repeatability. In most laboratory work, we usually have no reason to suspect a piece of equipment is giving inaccurate measurements (is biased), so making precise measures is usually the most important consideration. We can test the precision of our measurements by taking repeated measurements from individual samples.

Population studies present us with an additional problem. When a researcher makes measurements of some variable in a study (e.g. fish length), they are usually trying to obtain an estimate of the true value for a parameter of interest (e.g. the mean size, therefore age, of fish). Populations are variable, so we can more accurately estimate a population parameter if we take a large number of random samples from the population.

pHScan 2

RA

A digital device such as this pH meter (above left) will deliver precise measurements, but its accuracy will depend on correct calibration. The precision of measurements taken with instruments such as callipers (above) will depend on the skill of the operator.

1. Distinguish between accuracy and precision: ______

2. Describe why it is important to take measurements that are both accurate and precise: ______

3. A researcher is trying to determine at what temperature enzyme A becomes denatured. Their temperature probe is incorrectly calibrated. Discuss how this might affect the accuracy and precision of the data collected: ______

Related activities: *Terms and Notation*

ISBN: 978-1-877462-96-2

Variables and Data

When planning any kind of biological investigation, it is important to consider the type of data that will be collected. It is best, whenever possible, to collect quantitative or numerical data, as these data lend themselves well to analysis and statistical testing. Recording data in a systematic way as you collect it, e.g. using a table or spreadsheet, is important, especially if data manipulation and transformation are required. It is also useful to calculate summary, descriptive statistics (e.g. mean, median) as you proceed. These will help you to recognise important trends and features in your data as they become apparent.

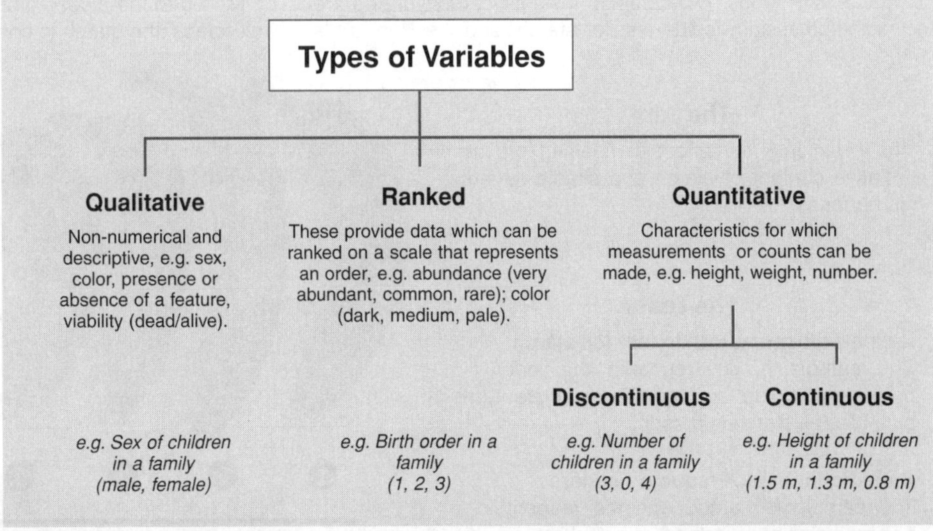

The values for monitored or measured variables, collected during the course of the investigation, are called data. Like their corresponding variables, data may be quantitative, qualitative, or ranked.

A: Leaf shape

B: Number per litter

C: Fish length

1. For each of the photographic examples (A – C above), classify the variables as quantitative, ranked, or qualitative:

   (a) Leaf shape: ______

   (b) Number per litter: ______

   (c) Fish length: ______

2. Why it is desirable to collect quantitative data where possible in biological studies? ______

3. How you might measure the color of light (red, blue, green) quantitatively? ______

4. (a) Give an example of data that could not be collected in a quantitative manner, explaining your answer:

   (b) Sometimes, ranked data are given numerical values, e.g. rare = 1, occasional = 2, frequent = 3, common = 4, abundant = 5. Suggest why these data are sometimes called **semi-quantitative:**

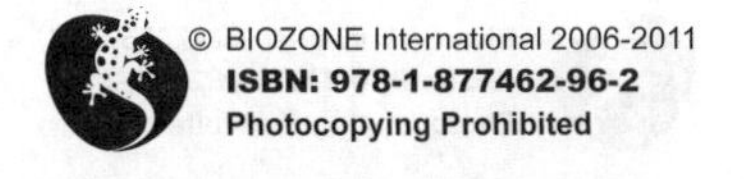

ISBN: 978-1-877462-96-2

Periodicals:
Descriptive Statistics

Related activities: *Descriptive Statistics*

A Qualitative Practical Task

Not all the experimental work you carry out in biology will yield quantitative data. It is preferable to collect quantitative data; it is more easily analyzed and interpreted and it can be collected without bias more easily. However, some situations do warrant the collection of qualitative data, for example, when recording color changes in simple biochemical tests for common components of foods. Two common tests for carbohydrates are the iodine/potassium iodide test for starch, and the Benedict's test for reducing sugars such as glucose (specifically, Benedict's reagent detects the presence of an aldehyde functional group, –CHO). These tests indicate the presence of a substance with a color change. All monosaccharides are reducing sugars as are the disaccharides, lactose and maltose. The monosaccharide fructose is a ketose, but it gives a positive test because it is converted to the aldose glucose in the reagent. When a starchy fruit ripens, the starch is converted to simple reducing sugars.

The Aim

To investigate the effect of ripening on the relative content of starch and simple sugars in bananas.

The Tests

Iodine-potassium iodide test for starch
The sample is covered with the iodine in potassium iodide solution. The sample turns blue-black if starch is present.

Benedict's test for reducing sugars
The sample is heated with the reagent in a boiling water bath. After 2 minutes, the sample is removed and stirred, and the color recorded immediately after stirring. A change from a blue to a brick red color indicates a reducing sugar.

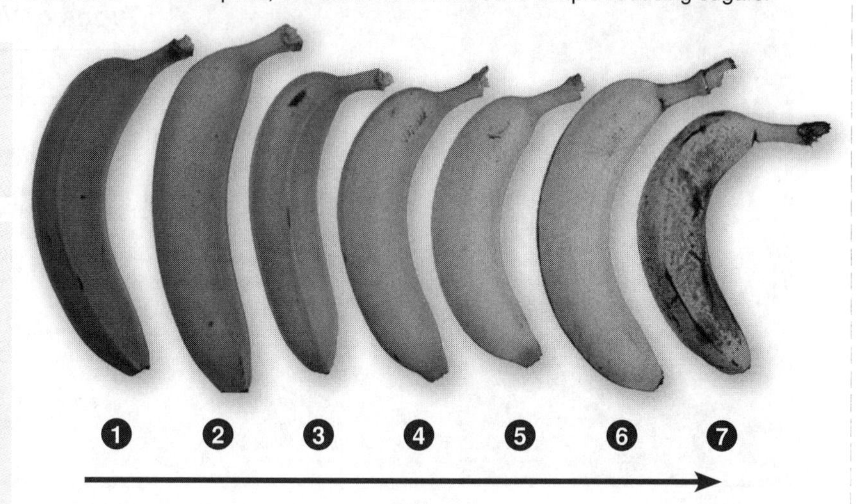

Summary of the Method

Two 1 cm thick slices of banana from each of seven stages of ripeness were cut and crushed to a paste. One slice from each stage was tested using the I/KI test for starch, and the other was tested using the Benedict's test.

The color changes were recorded in a table. Signs (+/–) were used to indicate the intensity of the reaction relative to those in bananas that were either less or more ripe.

Stage of ripeness	Starch-iodine test		Benedict's test	
1	blue-black	+++++	blue clear	–
2	blue-black	++++	blue clear	–
3	blue-black	+++	green	+
4	blue-black	++	yellow cloudy	++
5	slight darkening	+	orange thick	+++
6	no change	–	orangey-red thick	++++
7	no change	–	brick-red thick	+++++

1. Explain why each of the following protocols was important:

   (a) All samples of banana in the Benedict's reagent were heated for 2 minutes: ______

   (b) The contents of the banana sample and Benedict's reagent were stirred after heating: ______

2. Explain what is happening to the relative levels of starch and glucose as bananas ripen: ______

3. Fructose is a ketose sugar (not an aldose with an aldehyde functional group like glucose).

   (a) Explain why fructose also gives a positive result in a Benedict's test: ______

   (b) What could this suggest to you about the results of this banana test? ______

ISBN: 978-1-877462-96-2

Related activities: *Biochemical Tests*

Planning a Quantitative Investigation

The middle stage of any investigation (following the planning) is the practical work when the data are collected. Practical work may be laboratory or field based. Typical laboratory based experiments involve investigating how a biological response is affected by manipulating a particular **variable**, e.g. temperature. The data collected for a quantitative practical task should be recorded systematically, with due attention to safe practical techniques, a suitable quantitative method, and accurate measurements to a an appropriate degree of precision. If your quantitative practical task is executed well, and you have taken care throughout, your evaluation of the experimental results will be much more straightforward and less problematic.

Carrying Out Your Practical Work

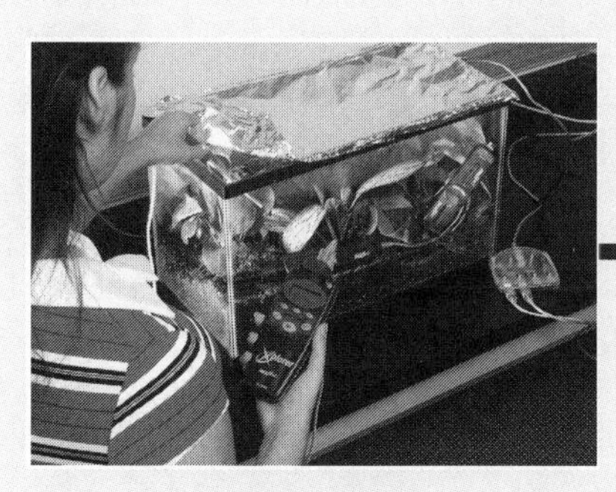

Preparation

Familiarise yourself with the equipment and how to set it up. If necessary, calibrate equipment to give accurate measurements.

Read through the methodology and identify key stages and how long they will take.

Execution

Know how you will take your measurements, how often, and to what degree of precision.

If you are working in a group, assign tasks and make sure everyone knows what they are doing.

Recording

Record your results systematically, in a hand-written table or on a spreadsheet.

Record your results to the appropriate number of significant figures according to the precision of your measurement.

Identifying Variables

A variable is any characteristic or property able to take any one of a range of values. Investigations often look at the effect of changing one variable on another. It is important to identify all variables in an investigation: independent, dependent, and controlled, although there may be nuisance factors of which you are unaware. In all fair tests, only one variable is changed by the investigator.

Dependent variable

- Measured during the investigation.
- Recorded on the y axis of the graph.

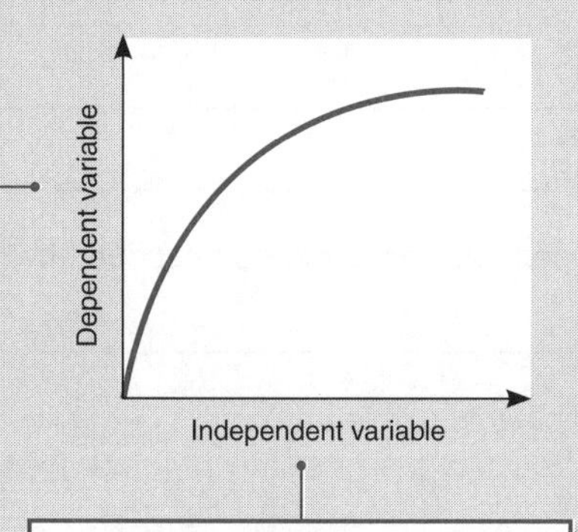

Controlled variables

- Factors that are kept the same or controlled.
- List these in the method, as appropriate to your own investigation.

Independent variable

- Set by the experimenter.
- Recorded on the graph's x axis.

Experimental Controls

A control refers to standard or reference treatment or group in an experiment. It is the same as the experimental (test) group, except that it lacks the one variable being manipulated by the experimenter. Controls are used to demonstrate that the response in the test group is due a specific variable (e.g. temperature). The control undergoes the same preparation, experimental conditions, observations, measurements, and analysis as the test group. This helps to ensure that responses observed in the treatment groups can be reliably interpreted.

The experiment above tests the effect of a certain nutrient on microbial growth. All the agar plates are prepared in the same way, but the control plate does not have the test nutrient applied. Each plate is inoculated from the same stock solution, incubated under the same conditions, and examined at the same set periods. The control plate sets the baseline; any growth above that seen on the control plate is attributed to the presence of the nutrient.

Examples of Investigations

Aim		Variables	
Investigating the effect of varying...	**on the following...**	**Independent variable**	**Dependent variable**
Temperature	Leaf width	Temperature	Leaf width
Light intensity	Activity of woodlice	Light intensity	Woodlice activity
Soil pH	Plant height at age 6 months	pH	Plant height

ISBN: 978-1-877462-96-2

Periodicals: Experiments

Related activities: *A Guide to Research Topics, Variables and Data, Terms and Notation*

In order to write a sound method for your investigation, you need to determine how the independent, dependent, and controlled variables will be set and measured (or monitored). A good understanding of your methodology is crucial to a successful investigation. You need to be clear about how much data, and what type of data, you will collect. You should also have a good idea about how you plan to analyze those data. Use the example below to practise identifying this type of information.

Case Study: Catalase Activity

Catalase is an enzyme that converts hydrogen peroxide (H_2O_2) to oxygen and water. An experiment investigated the effect of temperature on the rate of the catalase reaction. Small (10 cm^3) test tubes were used for the reactions, each containing 0.5 cm^3 of enzyme and 4 cm^3 of hydrogen peroxide. Reaction rates were assessed at four temperatures (10°C, 20°C, 30°C, and 60°C). For each temperature, there were two reaction tubes (e.g. tubes 1 and 2 were both kept at 10°C). The height of oxygen bubbles present after one minute of reaction was used as a measure of the reaction rate; a faster reaction rate produced more bubbles. The entire experiment, involving eight tubes, was repeated on two separate days.

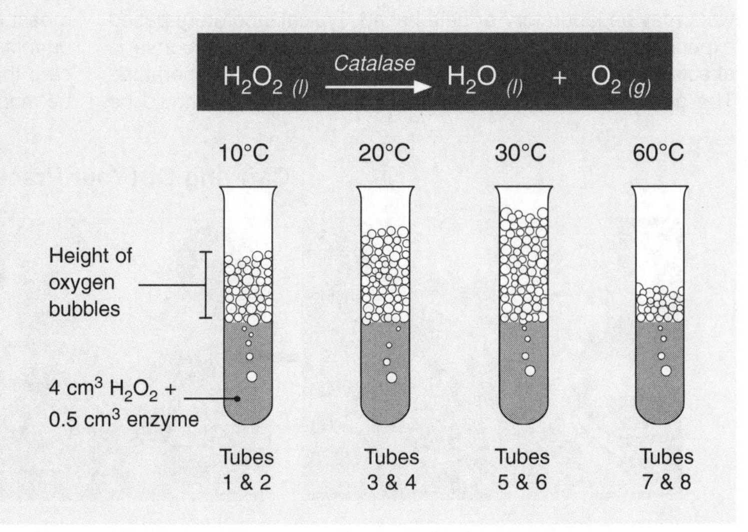

1. Write a suitable aim for this experiment: ______

2. Write a suitable hypothesis for this experiment: ______

3. (a) Identify the **independent variable:** ______

   (b) State the range of values for the independent variable: ______

   (c) Name the unit for the independent variable: ______

   (d) List the equipment needed to set the independent variable, and describe how it was used: ______

4. (a) Identify the **dependent variable**: ______

   (b) Name the unit for the dependent variable: ______

   (c) List the equipment needed to measure the dependent variable, and describe how it was used: ______

5. (a) Each temperature represents a treatment/sample/trial (circle one):

   (b) State the number of tubes at each temperature: ______

   (c) State the sample size for each treatment: ______

   (d) State how many times the whole investigation was repeated: ______

6. Explain why it would have been desirable to have included an extra tube containing no enzyme: ______

7. Identify three variables that might have been controlled in this experiment, and how they could have been monitored:

   (a) ______

   (b) ______

   (c) ______

8. Explain why controlled variables should be monitored carefully: ______

ISBN: 978-1-877462-96-2

Investigating Plant Growth

Recording data from an experiment is an important skill. Using a table is the preferred way to record your results **systematically**, both during the course of your experiment and in presenting your results. A table can also show calculated values, such as rates or means. An example of a table for recording results is shown below. It relates to a student investigation that followed the observation that plants in a paddock fertilized with a nitrogen fertiliser grew more vigorously than plants in a non-fertilized paddock. The table's first column shows the range of the independent variable. There are spaces for multiple samples, and calculated mean values. The students tested which concentration of a soluble nitrogen fertiliser produced optimal growth.

Radishes

The Aim

To investigate the effect of a nitrogen fertilizer on the growth of plants.

Background

Inorganic fertilizers revolutionized crop farming when they were introduced during the late 19th and early 20th century. Crop yields soared and today it is estimated around 50% of crop yield is attributable to the use of fertiliser. Nitrogen is a very important element for plant growth and several types of purely nitrogen fertiliser are manufactured to supply it, e.g. urea.

Experimental Method

This experiment was designed to test the effect of nitrogen fertilizer on plant growth. Radish seeds were planted in separate identical pots (5 cm x 5 cm wide x 10 cm deep) and grown together in normal room conditions. The radishes were watered every day at 10 am and 3 pm with 1.25 L per treatment. Water soluble fertiliser was mixed and added with the first watering on the 1st, 11th and 21st days. The fertilizer concentrations used were: 0.00, 0.06, 0.12, 0.18, 0.24, and 0.30 g L^{-1} with each treatment receiving a different concentration. The plants were grown for 30 days before being removed, washed, and the root (radish) weighed. Results were tabulated below:

To investigate the effect of nitrogen on plant growth, a group of students set up an experiment using different concentrations of nitrogen fertiliser. Radish seeds were planted into a standard soil mixture and divided into six groups each, with five sample plants (30 plants in total).

Tables should have an accurate, descriptive title. Number tables consecutively through the report.

Heading and subheadings identify each set of data and show units of measurement.

Independent variable in the left column.

Table 1: Mass (g) of radish plant roots under six different fertilizer concentrations (data given to 1dp).

Fertilizer concentration (g L^{-1})	Mass of radish root (g)†						
	Sample (*n*)					Total mass	Mean mass
	1	2	3	4	5		
0	80.1	83.2	82.0	79.1	84.1	408.5	81.7
0.06	109.2	110.3	108.2	107.9	110.7		
0.12	117.9	118.9	118.3	119.1	117.2		
0.18	128.3	127.3	127.7	126.8	DNG*		
0.24	23.6	140.3	139.6	137.9	141.1		
0.30	122.3	121.1	122.6	121.3	123.1		

* DNG: Did not germinate

Control values (if present) should be placed at the beginning of the table.

Values should be shown only to the level of significance allowable by your measuring technique.

Organise the columns so that each category of like numbers or attributes is listed vertically.

Each row should show a different experimental treatment, organism, sampling site etc.

† Based on data from M S Jilani, *et al* Journal Agricultural Research

ISBN: 978-1-877462-96-2

Related activities: *Planning a Quantitative Investigation, Descriptive Statistics*
Weblinks: *Introduction to Descriptive Statistics*

1. Identify the independent variable for the experiment and its range: ______

______

2. What is the sample size for each concentration of fertilizer? ______

3. One of the radishes recorded in Table 1 did not grow as expected and produced an extreme value. Record the **outlying value** here and decide whether or not you should include it in future calculations:

______

______

4. Complete the table on the previous page by calculating the **total mass** and **mean mass** of the radish roots:

5. Use the grid below to draw a **line graph** of the experimental results. Use your calculated means and remember to include a title and correctly labelled axes.

6. The students recorded the wet mass of the root (the root still containing water) in their table. What mass should they have actually recorded to get a better representation of the effect of the fertilizer on root mass?

______

______

7. Why would measuring just root mass not be a totally accurate way of measuring the effect of fertilizer on radish growth?

______

______

8. Describe some other measurements the students could have taken to make their experiment more complete:

______

______

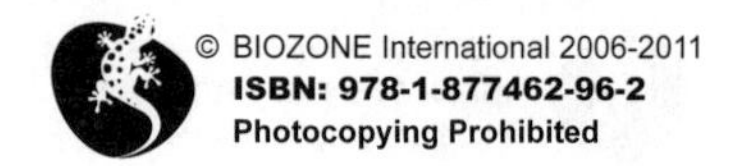

ISBN: 978-1-877462-96-2

Calculating Simple Statistics for a Data Set

Statistic	Definition and use	Method of calculation
Mean	• The average of all data entries. • Measure of central tendency for normally distributed data.	• Add up all the data entries. • Divide by the total number of data entries.
Median	• The middle value when data entries are placed in rank order. • A good measure of central tendency for skewed distributions.	• Arrange the data in increasing rank order. • Identify the middle value. • For an even number of entries, find the mid point of the two middle values.
Mode	• The most common data value. • Suitable for bimodal distributions and qualitative data.	• Identify the category with the highest number of data entries using a tally chart or a bar graph.
Range	• The difference between the smallest and largest data values. • Provides a crude indication of data spread.	• Identify the smallest and largest values and find the difference between them.

Data can be simply summarized using **descriptive statistics**. Descriptive statistics, such as mean, median, and mode, can highlight trends or patterns in the data. The mean can be used to compare different groups. You can use more complex statistics to determine if the means of different groups are significantly different.

When NOT to calculate a mean:

In certain situations, calculation of a simple arithmetic mean is inappropriate.

Remember:

- *DO NOT* calculate a mean from values that are already means (averages) themselves.
- *DO NOT* calculate a mean of ratios (e.g. percentages) for several groups of different sizes; go back to the raw values and recalculate.
- *DO NOT* calculate a mean when the measurement scale is not linear, e.g. pH units are not measured on a linear scale.

The students decided to further their experiment by recording the number of leaves on each radish plant:

Table 2: Number of leaves on radish plant under six different fertilizer concentrations.

Fertilizer concentration (g L^{-1})	Number of leaves: Sample (*n*) 1	2	3	4	5	Mean	Median	Mode
0	9	9	10	8	7			
0.06	15	16	15	16	16			
0.12	16	17	17	17	16			
0.18	18	18	19	18	DNG*			
0.24	6	19	19	18	18			
0.30	18	17	18	19	19			

* DNG: Did not germinate

9. Complete Table 2 by calculating the mean, median and mode for each concentration of fertilizer:

10. Which concentration of fertilizer appeared to produce the best growth results? ______________________

11. Describe some sources of error for the experiment: ______________________

12. Write a brief conclusion for the experiment. Include a reference to the aim and results: ______________________

13. The students decided to replicate the experiment (carry it out again). How might this improve the experiment's results?

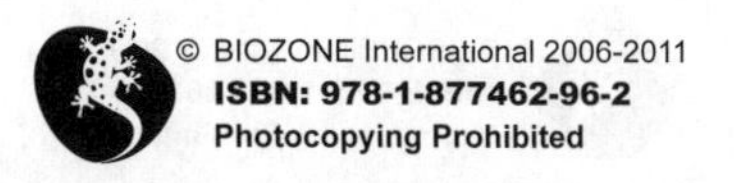

ISBN: 978-1-877462-96-2

Constructing Tables

Tables provide a convenient way to systematically record and condense a large amount of information for later presentation and analysis. The protocol for creating tables for recording data during the course of an investigation is provided elsewhere, but tables can also provide a useful summary in the results section of a finished report. They provide an accurate record of numerical values and allow you to organise your data in a way that allows you to clarify the relationships and trends that are apparent. Columns can be provided to display the results of any data transformations such as rates. Some basic descriptive statistics (such as mean or standard deviation) may also be included prior to the data being plotted. For complex data sets, graphs tend to be used in preference to tables, although the latter may be provided as an appendix.

Presenting Data in Tables

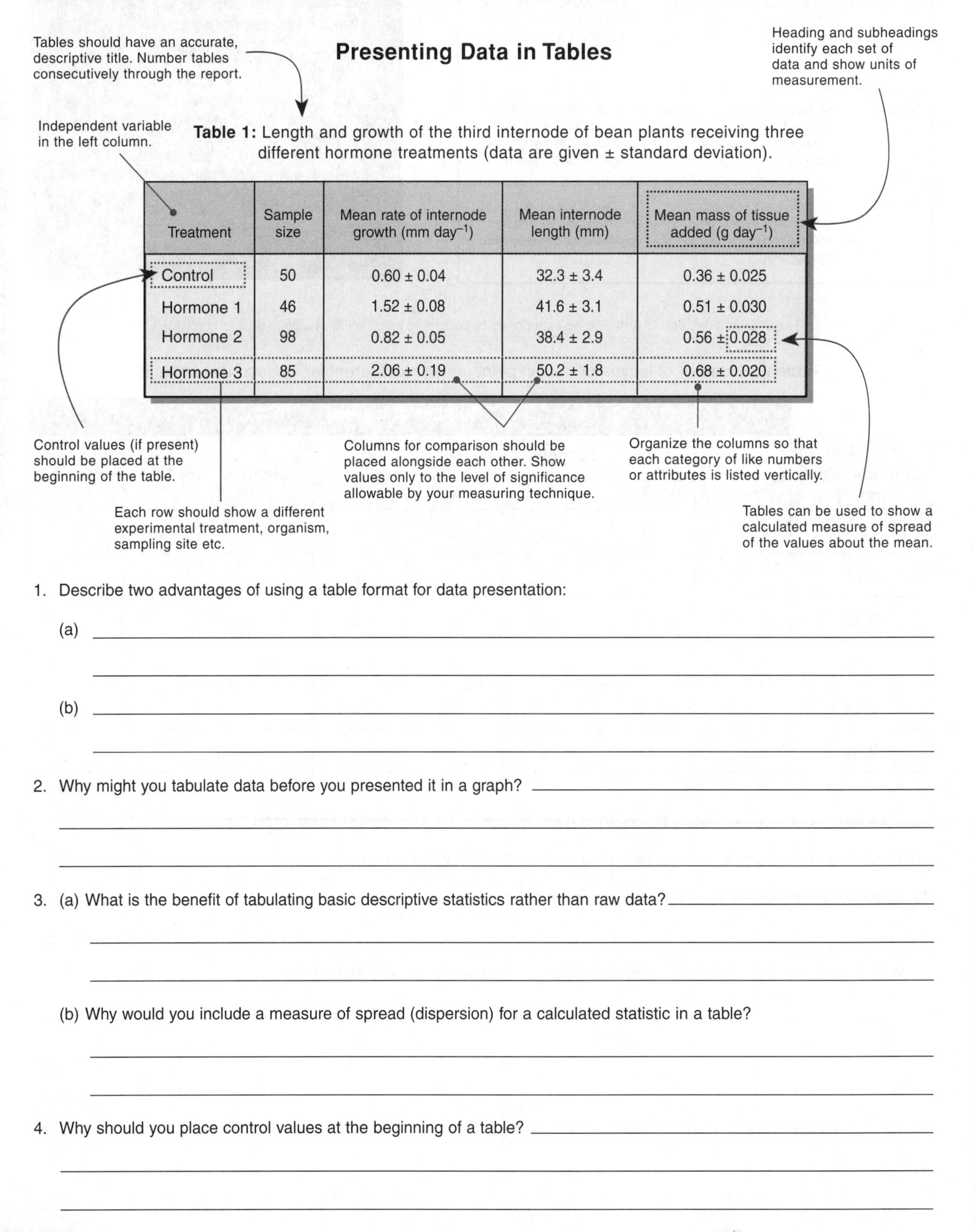

Table 1: Length and growth of the third internode of bean plants receiving three different hormone treatments (data are given ± standard deviation).

Treatment	Sample size	Mean rate of internode growth (mm day^{-1})	Mean internode length (mm)	Mean mass of tissue added (g day^{-1})
Control	50	0.60 ± 0.04	32.3 ± 3.4	0.36 ± 0.025
Hormone 1	46	1.52 ± 0.08	41.6 ± 3.1	0.51 ± 0.030
Hormone 2	98	0.82 ± 0.05	38.4 ± 2.9	0.56 ± 0.028
Hormone 3	85	2.06 ± 0.19	50.2 ± 1.8	0.68 ± 0.020

1. Describe two advantages of using a table format for data presentation:

   (a) ______________________________

   (b) ______________________________

2. Why might you tabulate data before you presented it in a graph? ______________________________

3. (a) What is the benefit of tabulating basic descriptive statistics rather than raw data? ______________________________

   (b) Why would you include a measure of spread (dispersion) for a calculated statistic in a table?

   ____

4. Why should you place control values at the beginning of a table? ______________________________

Related activities: Variables and Data, Descriptive Statistics

Periodicals: Descriptive Statistics

ISBN: 978-1-877462-96-2

Constructing Graphs

Presenting results in a graph format provides a visual image of trends in data in a minimum of space. The choice between graphing or tabulation depends on the type and complexity of the data and the information that you are wanting to convey. Presenting graphs properly requires attention to a few basic details, including correct orientation and labelling of the axes, and accurate plotting of points. Common graphs include scatter plots and line graphs (for continuous data), and bar charts and histograms (for categorical data). Where there is an implied trend, a line of best fit can be drawn through the data points, as indicated in the figure below. Further guidelines for drawing graphs are provided on the following pages.

Presenting Data in Graph Format

Fig. 1: Cumulative water loss in μL from a geranium shoot in still and moving air.

Graphs (called figures) should have a concise, explanatory title. If several graphs appear in your report they should be numbered consecutively.

A key identifies symbols. This information sometimes appears in the title.

Still air
Moving air

Plot points accurately. Different responses can be distinguished using different symbols, lines or bar colors.

Label both axes and provide appropriate units of measurement if necessary.

Volume of water loss (μL)

220
200
180
160
140
120
100
80
60
40
20
0

Two or more sets of results can be plotted on the same figure and distinguished by a key. For time series it is appropriate to join the plotted points with a line.

Place the dependent variable e.g. biological response, on the vertical (Y) axis (if you are drawing a scatter graph it does not matter).

30 60 90 120 150 180

Time (s)

Each axis should have an appropriate scale. Decide on the scale by finding the maximum and minimum values for each variable.

Place the independent variable e.g. treatment, on the horizontal (X) axis

1. Describe an advantage of using a graph format for data presentation:

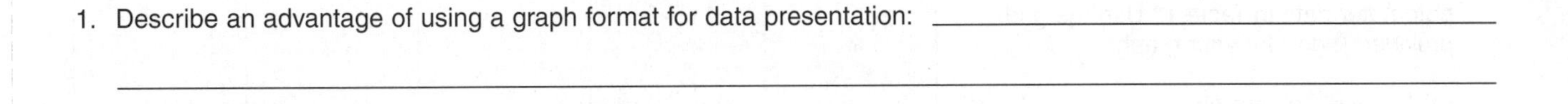

2. (a) Why is it important to use an appropriate scale on a graph?

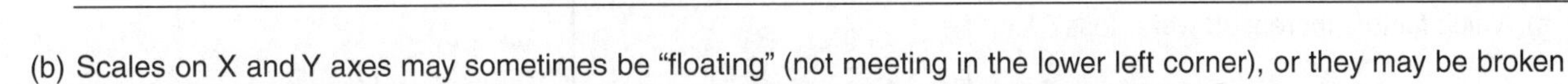

(b) Scales on X and Y axes may sometimes be "floating" (not meeting in the lower left corner), or they may be broken using a double slash and recontinued. When and why would you use these techniques?

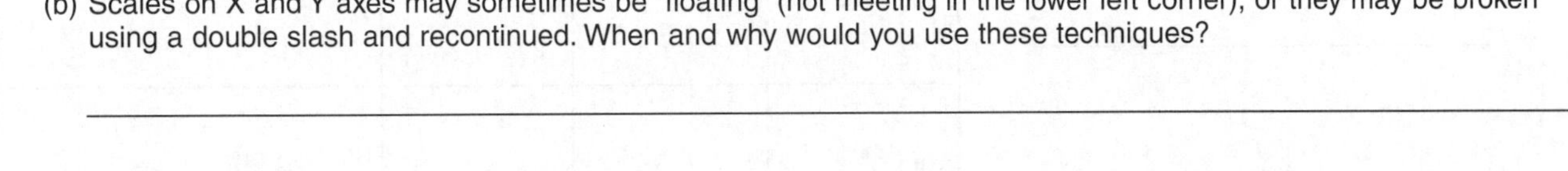

3. (a) What is wrong with the graph plotted to the right:

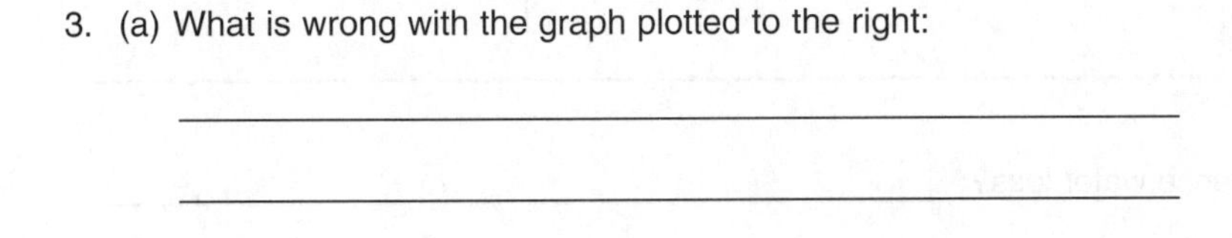

(b) Describe the graph's appearance if it were plotted correctly:

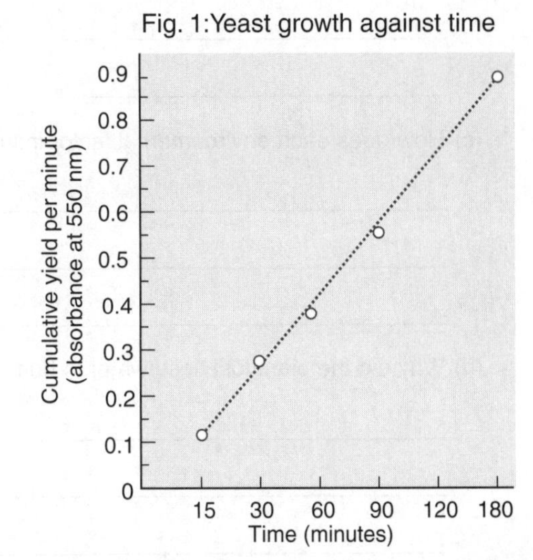

ISBN: 978-1-877462-96-2

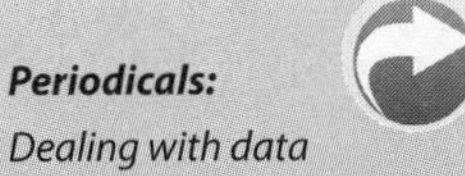

Graphing Time Dependent Data

Once you have completed an experiment it is often helpful to graph the information. Graphs display data in a way that makes it easy to see trends or relationships between different variables. Presenting graphs properly requires attention to a few basic details, including correct orientation and labelling of the axes, and accurate plotting of points. This activity describes a plant transpiration experiment. Use the transpiration data provided below to practice graphing and analyzing data.

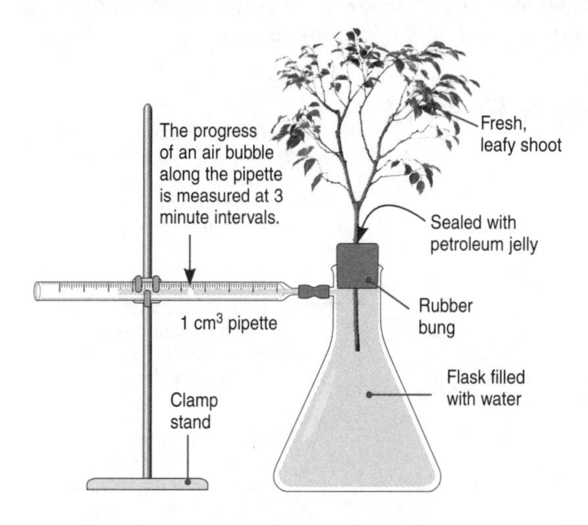

Background

- Plants lose water all the time by evaporation from the leaves and stem. This loss, mostly through stomata, is called **transpiration**.
- Students carried out a transpiration experiment to see how environmental conditions affected transpiration rate.
- The environmental conditions tested were **ambient**, **wind**, **humidity**, and **bright light**.
- A **potometer** (left) was used to measure transpiration.
- The apparatus was equilibrated for 10 minutes, and the position of the air bubble in the pipette was recorded. This is the time 0 reading.
- The plant was then exposed to one of the environmental conditions. Students recorded the location of the air bubble every three minutes over a 30 minute period. Results are given below in Table 1.

Table 1. Potometer readings

Treatment \ Time (min)	0	3	6	9	12	15	18	21	24	27	30
Ambient	0	0.002	0.005	0.008	0.012	0.017	0.022	0.028	0.032	0.036	0.042
Wind	0	0.025	0.054	0.088	0.112	0.142	0.175	0.208	0.246	0.283	0.325
High humidity	0	0.002	0.004	0.006	0.008	0.011	0.014	0.018	0.019	0.021	0.024
Bright light	0	0.021	0.042	0.070	0.091	0.112	0.141	0.158	0.183	0.218	0.239

1. Using an appropriate graph, plot the potometer data in Table 1. Use the grid provided (right) for your graph:

2. (a) Identify the control: ____________

   ____

   (b) Which factors increased water loss?

   ____

   (c) How does each environmental factor influence water loss? ______________________

   (d) Why did the plant lose less water in humid conditions? ______________________

Related activities: Constructing Graphs

ISBN: 978-1-877462-96-2

Evaluating Time Dependent Data

Any practical investigation requires you to critically evaluate your results in the light of your own hypothesis and your biological knowledge. A critical evaluation of any study involves analyzing, presenting, and discussing the results, as well as accounting for any deficiencies in your procedures and erroneous results. This activity describes an experiment comparing different carbohydrates for their effectiveness as substrates for fermentation. Brewer's yeast is a facultative anaerobe that will preferentially use alcoholic fermentation when sugars are in excess. One would expect glucose to be the preferred substrate, as it is the starting molecule in cellular respiration, but yeast are capable of utilizing a variety of sugars, which may be isomers of glucose or disaccharides that can be broken down into their constituent monomers. Completing this activity, which involves a critical evaluation of the second-hand data provided, will help to prepare you for your own evaluative task.

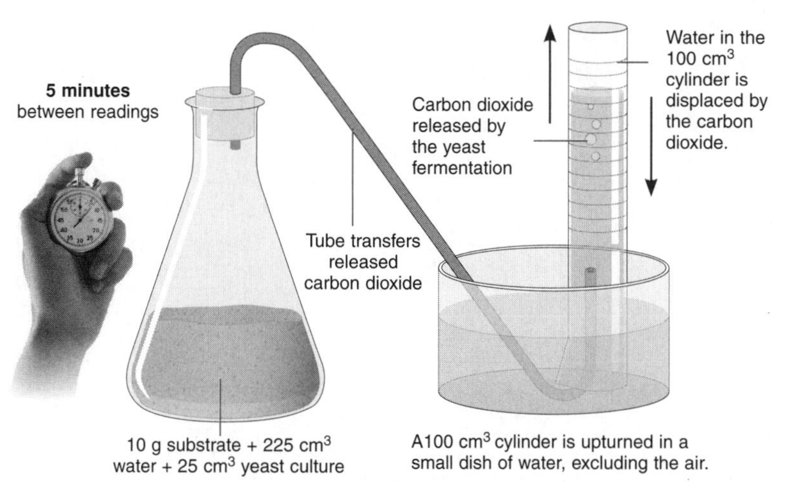

The Apparatus

In this experiment, all substrates tested used the same source culture of 30 g active yeast dissolved in 150 cm^3 of room temperature (24°C) tap water. For each substrate, 25 g of the substrate to be tested was added to 225 cm^3 room temperature (24°C) tap water buffered to pH 4.5. Then 25 cm^3 of source culture was added to the test solution. The control contained yeast solution but no substrate:

Substrate / Time / min	**Group 1**: Volume of carbon dioxide collected (cm^3)				
	None	**Glucose**	**Maltose**	**Sucrose**	**Lactose**
0	0	0	0	0	0
5	0	0	0.8	0	0
10	0	0	0.8	0	0
15	0	0	0.8	0.1	0
20	0	0.5	2.0	0.8	0
25	0	1.2	3.0	1.8	0
30	0	2.8	3.6	3.0	0.5
35	0	4.2	5.4	4.8	0.5
40	0	4.6	5.6	4.8	0.5
45	0	7.4	8.0	7.2	1.0
50	0	10.8	8.9	7.6	1.3
55	0	13.6	9.6	7.7	1.3
60	0	16.1	10.4	9.6	1.3
65	0	22.0	12.1	10.2	1.8
70	0	23.8	14.4	12.0	1.8
75	0	26.7	15.2	12.6	2.0
80	0	32.5	17.3	14.3	2.1
85	0	37.0	18.7	14.9	2.4
90	0	39.9	21.6	17.2	2.6

Substrate / Time / min	**Group 2**: Volume of carbon dioxide collected (cm^3)				
	None	**Glucose**	**Maltose**	**Sucrose**	**Lactose**
90	0	24.4	19.0	17.5	0

The Aim

To investigate the suitability of different mono- and disaccharide sugars as substrates for alcoholic fermentation in yeast.

Background

The rate at which brewer's or baker's yeast (*Saccharomyces cerevisiae*) metabolizes carbohydrate substrates is influenced by factors such as temperature, solution pH, and type of carbohydrate available. The literature describes yeast metabolism as optimal in warm, slightly acid environments. High levels of sugars suppress aerobic respiration in yeast, so yeast will preferentially use the fermentation pathway in the presence of excess substrate.

Substrates: Glucose is a monosaccharide, maltose (glucose-glucose), sucrose (glucose-fructose), and lactose (glucose-galactose) are disaccharides.

1. Write the equation for the fermentation of glucose by yeast:

____

2. Calculate the rate of carbon dioxide production per minute for each substrate in group 1's results:

(a) None: _______________

(b) Glucose: _______________

(c) Maltose: _______________

(d) Sucrose: _______________

(e) Lactose: _______________

3. A second group of students performed the same experiment. Their results are summarized, below left. Calculate the rate of carbon dioxide production per minute for each substrate in group 2's results:

(a) None: _______________

(b) Glucose: _______________

(c) Maltose: _______________

(d) Sucrose: _______________

(e) Lactose: _______________

Experimental design and results adapted from Tom Schuster, Rosalie Van Zyl, & Harold Coller , California State University Northridge 2005

ISBN: 978-1-877462-96-2

4. What assumptions are being made in this experimental design and do you think they were reasonable?

5. Use the tabulated data to plot an appropriate graph of group 1's results on the grid provided:

6. (a) Summarize the results of group 1's fermentation experiment:

(b) Explain the findings based on your understanding of cellular respiration and carbohydrate chemistry:

7. (a) Plot a column chart to compare the results of the two groups in the volume of CO_2 collected after 90 minutes for each substrate (axes have been completed):

(b) Compare the results of the two groups:

Vol. CO_2 produced in 90 minutes (cm^3)

50
45
40
35
30
25
20
15
10
5
0

None Glucose Maltose Sucrose Lactose

Substrate type

(c) Provide a probable explanation for any differences in the results:

(d) Describe one improvement you could make to the experiment in order to generate more reliable data:

ISBN: 978-1-877462-96-2

Evaluating Your Results

Once you have completed the practical part of an experiment, the next task is to evaluate your results in the light of your own hypothesis and your current biological knowledge. A critical evaluation of any study involves analyzing, presenting, and discussing the results, as well as accounting for any deficiencies in your procedures and erroneous results. This activity describes an experiment in which germinating seeds of different ages were tested for their level of catalase activity using hydrogen peroxide solution as the substrate and a simple apparatus to measure oxygen production (see background). Completing this activity, which involves a critical evaluation of the second-hand data provided will help to prepare you for your own evaluative task.

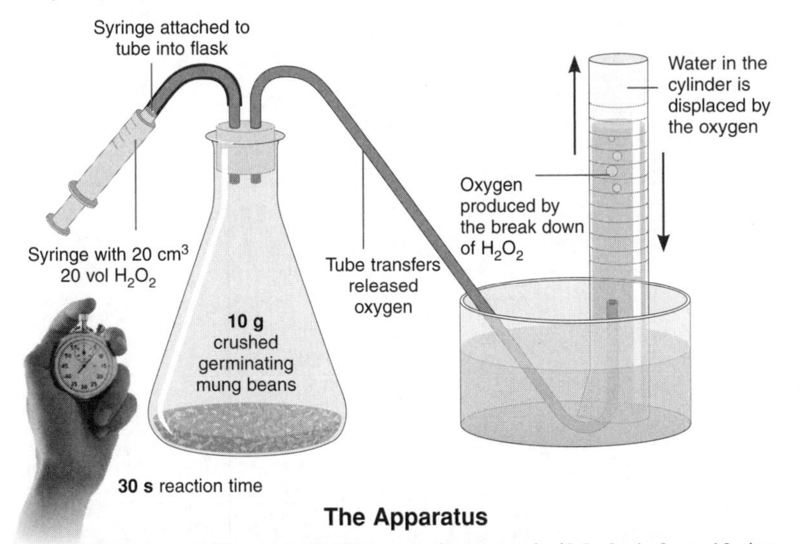

The Apparatus

In this experiment, 10 g germinating mung bean seeds (0.5, 2, 4, 6, or 10 days old) were ground by hand with a mortar and pestle and placed in a conical flask as above. There were six trials at each of the five seedling ages. With each trial, 20 cm^3 of 20 vol H_2O_2 was added to the flask at time 0 and the reaction was allowed to run for 30 seconds. The oxygen released by the decomposition of the H_2O_2 by catalase in the seedlings was collected via a tube into an inverted measuring cylinder. The volume of oxygen produced is measured by the amount of water displaced from the cylinder. The results from all trials are tabulated below:

The Aim

To investigate the effect of germination age on the level of catalase activity in mung beans.

Background

Germinating seeds are metabolically very active and this metabolism inevitably produces reactive oxygen species, including hydrogen peroxide (H_2O_2). H_2O_2 is helps germination by breaking dormancy, but it is also toxic. To counter the toxic effects of H_2O_2 and prevent cellular damage, germinating seeds also produce **catalase**, an enzyme that catalyses the breakdown of H_2O_2 to water and oxygen.

A class was divided into six groups with each group testing the seedlings of each age. Each group's set of results (for 0.5, 2, 4, 6, and 10 days) therefore represents one trial.

Stage of germination / days \ Trial #	Volume of oxygen collected after 30s (cm^3)								Mean rate ($cm^3\ s^{-1}\ g^{-1}$)
	1	2	3	4	5	6	Mean	Standard deviation	
0.5	9.5	10	10.7	9.5	10.2	10.5			
2	36.2	30	31.5	37.5	34	40			
4	59	66	69	60.5	66.5	72			
6	39	31.5	32.5	41	40.3	36			
10	20	18.6	24.3	23.2	23.5	25.5			

1. Write the equation for the catalase reaction with hydrogen peroxide: ____________________

2. Complete the table above to summarize the data from the six trials:

   (a) Calculate the mean volume of oxygen for each stage of germination and enter the values in the table.

   (b) Calculate the standard deviation for each mean and enter the values in the table (you may use a spreadsheet).

   (c) Calculate the mean rate of oxygen production in cm^3 per second per gram. For the purposes of this exercise, assume that the weight of germinating seed in every case was 10.0 g.

3. In another scenario, group (trial) #2 obtained the following measurements for volume of oxygen produced: 0.5 d: 4.8 cm^3, 2 d: 29.0 cm^3, 4 d: 70 cm^3, 6 d: 30.0 cm^3, 10 d: 8.8 cm^3 (pencil these values in beside the other group 2 data set).

   (a) Describe how group 2's new data accords with the measurements obtained from the other groups: ____________________

   (b) Describe how you would approach a reanalysis of the data set incorporating group 2's new data: ____________________

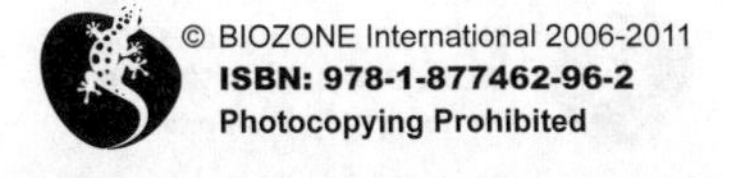

ISBN: 978-1-877462-96-2

Periodicals: *Estimating the mean and standard deviation*

Related activities: *Planning An Investigation*

(c) Explain the rationale for your approach ______________________________

____

4. Use the tabulated data to plot an appropriate graph of the results on the grid provided:

5. (a) Describe the trend in the data: ______________________________

____

____

(b) Explain the relationship between stage of germination and catalase activity shown in the data: ______________________________

____

____

6. Describe any potential sources of errors in the apparatus or the procedure: ______________________________

____

____

7. Describe two things that might affect the validity of findings in this experimental design: ______________________________

____

____

8. Describe one improvement you could make to the experiment in order to generate more reliable data: ______________________________

____

____

____

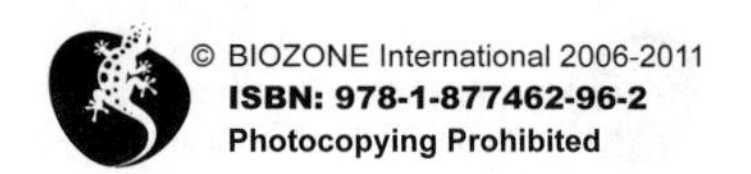

ISBN: 978-1-877462-96-2

Manipulating Raw Data

The data collected by measuring or counting in the field or laboratory are called **raw data.** They often need to be changed (**transformed**) into a form that makes it easier to identify important features of the data (e.g. trends). Some basic calculations, such as totals (the sum of all data values for a variable), are made as a matter of course to compare replicates or as a prelude to other transformations. The calculation of **rate** (amount per unit time) is another example of a commonly performed calculation, and is appropriate for many biological situations (e.g. measuring growth or weight loss or gain). For a line graph, with time as the independent variable plotted against the values of the biological response, the slope of the line is a measure of the rate. Biological investigations often compare the rates of events in different situations (e.g. the rate of photosynthesis in the light and in the dark). Other typical transformations include frequencies (number of times a value occurs) and percentages (fraction of 100).

Tally Chart

Records the number of times a value occurs in a data set

HEIGHT (cm)	TALLY	TOTAL
0-0.99	III	3
1-1.99	~~IIII~~ I	6
2-2.99	~~IIII~~ ~~IIII~~	10
3-3.99	~~IIII~~ ~~IIII~~ II	12
4-4.99	III	3
5-5.99	II	2

- A useful first step in analysis; a neatly constructed tally chart doubles as a simple histogram.
- Cross out each value on the list as you tally it to prevent double entries. Check all values are crossed out at the end and that totals agree.

Example: Height of 6d old seedlings

Percentages

Expressed as a fraction of 100

Women	Body mass in Kg	Lean body mass in Kg	% lean body mass
Athlete	50	38	76.0
Lean	56	41	73.2
Normal weight	65	46	70.8
Overweight	80	48	60.0
Obese	95	52	54.7

- Percentages provide a clear expression of what proportion of data fall into any particular category, e.g. for pie graphs.
- Allows meaningful comparison between different samples.
- Useful to monitor change (e.g. % increase from one year to the next).

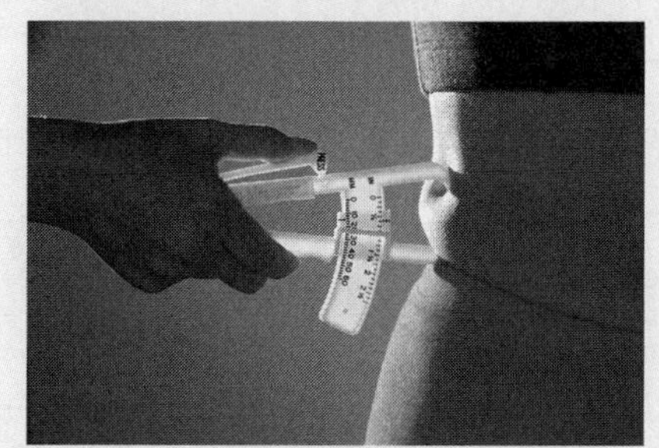

Example: Percentage of lean body mass in women

Rates

Expressed as a measure per unit time

Time (minutes)	Cumulative sweat loss (cm^3)	Rate of sweat loss ($cm^3\ min^{-1}$)
0	0	0
10	50	5
20	130	8
30	220	9
60	560	11.3

- Rates show how a variable changes over a standard time period (e.g. one second, one minute, or one hour).
- Rates allow meaningful comparison of data that may have been recorded over different time periods.

Example: Rate of sweat loss during cycling

1. (a) Explain what it means to transform data: ______________________

   (b) Briefly explain the general purpose of transforming data: ______________________

2. For each of the following examples, state a suitable transformation, together with a reason for your choice:

   (a) Determining relative abundance from counts of four plant species in two different habitat areas:

   Suitable transformation: ______________________

   Reason: ______________________

   (b) Determining the effect of temperature on the production of carbon dioxide by respiring seeds:

   Suitable transformation: ______________________

   Reason: ______________________

ISBN: 978-1-877462-96-2

3. Complete the transformations for each of the tables on the right. The first value is provided in each case.

(a) TABLE: Incidence of cyanogenic clover in different areas:

Working: 124 ÷ 159 = 0.78 = 78%

This is the number of cyanogenic clover out of the total.

Incidence of cyanogenic clover in different areas

Clover plant type	Frost free area		Frost prone area		Totals
	Number	%	Number	%	
Cyanogenic	124	78	26		
Acyanogenic	35		115		
Total	159				

(b) TABLE: Plant water loss using a bubble potometer

Working: (9.0 – 8.0) ÷ 5 min = 0.2

This is the distance the bubble moved over the first 5 minutes. Note that there is no data entry possible for the first reading (0 min) because no difference can be calculated.

Plant water loss using a bubble potometer

Time (min)	Pipette arm reading (cm^3)	Plant water loss ($cm^3\ min^{-1}$)
0	9.0	–
5	8.0	0.2
10	7.2	
15	6.2	
20	4.9	

(c) TABLE: Photosynthetic rate at different light intensities:

Working: 1 ÷ 15 = 0.067

This is time taken for the leaf to float. A reciprocal gives a per minute rate (the variable measured is the time taken for an event to occur).

NOTE: In this experiment, the flotation time is used as a crude measure of photosynthetic rate. As oxygen bubbles are produced as a product of photosynthesis, they stick to the leaf disc and increase its buoyancy. The faster the rate, the sooner they come to the surface. The rates of photosynthesis should be measured over similar time intervals, so the rate is transformed to a 'per minute' basis (the reciprocal of time).

Photosynthetic rate at different light intensities

Light intensity (%)	Average time for leaf disc to float (min)	Reciprocal of time (min^{-1})
100	15	0.067
50	25	
25	50	
11	93	
6	187	

(d) TABLE: Frequency of size classes in a sample of eels:

Working: (7 ÷ 270) x 100 = 2.6 %

This is the number of individuals out of the total that appear in the size class 0-50 mm. The relative frequency is rounded to one decimal place.

Frequency of size classes in a sample of eels

Size class (mm)	Frequency	Relative frequency (%)
0-50	7	2.6
50-99	23	
100-149	59	
150-199	98	
200-249	50	
250-299	30	
300-349	3	
Total	270	

ISBN: 978-1-877462-96-2

Drawing Bar Graphs

Guidelines for Bar Graphs

Bar graphs are appropriate for data that are non-numerical and **discrete** for at least one variable, i.e. they are grouped into separate categories. There are no dependent or independent variables. Important features of this type of graph include:

- Data are collected for discontinuous, non-numerical categories (e.g. place, color, and species), so the bars do not touch.
- Data values may be entered on or above the bars if you wish.
- Multiple sets of data can be displayed side by side for direct comparison (e.g. males and females in the same age group).
- Axes may be reversed so that the categories are on the x axis, i.e. the bars can be vertical or horizontal. When they are vertical, these graphs are sometimes called column graphs.

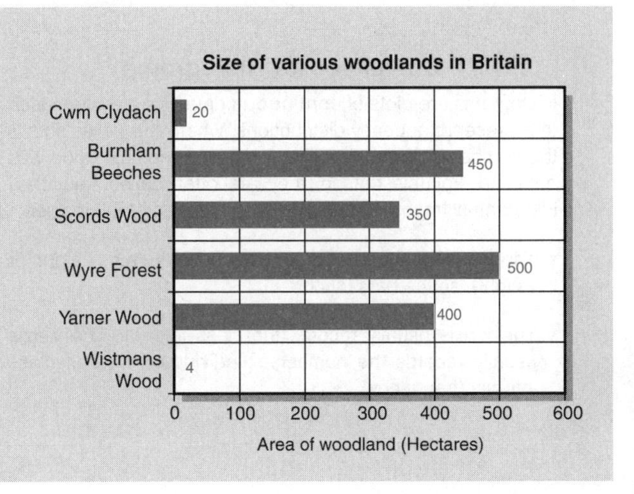

1. Counts of eight mollusc species were made from a series of quadrat samples at two sites on a rocky shore. The summary data are presented here.
   (a) Tabulate the **mean** (average) numbers per square meter at each site in Table 1 (below left).
   (b) Plot a **bar graph** of the tabulated data on the grid below. For each species, plot the data from both sites side by side using different colors to distinguish the sites.

Field data notebook

Total counts at site 1 (11 quadrats) and site 2 (10 quadrats). Quadrats 1 sq m.

Species	Site 1 No (m^{-2}) Total	Site 1 Mean	Site 2 No (m^{-2}) Total	Site 2 Mean
Ornate limpet	232	21	299	30
Radiate limpet	68	6	344	34
Limpet sp. A	420	38	0	0
Cats-eye	68	6	16	2
Top shell	16	2	43	4
Limpet sp. B	628	57	389	39
Limpet sp. C	0	0	22	2
Chiton	12	1	30	3

Mean abundance of 8 mollusc species from two sites along a rocky shore.

Species	Mean (no m^{-2})	
	Site 1	Site 2

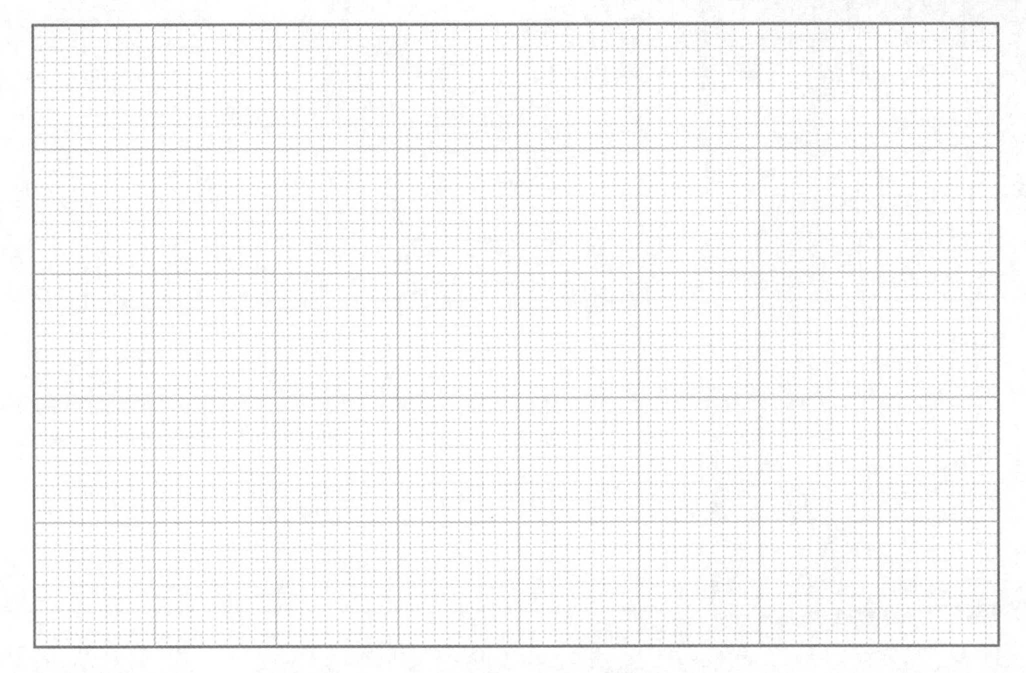

ISBN: 978-1-877462-96-2

Periodicals: *Drawing graphs*

Related activities: *Constructing Tables, Descriptive Statistics*

Drawing Histograms

Guidelines for Histograms

Histograms are plots of **continuous** data and are often used to represent frequency distributions, where the y-axis shows the number of times a particular measurement or value was obtained. For this reason, they are often called frequency histograms. Important features of this type of graph include:

- The data are numerical and continuous (e.g. height or weight), so the bars touch.
- The x-axis usually records the class interval. The y-axis usually records the number of individuals in each class interval (frequency).

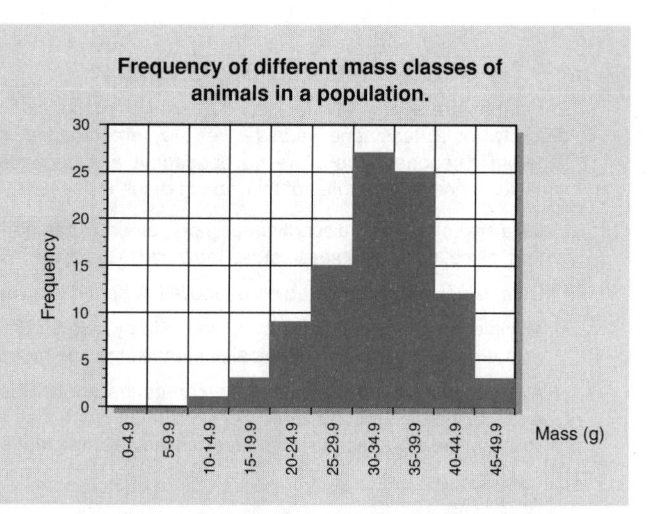

1. The weight data provided below were recorded from 95 individuals (male and female), older than 17 years.
   (a) Create a tally chart (frequency table) in the frame provided, organizing the weight data into a form suitable for plotting. An example of the tally for the weight grouping 55-59.9 kg has been completed for you as an example. Note that the raw data values, once they are recorded as counts on the tally chart, are crossed off the data set in the notebook. It is important to do this in order to prevent data entry errors.
   (b) Plot a **frequency histogram** of the tallied data on the grid provided below.

Weight (kg)	Tally	Total
45-49.9		
50-54.9		
55-59.9	~~||||~~ //	7
60-64.9		
65-69.9		
70-74.9		
75-79.9		
80-84.9		
85-89.9		
90-94.9		
95-99.9		
100-104.9		
105-109.9		

Lab notebook

Weight (in kg) of 95 individuals

63.4	81.2	65
~~56.5~~	83.3	75.6
84	95	76.8
81.5	105.5	67.8
73.4	82	68.3
~~56~~	73.5	63.5
60.4	75.2	~~58~~
83.5	63	~~58.5~~
82	70.4	50
61	82.2	92
~~55.2~~	87.8	91.5
48	86.5	88.3
53.5	85.5	81
63.8	87	72
69	98	66.5
82.8	71	61.5
68.5	76	66
67.2	72.5	65.5
82.5	61	67.4
83	60.5	73
78.4	67	67
76.5	86	71
83.4	85	70.5
77.5	93.5	65.5
77	62	68
87	62.5	90
89	63	83.5
93.4	60	73
83	71.5	66
80	73.8	~~57.5~~
76	77.5	76
~~56~~	74	

Related activities: *Manipulating Raw Data*

Periodicals: *Drawing graphs*

ISBN: 978-1-877462-96-2

Drawing Pie Graphs

Guidelines for Pie Graphs

Pie graphs can be used instead of bar graphs, generally in cases where there are six or fewer categories involved. A pie graph provides strong visual impact of the relative proportions in each category, particularly where one of the categories is very dominant. Features of pie graphs include:

- The data for one variable are discontinuous (non-numerical or categories).
- The data for the dependent variable are usually in the form of counts, proportions, or percentages.
- Pie graphs are good for visual impact and showing relative proportions.
- They are not suitable for data sets with a large number of categories.

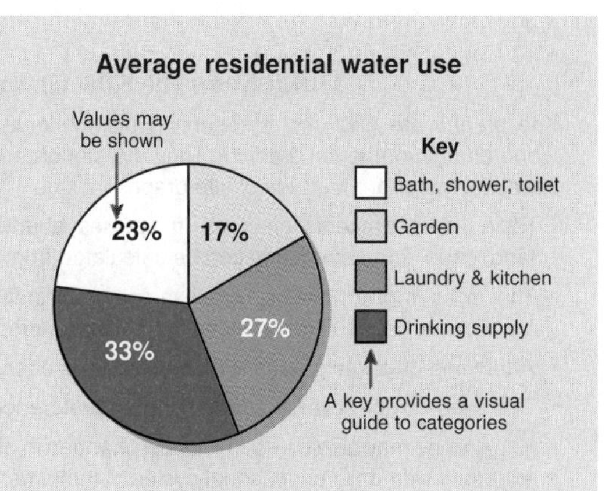

1. The data provided below are from a study of the diets of three vertebrates.

   (a) Tabulate the data from the notebook shown. Calculate the angle for each percentage, given that each percentage point is equal to 3.6° (the first example is provided: 23.6 x 3.6 = 85).

   (b) Plot a pie graph for each animal in the circles provided. The circles have been marked at 5° intervals to enable you to do this exercise without a protractor. For the purposes of this exercise, begin your pie graphs at the 0° (= 360°) mark and work in a clockwise direction from the largest to the smallest percentage. Use one key for all three pie graphs.

Field data notebook

Percentage of different food items in the diet

Food item	Ferrets	Rats	Cats
Birds	23.6	1.4	6.9
Crickets	15.3	23.6	0
Other insects (not crickets)	15.3	20.8	1.9
Voles	9.2	0	19.4
Rabbits	8.3	0	18.1
Rats	6.1	0	43.1
Mice	13.9	0	10.6
Fruits and seeds	0	40.3	0
Green leaves	0	13.9	0
Unidentified	8.3	0	0

Percentage occurrence of foods in the diet of ferrets, rats, and cats. Graph angle representing the % is shown to help plotting.

Food item in diet	Ferrets		Rats		Cats	
	% in diet	Angle (°)	% in diet	Angle (°)	% in diet	Angle (°)
Birds	23.6	85				

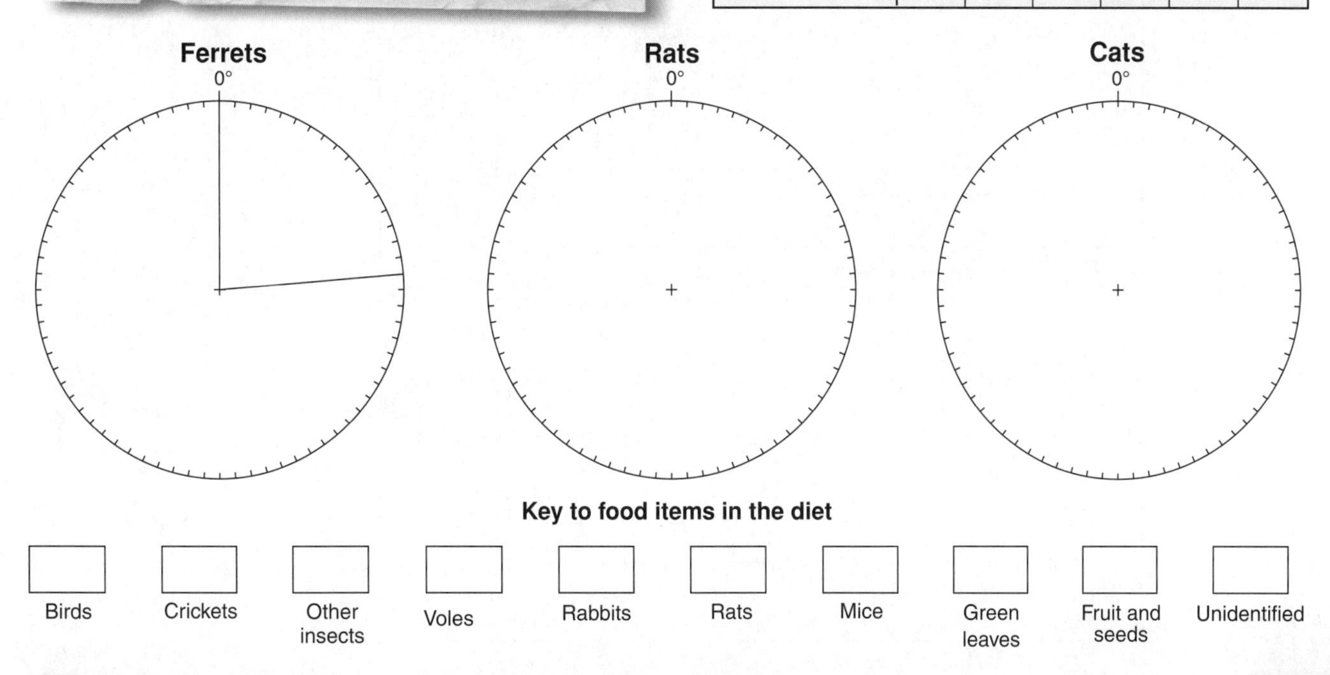

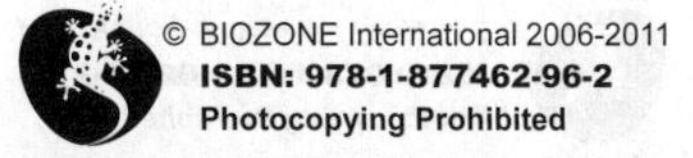

ISBN: 978-1-877462-96-2

Periodicals:
Drawing graphs

Related activities: *Manipulating Raw Data*

Drawing Kite Graphs

Guidelines for Kite Graphs

Kite graphs are ideal for representing distributional data, e.g. abundance along an environmental gradient. They are elongated figures drawn along a baseline. Important features of kite graphs include:

- Each kite represents changes in species abundance across a landscape. The abundance can be calculated from the kite width.
- They often involve plots for more than one species; this makes them good for highlighting probable differences in habitat preferences between species.
- A thin line on a kite graph represents species absence.
- The axes can be reversed depending on preference.
- Kite graphs may also be used to show changes in distribution with time, for example, with daily or seasonal cycles of movement.

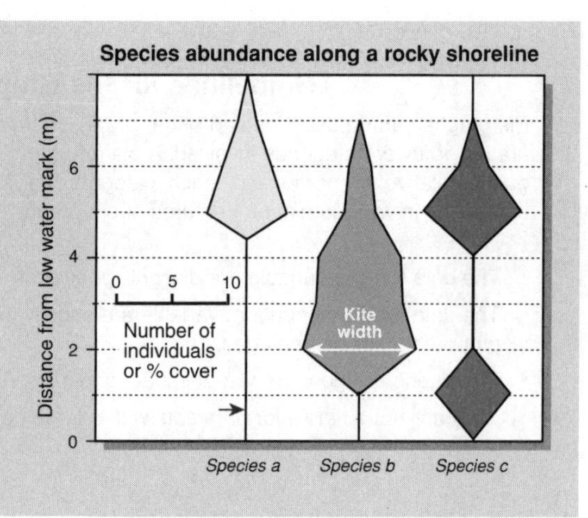

1. The following data were collected from three streams of different lengths and flow rates. Invertebrates were collected at 0.5 km intervals from the headwaters (0 km) to the stream mouth. Their wet weight was measured and recorded (per m²).
   (a) Tabulate the data below for plotting.
   (b) Plot a **kite graph** of the data from all three streams on the grid provided below. Do not forget to include a scale so that the weight at each point on the kite can be calculated.

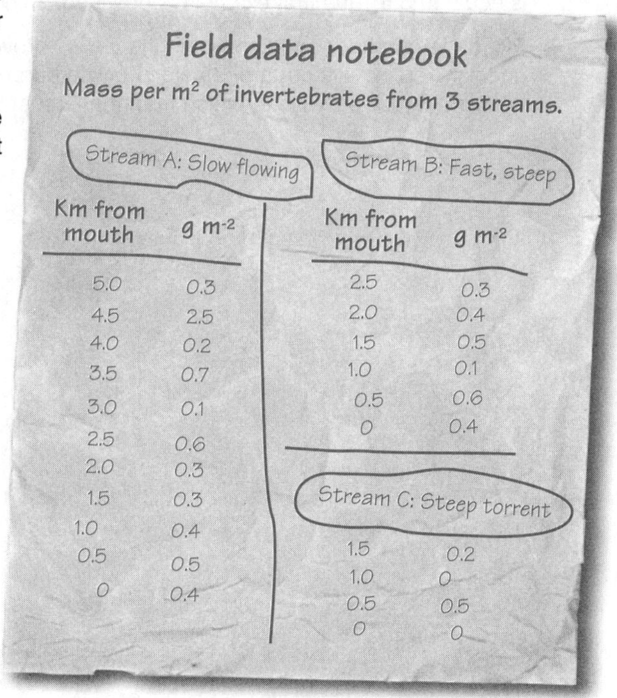

Field data notebook

Mass per m² of invertebrates from 3 streams.

Stream A: Slow flowing

Km from mouth	g m⁻²
5.0	0.3
4.5	2.5
4.0	0.2
3.5	0.7
3.0	0.1
2.5	0.6
2.0	0.3
1.5	0.3
1.0	0.4
0.5	0.5
0	0.4

Stream B: Fast, steep

Km from mouth	g m⁻²
2.5	0.3
2.0	0.4
1.5	0.5
1.0	0.1
0.5	0.6
0	0.4

Stream C: Steep torrent

Km from mouth	g m⁻²
1.5	0.2
1.0	0
0.5	0.5
0	0

Wet mass of invertebrates along three different streams

Distance from mouth (km)	Wet mass (g m⁻²)		
	Stream A	Stream B	Stream C

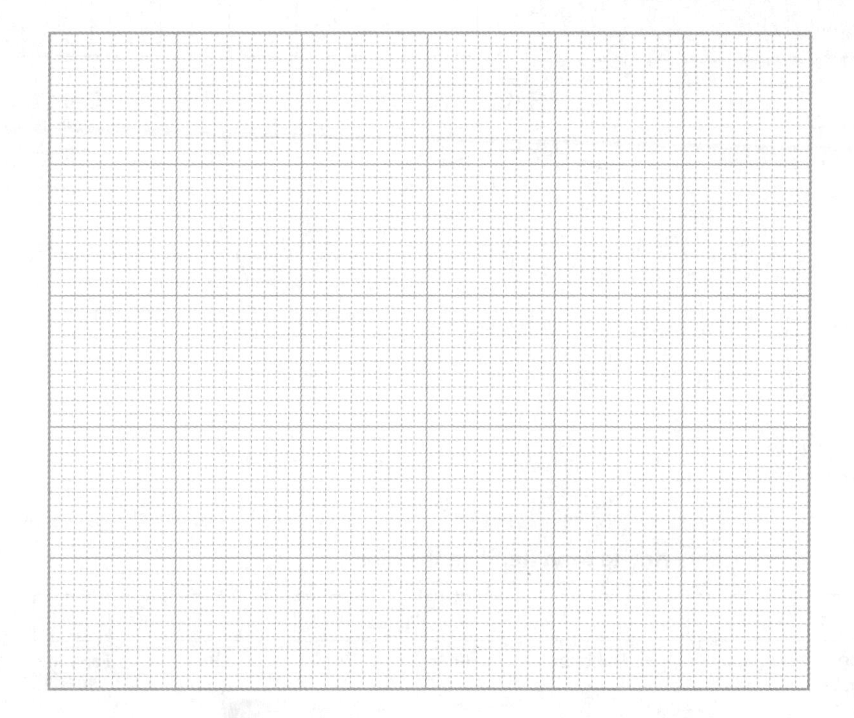

Related activities: Manipulating Raw Data

Periodicals: Drawing graphs

ISBN: 978-1-877462-96-2

Drawing Scatter Plots

Guidelines for Scatter Graphs

A scatter graph is a common way to display continuous data where there is a relationship between two interdependent variables.

- The data for this graph must be continuous for both variables.
- There is no independent (manipulated) variable, but the variables are often correlated, i.e. they vary together in some predictable way.
- Scatter graphs are useful for determining the relationship between two variables.
- The points on the graph are not connected, but a line of best fit is often drawn through the points to show the relationship between the variables (this may be drawn by eye or computer generated).

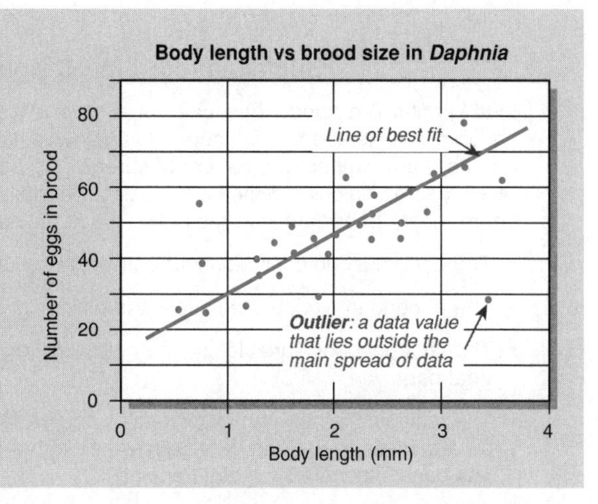

1. In the example below, metabolic measurements were taken from seven Antarctic fish *Pagothenia borchgrevinski*. The fish are affected by a gill disease, which increases the thickness of the gas exchange surfaces and affects oxygen uptake. The results of oxygen consumption of fish with varying amounts of affected gill (at rest and swimming) are tabulated below.

   (a) Using **one** scale only for oxygen consumption, plot the data on the grid below to show the relationship between oxygen consumption and the amount of gill affected by disease. Use different symbols or colors for each set of data (at rest and swimming).

   (b) Draw a line of best fit through each set of points.

Oxygen consumption of fish with affected gills

Fish number	Percentage of gill affected	Oxygen consumption ($cm^3\ g^{-1}\ h^{-1}$)	
		At rest	Swimming
1	0	0.05	0.29
2	95	0.04	0.11
3	60	0.04	0.14
4	30	0.05	0.22
5	90	0.05	0.08
6	65	0.04	0.18
7	45	0.04	0.20

2. Describe the relationship between the amount of gill affected and oxygen consumption in the fish:

   (a) For the **at rest** data set:

   (b) For the **swimming** data set:

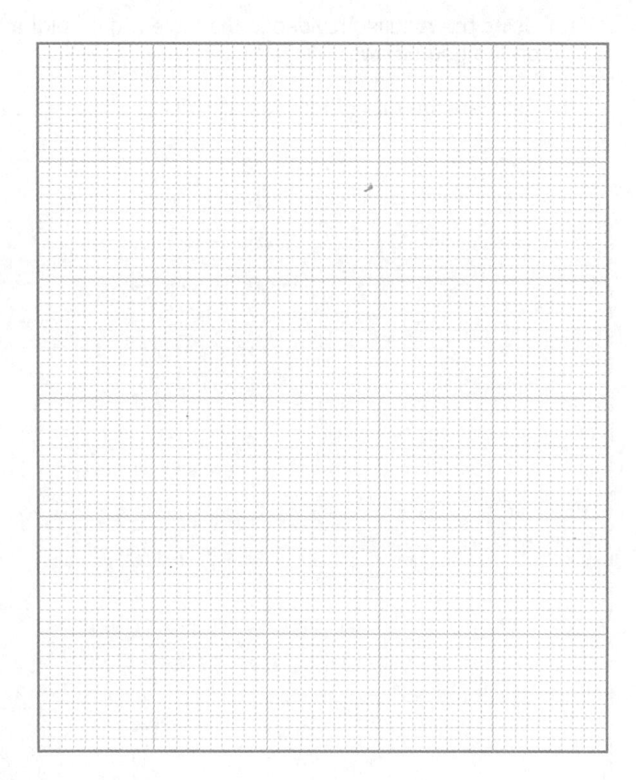

3. Describe how the gill disease affects oxygen uptake in resting fish:

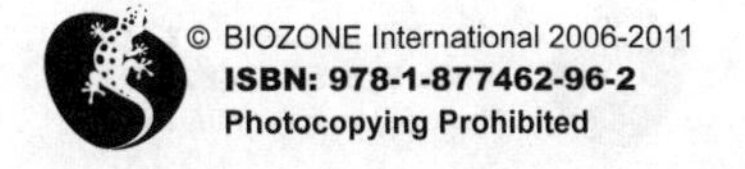

ISBN: 978-1-877462-96-2

Periodicals: *Drawing graphs*

Related activities: *Interpreting Line Graphs, Linear Regression*

Drawing Line Graphs

Guidelines for Line Graphs

Line graphs are used when one variable (the independent variable) affects another, the dependent variable. Line graphs can be drawn without a measure of spread (top figure, right) or with some calculated measure of data variability (bottom figure, right). Important features of line graphs include:

- The data must be continuous for both variables.
- The dependent variable is usually the biological response.
- The independent variable is often time or experimental treatment.
- The relationship between two variables can be represented as a continuum and the data points are plotted accurately and connected directly (point to point).
- Line graphs may be drawn with measure of error. The data are presented as points (which are the calculated means), with bars above and below, indicating a measure of variability or spread in the data (e.g. standard error, standard deviation, or 95% confidence intervals).
- Where no error value has been calculated, the scatter can be shown by plotting the individual data points vertically above and below the mean. By convention, bars are not used to indicate the range of raw values in a data set.

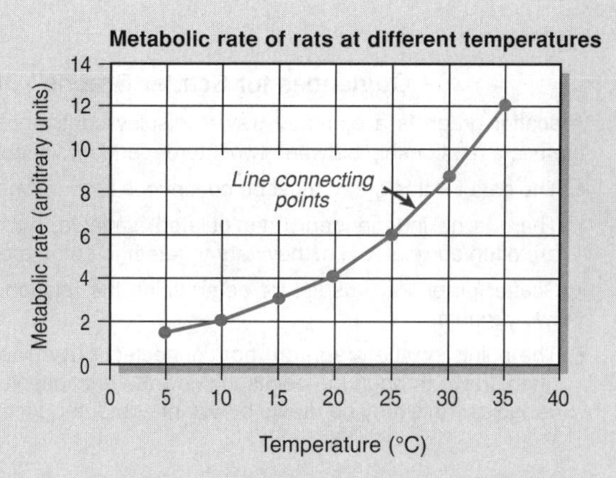

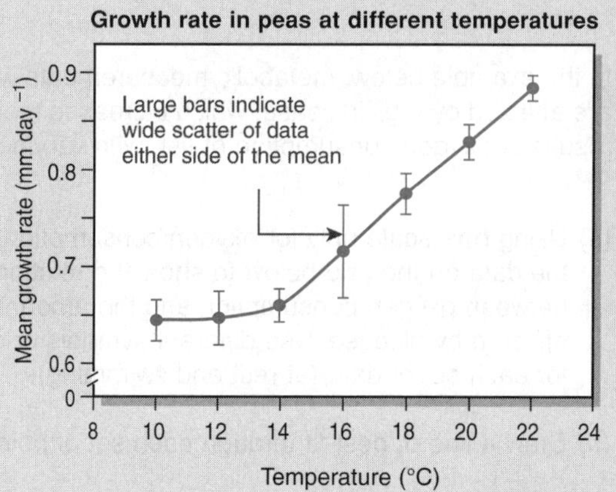

1. The results (shown right) were collected in a study investigating the effect of temperature on the activity of an enzyme.

   (a) Using the results provided in the table (right), plot a line graph on the grid below:

   (b) Estimate the rate of reaction at 15°C: ____________________

Lab Notebook

An enzyme's activity at different temperatures

Temperature (°C)	Rate of reaction (mg of product formed per minute)
10	1.0
20	2.1
30	3.2
35	3.7
40	4.1
45	3.7
50	2.7
60	0

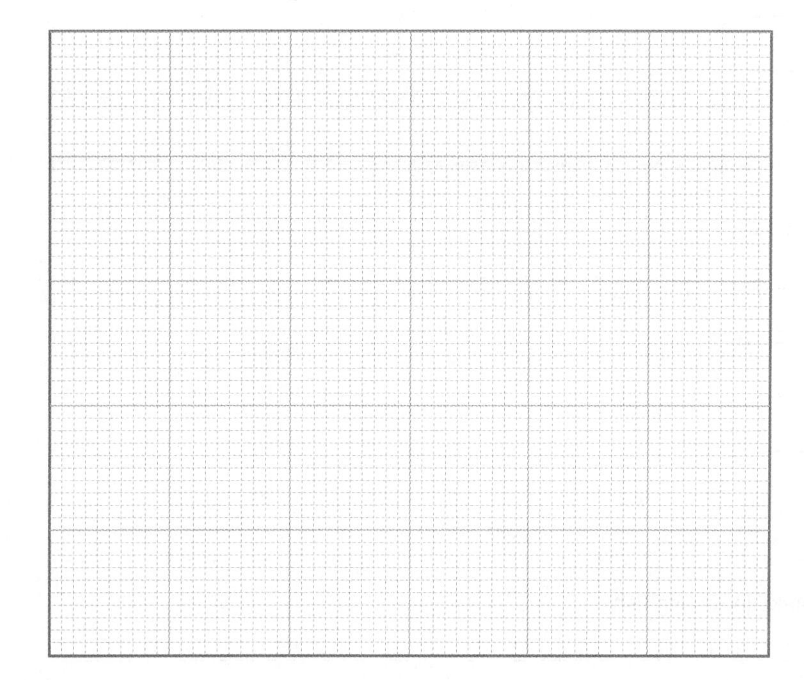

Related activities: *Interpreting Line Graphs, The Reliability of the Mean*

Periodicals: *Drawing graphs*

ISBN: 978-1-877462-96-2

Plotting Multiple Data Sets

A single figure can be used to show two or more data sets, i.e. more than one curve can be plotted per set of axes. This type of presentation is useful when you want to visually compare the trends for two or more treatments, or the response of one species against the response of another. Important points regarding this format are:

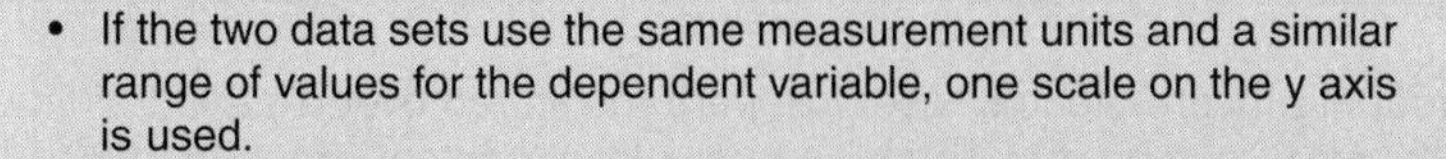

- If the two data sets use the same measurement units and a similar range of values for the dependent variable, one scale on the y axis is used.
- If the two data sets use different units and/or have a very different range of values for the dependent variable, two scales for the y axis are used (see example provided). The scales can be adjusted if necessary to avoid overlapping plots
- The two curves must be distinguished with a key.

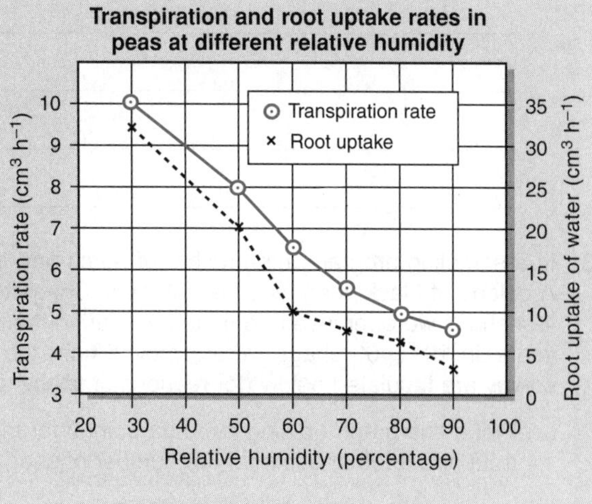

2. A census of a deer population on an island indicated a population of 2000 animals in 1960. In 1961, ten wolves (natural predators of deer) were brought to the island in an attempt to control deer numbers. Over the next nine years, the numbers of deer and wolves were monitored. The results of these population surveys are presented in the table, right.

   (a) Plot a line graph (joining the data points) for the tabulated results. Use one scale (on the left) for numbers of deer and another scale (on the right) for the number of wolves. Use different symbols or colors to distinguish the lines and include a key.

Field data notebook

Results of a population survey on an island

Time (year)	Wolf numbers	Deer numbers
1961	10	2000
1962	12	2300
1963	16	2500
1964	22	2360
1965	28	2244
1966	24	2094
1967	21	1968
1968	18	1916
1969	19	1952

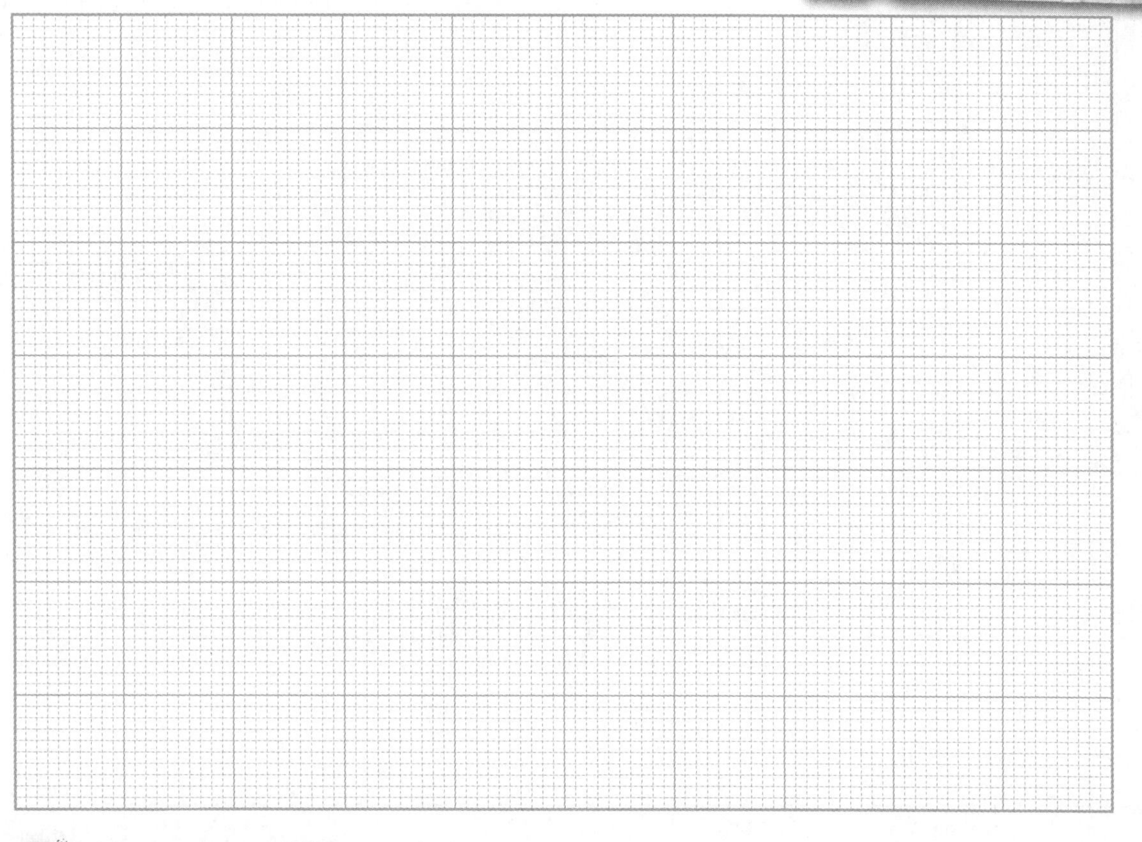

ISBN: 978-1-877462-96-2

(b) Study the line graph that you plotted for the wolf and deer census on the previous page. Provide a plausible explanation for the pattern in the data, stating the evidence available to support your reasoning:

3. In a sampling program, the number of perch and trout in a hydro-electric reservoir were monitored over a period of time. A colony of black shag was also present. Shags take large numbers of perch and (to a lesser extent) trout. In 1960-61, 424 shags were removed from the lake during the nesting season and nest counts were made every spring in subsequent years. In 1971, 60 shags were removed from the lake, and all existing nests dismantled. The results of the population survey are tabulated below (for reasons of space, the entire table format has been repeated to the right for 1970-1978).

(a) Plot a line graph (joining the data points) for the survey results. Use one scale (on the left) for numbers of perch and trout and another scale for the number of shag nests. Use different symbols to distinguish the lines and include a key.

(b) Use a vertical arrow to indicate the point at which shags and their nests were removed.

Results of population survey at reservoir

Time (year)	Fish number (mean number per haul)		Shag nest numbers	Time (year continued)	Fish number (mean number per haul)		Shag nest numbers
	Trout	Perch			Trout	Perch	
1960	–	–	16	1970	1.5	6	35
1961	–	–	4	1971	0.5	0.7	42
1962	1.5	11	5	1972	1	0.8	0
1963	0.8	9	10	1973	0.2	4	0
1964	0	5	22	1974	0.5	6.5	0
1965	1	1	25	1975	0.6	7.6	2
1966	1	2.9	35	1976	1	1.2	10
1967	2	5	40	1977	1.2	1.5	32
1968	1.5	4.6	26	1978	0.7	2	28
1969	1.5	6	32				

Source: Data adapted from 1987 Bursary Examination

ISBN: 978-1-877462-96-2

Interpreting Line Graphs

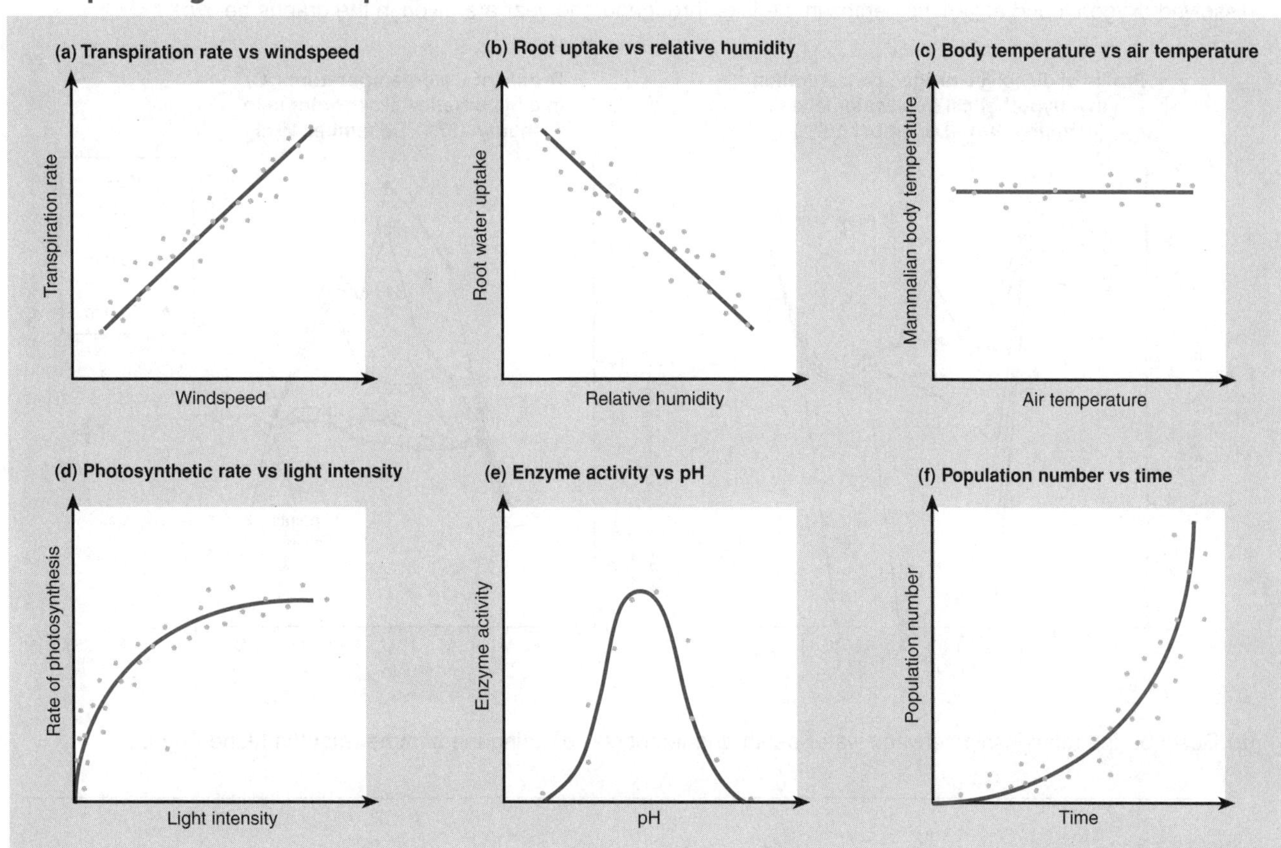

1. For each of the graphs (b-f) above, give a description of the slope and an interpretation of how one variable changes with respect to the other. For the purposes of your description, call the independent variable (horizontal or x-axis) in each example "variable X" and the dependent variable (vertical or y-axis) "variable Y". Be aware that the existence of a relationship between two variables does not necessarily mean that the relationship is causative (although it may be).

   (a) Slope: Positive linear relationship, with constantly rising slope

   Interpretation: Variable Y (transpiration) increases regularly with increase in variable X (windspeed)

   (b) Slope: ______

   Interpretation: ______

   (c) Slope: ______

   Interpretation: ______

   (d) Slope: ______

   Interpretation: ______

   (e) Slope: ______

   Interpretation: ______

   (f) Slope: ______

   Interpretation: ______

2. Study the line graph of trout, perch and shag numbers that you plotted on the previous page:

   (a) Describe the evidence suggesting that the shag population is exercising some control over perch numbers:

   ______

   (b) Describe evidence that the fluctuations in shag numbers are related to fluctuations in trout numbers: ______

   ______

   ______

ISBN: 978-1-877462-96-2

Periodicals:
Dealing with data

Related activities: *Drawing Scatter Plots, Drawing Line Graphs, Linear Regression, Non-Linear Regression*

3. A survey of two species of bottom dwelling bloodworm was carried out in a lake (for the purposes of this exercise, this is a hypothetical lake). The two species were *Chironomus species a*, and *Chironomus species b*. The water temperature and dissolved oxygen found at various depths in the lake throughout the year are given in the graphs below:

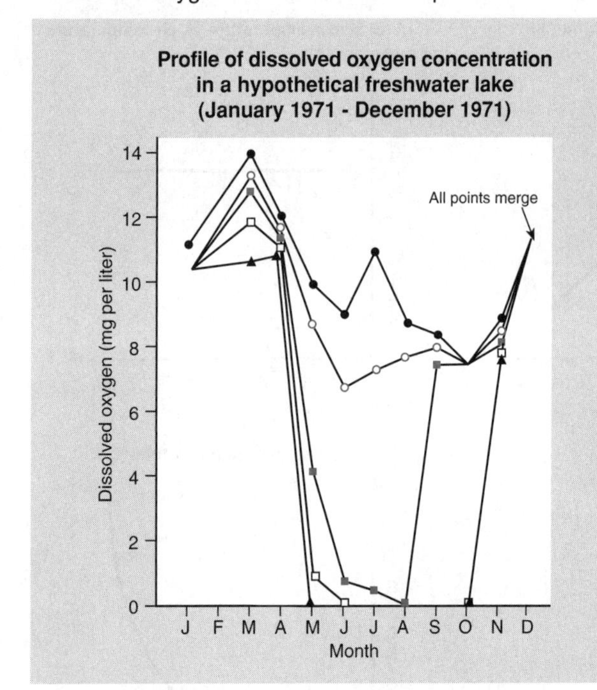

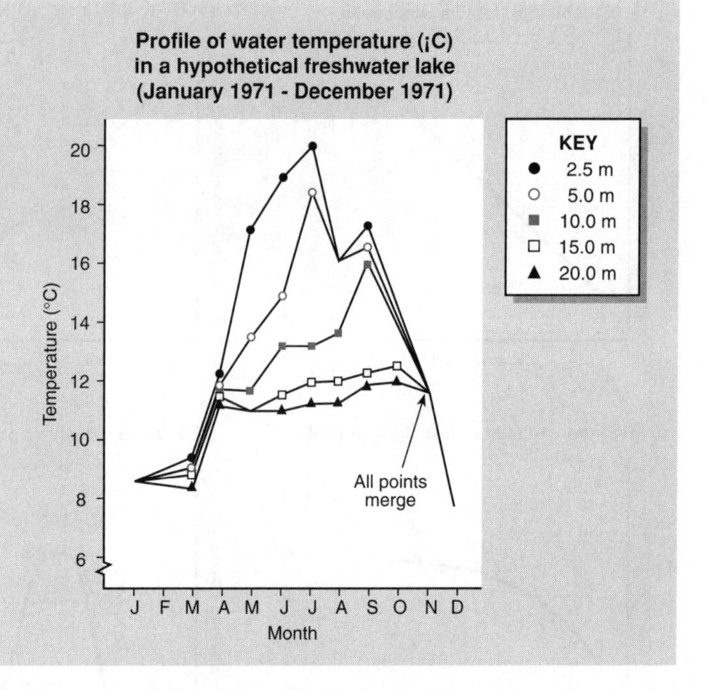

(a) Describe the relationship between water depth and temperature during the summer months (June-August):

(b) Describe the relationship between water depth and dissolved oxygen during the summer months:

4. The column graphs on the right show depth distributions of similar aged individuals of the two bloodworm species described above.

(a) Describe the difference between summer (June-August) and winter (Dec-Feb) distributions. Suggest a reason for this:

(b) Explain why the population density of both species is higher at greater depth during December:

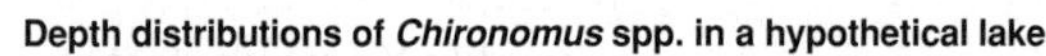

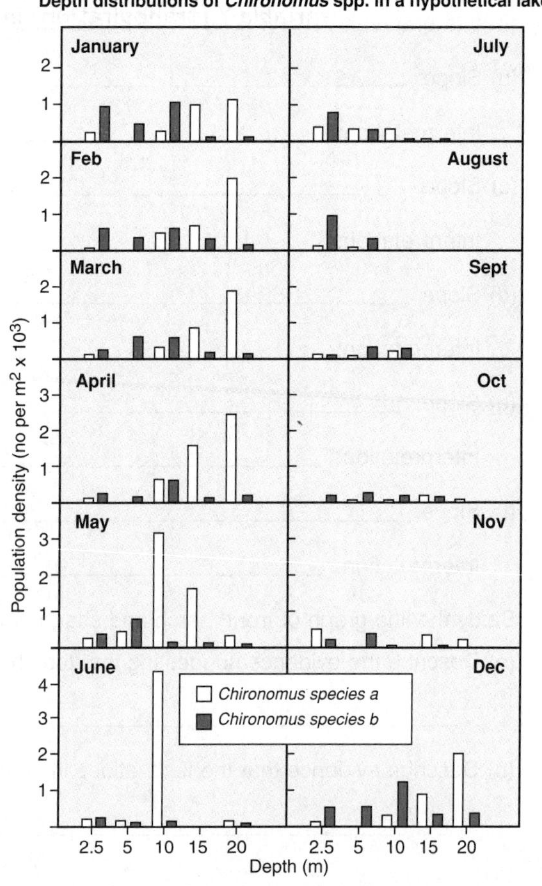

ISBN: 978-1-877462-96-2

KEY TERMS: Flash Card Game

The cards below have a keyword or term printed on one side and its definition printed on the opposite side. The aim is to win as many cards as possible from the table. To play the game.....

1) Cut out the cards and lay them definition side down on the desk. You will need one set of cards between two students.
2) Taking turns, choose a card and, BEFORE you pick it up, state your own best definition of the keyword to your opponent.
3) Check the definition on the opposite side of the card. If both you and your opponent agree that your stated definition matches, then keep the card. If your definition does not match then return the card to the desk.
4) Once your turn is over, your opponent may choose a card.

Accuracy	Table	Mean
Hypothesis	Variable	Precision
Qualitative data	Control	Graph
Independent variable	Dependent variable	Mode
Observation	Trend (of data)	Raw data
y-axis	Median	Scientific method

ISBN: 978-1-877462-96-2

When you've finished the game keep these cutouts and use them as flash cards!

The sum of the data divided by the number of data entries (*n*).

A systematic way to record and condense a large amount of information, that can be analyzed and presented later.

How close a measured value is to the true value.

The repeatability of a measurement.

A factor in an experiment that is subject to change.

A tentative explanation of an observation, capable of being tested by experimentation.

A diagram that often displays numerical information, often in a way that can be used to identify trends in the data.

A standard (reference) treatment that helps to ensure that the responses to the other treatments can be reliably interpreted.

Data described in descriptors or terms rather than by numbers.

The value that occurs most often in a data set.

A variable whose values are determined by another variable.

A variable whose values are set, or systematically altered, by the investigator.

Data that have not been processed or manipulated in any way.

A pattern observed in processed data showing that data values may be linked.

The act of seeing and noting an occurrence in the object or substance being studied.

The use of an ordered, repeatable method to investigate, manipulate, gather, and record data.

The number that occurs in the middle of a set of sorted numbers. It divides the upper half of the number data set from the lower half.

The vertical axis in a two-dimensional coordinate system such as a graph.

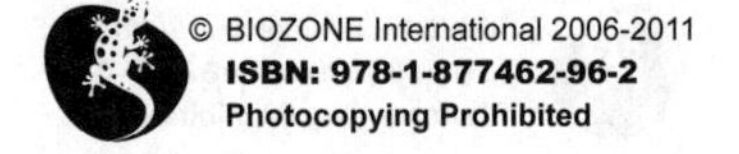

ISBN: 978-1-877462-96-2

Analysis and Reporting

Key concepts

- Recording results systematically makes it easier to analyze and interpret results.
- Evaluating quantitative data involves analysis of processed data and objective assessment of sources of error.
- A report should present and discuss findings and acknowledge the work of others.

Key terms

95% confidence limit
analysis of variance (ANOVA)
bibliography
chi-squared test
citation
conclusion
data
discussion
mean
median
methods
mode
parameter
raw data
record systematically
report
results
sample mean
significance (statistical)
Spearman rank correlation
standard deviation
standard error
statistic
statistical test
student's *t* test
transformation (of data)
trend (of data)

Periodicals:
Listings for this chapter are on page 153

Weblinks:
www.thebiozone.com/weblink/Skills-2962.html

Objectives

☐ 1. Use the **KEY TERMS** to help you understand and complete these objectives.

Analyzing Data

pages 42-67

☐ 2. Use the flow chart provided in this topic to determine a appropriate analysis for specific types of data.

☐ 3. Recall simple data transformations (rates, percentages, and frequencies). Demonstrate an ability to perform for other **data transformations** including **reciprocal**, **square root**, and **$\log_{10}$**. Explain the rationale for each of these simple transformations.

☐ 4. Demonstrate an understanding of basic **descriptive statistics**, including sample **mean** and **standard deviation**, and sample **median** and **mode**.

☐ 5. Calculate measures of dispersion for your data, related to the true population **parameters**, e.g. **standard error** of the mean and **95% confidence limits**.

☐ 6. Explain what is meant by **significance**. Appreciate that different statistical tests are appropriate for different types of data.

☐ 7. Distinguish between tests for a trend and tests for difference. Identify the criteria for the tests in each case. If required, perform an appropriate statistical analysis to test the significance of any trends or differences in your data.

(a) Tests for a **trend**: **correlation**, **regression**, **Spearman rank.**

(b) Test for **difference** (e.g. between groups or treatments): **student's t test**, **chi-squared**, **analysis of variance**.

Evaluating and Presenting Your Data

pages 68-73

☐ 8. Critical evaluation of results is an essential part of any study. Understand and be prepared to explain important features of your investigation, including:

- Any **trends** in your processed data.
- **Discussion** of the biological concepts involved.
- Evaluation, including erroneous results and sources of error.
- **Conclusions** based on analysis of the data and the experimental aims.

☐ 9. Present the findings of your investigation in a well organized scientific **report**.

☐ 10. Identify and explain the important features of a scientific report including:

- Introduction to the study, including a synopsis of the current knowledge.
- **Methods** sufficient to enable the study to be repeated independently.
- Results as recorded and processed data, including figures and tables.
- Discussion of the results within the context of the biology and aims.
- Conclusions.
- References to works cited in the body of the report.

Taking the Next Step

By this stage, you will have completed many of the early stages of your investigation. Now is a good time to review what you have done and reflect on the biological significance of what you are investigating. Review the first page of this flow chart in light of your findings so far. You are now ready to begin a more in-depth analysis of your results. Never under-estimate the value of plotting your data, even at a very early stage. This will help you decide on the best type of data analysis (opposite).

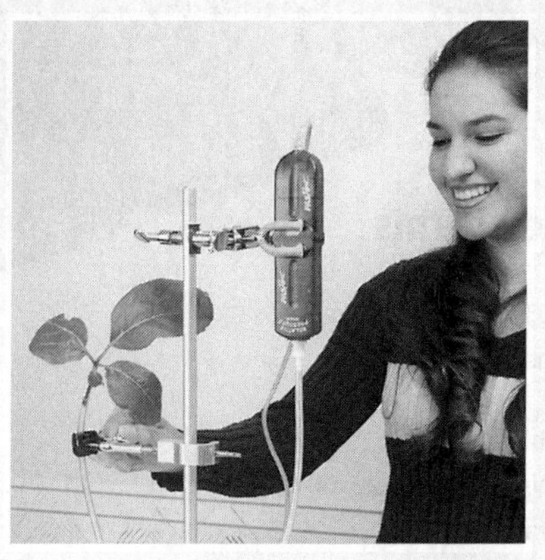

Photos courtesy of Pasco

Observation

Something...

- Changes or affects something else.
- Is more abundant, etc. along a transect, at one site, temperature, concentration, etc. than others.
- Is bigger, taller, or grows more quickly.

Research

To find out...

- Basic biology and properties.
- What other biotic or abiotic factors may have an effect.
- Its place within the broader biological context.

Variables

Next you need to...

- Identify the key variables likely to cause the effect.
- Identify variables to be controlled in order to give the best chance of showing the effect that you want to study.

Hypothesis

Must be...

- Testable
- Able to generate predictions

so that in the end you can say whether your data supports or allows you to reject your hypothesis.

Pilot study

Lets you check...

- Equipment, sampling sites, sampling interval.
- How long it takes to collect data.
- Problems with identification or other unforeseen issues.

Be prepared to revise your study design in the light of the results from your pilot study

Analysis

Are you looking for a...

- **Difference**.
- **Trend** or relationship.
- **Goodness of fit** (to a theoretical outcome).

GO TO NEXT PAGE

Related activities: *Linear Regression, Non-linear Regression, Student's t-Test, Chi-Squared Test, Chi-Squared Exercise in Ecology, Analysis of Variance*

ISBN: 978-1-877462-96-2

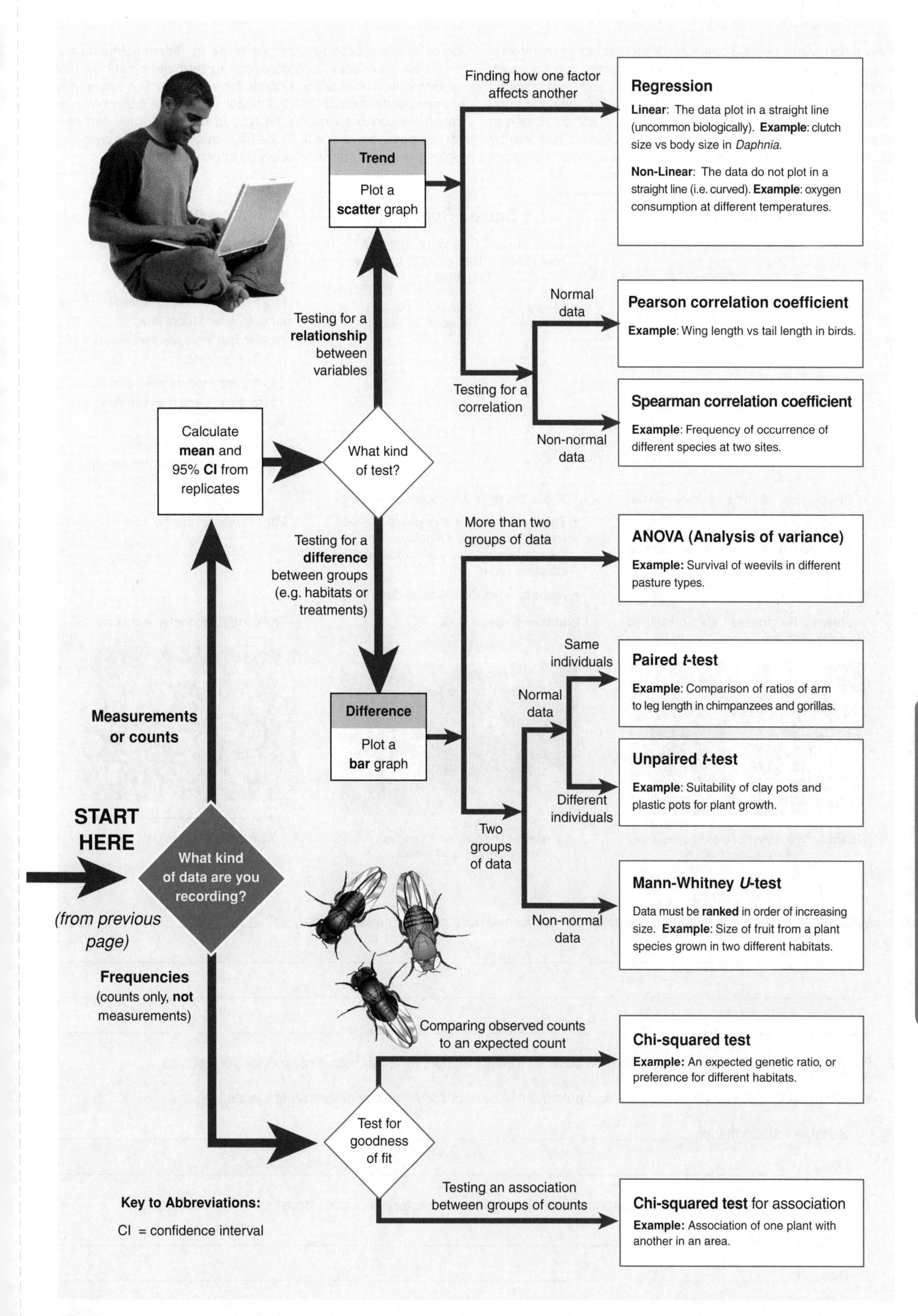

ISBN: 978-1-877462-96-2

Further Data Transformations

Raw data usually needs some kind of processing so that trends in the data and relationships between variables can be easily identified and tested statistically. The simplest and most powerful statistical tests generally require data to exhibit a normal distribution, yet many biological variables are not distributed in this way. It is possible to get around this apparent problem by transforming the data. Data transformation can help to account for differences between sample sizes in different treatments. It is also a perfectly legitimate way to normalize data so that its distribution meets the criteria for analysis. It is not a way to manipulate data to get the result you want. Your choice of transformation is based on the type of data you have and how you propose to analyze it. Some experimental results may be so clear, a complex statistical analysis is unnecessary.

Reciprocals

1 / x is the reciprocal of x.

Enzyme concentration ($\mu g\ mL^{-1}$)	Reaction time (min)	Reciprocal value
6	25	0.04
12.5	20	0.05
25	14	0.07
50	5	0.20
100	2.5	0.40
150	1.75	0.57

- Reciprocals of time (1/data value) can provide a crude measure of rate in situations where the variable measured is the total time taken to complete a task.

Problem: Responses are measured over different time scales.

Example: Time taken for color change in an enzyme reaction.

Square Root

A square root is a value that when multiplied by itself gives the original number.

Sampling site	No. of Woodlice	Square root
1	10	3.16
2	7	2.65
3	5	2.24
4	3	1.73
5	1	1
6	0	0
7	1	1
8	1	1

- Applied to data that counts something.
- The square root of a negative number cannot be taken. Negative numbers are made positive by the addition of a constant value.
- Helps to normalize skewed data.

Problem: Skewed data.

Example: The number of woodlice distributed across a transect.

Log_{10}

A log transformation has the effect of normalizing data.

- Log transformations are useful for data where there is an exponential increase in numbers (e.g. cell growth).
- Log transformed data will plot as a straight line and the numbers are more manageable.
- To find the log_{10} of a number, e.g. 32, using a calculator, key in (log) (32) = ___.

The answer should be 1.51.

Problem: Exponential increases.

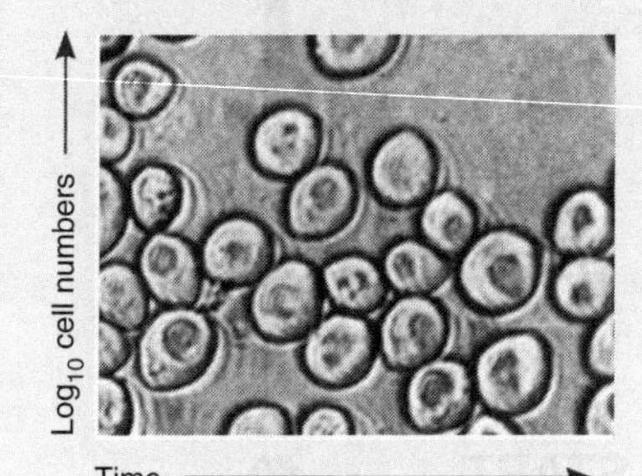

Example: Cell growth in a yeast culture

1. Why might a researcher transform skewed or non-normal data prior to statistical analysis? ____________________

2. For each of the following examples, state a suitable transformation, together with a reason for your choice:

(a) Comparing the time taken for chemical precipitation to occur in a flask at different pH values:

Suitable transformation: ____________________

Reason: ____________________

(b) Analyzing the effect of growth environment on the number of bacterial colonies developing in 50 agar plates:

Suitable transformation: ____________________

Reason: ____________________

Related activities: Manipulating Raw Data

ISBN: 978-1-877462-96-2

Descriptive Statistics

For most investigations, measures of the biological response are made from more than one sampling unit. The sample size (the number of sampling units) will vary depending on the resources available. In lab based investigations, the sample size may be as small as two or three (e.g. two test-tubes in each treatment). In field studies, each individual may be a sampling unit, and the sample size can be very large (e.g. 100 individuals). It is useful to summarize the data collected using **descriptive statistics.**

Descriptive statistics, such as mean, median, and mode, can help to highlight trends or patterns in the data. Each of these statistics is appropriate to certain types of data or distributions, e.g. a mean is not appropriate for data with a skewed distribution (see below). Frequency graphs are useful for indicating the distribution of data. Standard deviation and standard error are statistics used to quantify the amount of spread in the data and evaluate the reliability of estimates of the true (population) mean.

Variation in Data

Whether they are obtained from observation or experiments, most biological data show variability. In a set of data values, it is useful to know the value about which most of the data are grouped; the center value. This value can be the mean, median, or mode depending on the type of variable involved (see schematic below). The main purpose of these statistics is to summarize important trends in your data and to provide the basis for statistical analyses.

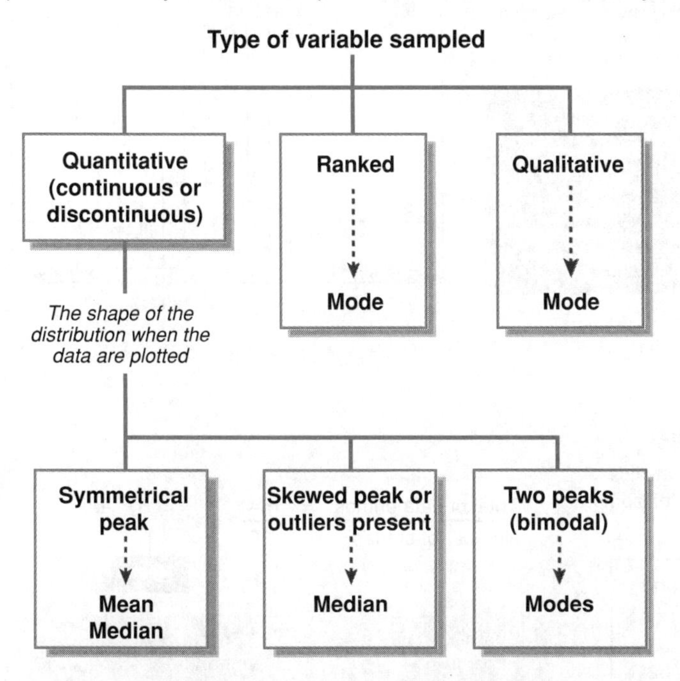

The shape of the distribution will determine which statistic (mean, median, or mode) best describes the central tendency of the sample data.

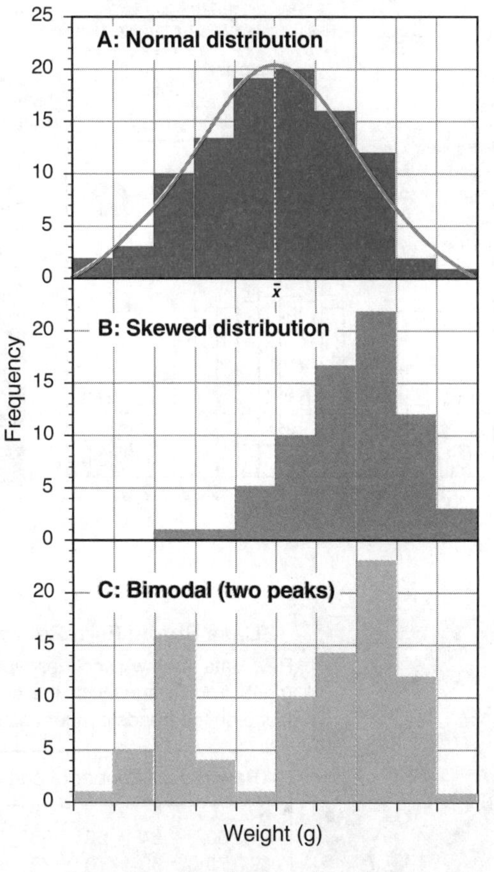

A **frequency distribution** will indicate whether the data are normal, skewed, or bimodal.

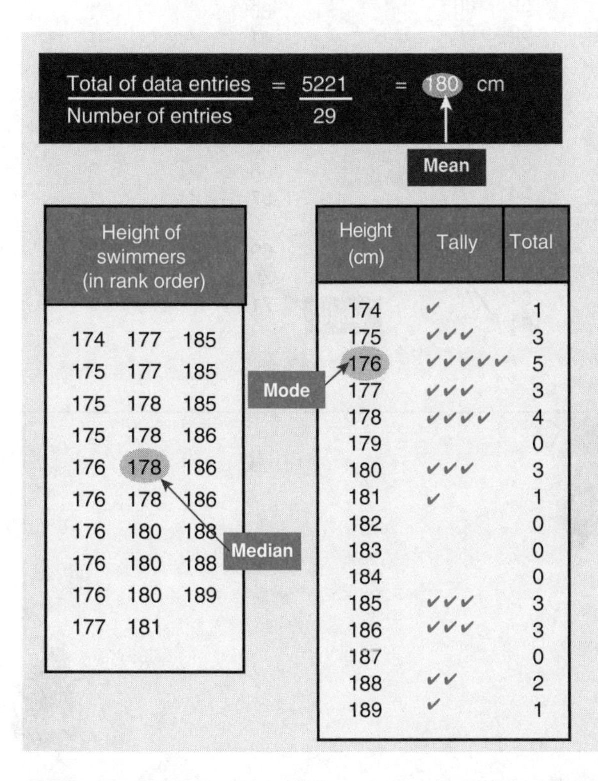

$$\frac{\text{Total of data entries}}{\text{Number of entries}} = \frac{5221}{29} = 180 \text{ cm}$$

Mean

Height of swimmers (in rank order)		
174	177	185
175	177	185
175	178	185
175	178	186
176	178	186
176	178	186
176	180	188
176	180	188
176	180	189
177	181	

Median: 178; Mode: 176

Height (cm)	Tally	Total
174	✓	1
175	✓✓✓	3
176	✓✓✓✓✓	5
177	✓✓✓	3
178	✓✓✓✓	4
179		0
180	✓✓✓	3
181	✓	1
182		0
183		0
184		0
185	✓✓✓	3
186	✓✓✓	3
187		0
188	✓✓	2
189	✓	1

Case Study: Height of Swimmers

Data (below) and descriptive statistics (left) from a survey of the height of 29 members of a male swim squad.

Raw data: Height (cm)					
178	177	188	176	186	175
180	181	178	178	176	175
180	185	185	175	189	174
178	186	176	185	177	176
176	188	180	186	177	

1. Give a reason for the difference between the mean, median, and mode for the swimmers' height data:

____

____

____

____

ISBN: 978-1-877462-96-2

Periodicals: *Describing the normal distribution*

Related activities: *Investigating Plant Growth, Interpreting Sample Variability, The Reliability of the Mean*

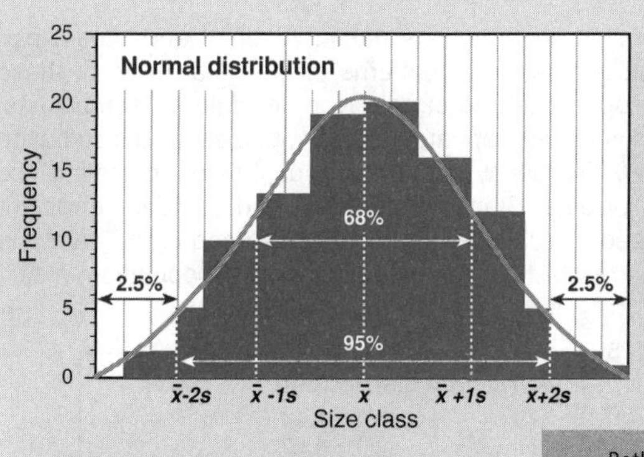

Measuring Spread

The **standard deviation** is a frequently used measure of the variability (spread) in a set of data. It is usually presented in the form $\bar{x} \pm s$. In a normally distributed set of data, 68% of all data values will lie within one standard deviation (s) of the mean ($\bar{x}$) and 95% of all data values will lie within two standard deviations of the mean (left).

Two different sets of data can have the same mean and range, yet the distribution of data within the range can be quite different. In both the data sets pictured in the histograms below, 68% of the values lie within the range $\bar{x} \pm 1s$ and 95% of the values lie within $\bar{x} \pm 2s$. However, in B, the data values are more tightly clustered around the mean.

Both plots show a normal distribution with a symmetrical spread of values about the mean.

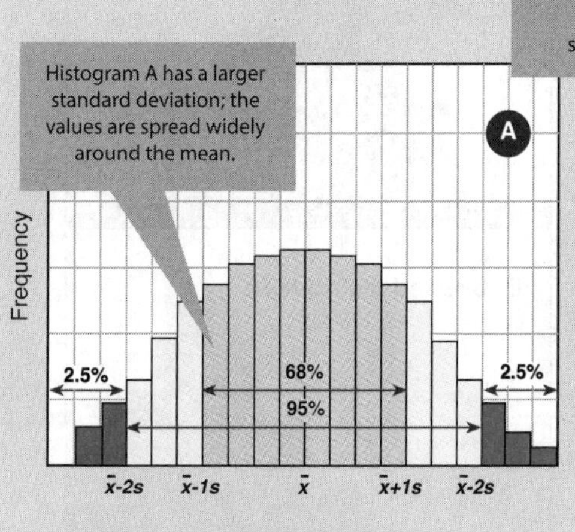

Calculating *s*

In calculating standard deviation, organize the data in columns to minimize calculation errors.

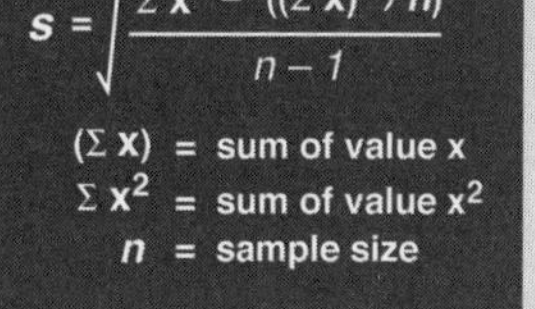

$$s = \sqrt{\frac{\Sigma x^2 - ((\Sigma x)^2 / n)}{n-1}}$$

(Σx) = sum of value x

Σx^2 = sum of value x^2

n = sample size

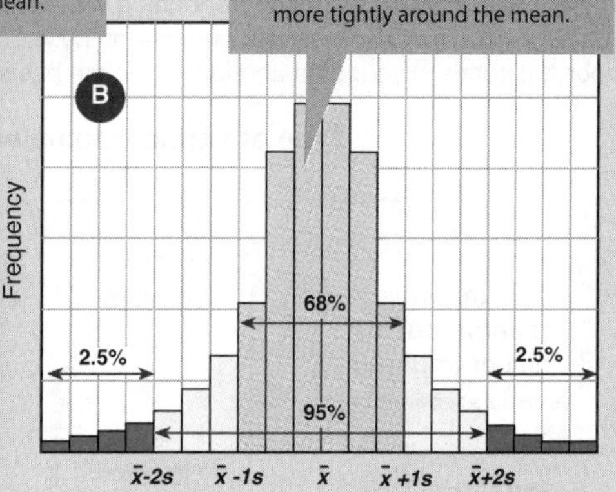

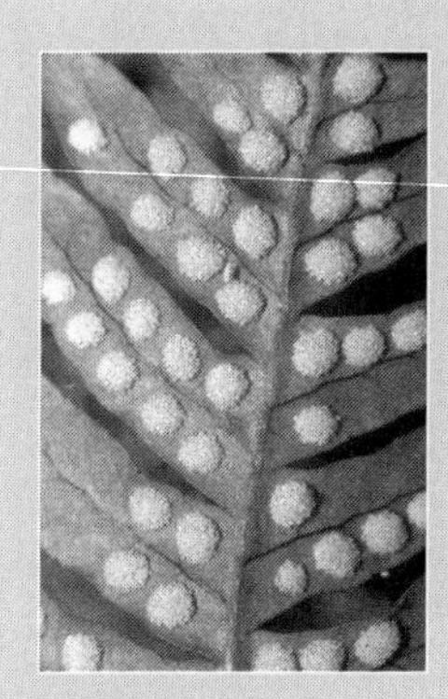

Fern spores

Case Study: Fern Reproduction

Raw data (below) and descriptive statistics (right) from a survey of the number of sori found on the fronds of a fern plant.

Raw data: Number of sori per frond						
64	60	64	62	68	66	63
69	70	63	70	70	63	62
71	69	59	70	66	61	70
67	64	63	64			

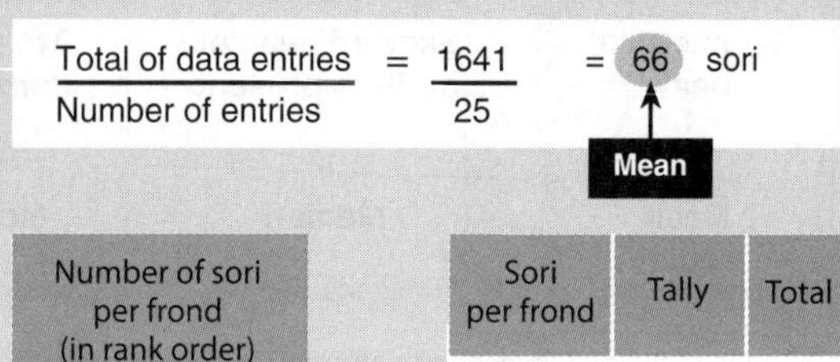

$$\frac{\text{Total of data entries}}{\text{Number of entries}} = \frac{1641}{25} = 66 \text{ sori}$$

Mean

Number of sori per frond (in rank order)	
59	66
60	66
61	67
62	68
62	69
63	69
63	70
63	70
63	70
64	70
64	70
64	71
64	

Median: 64

Sori per frond	Tally	Total
59	✓	1
60	✓	1
61	✓	1
62	✓✓	2
63	✓✓✓✓	4
64	✓✓✓✓	4
65		0
66	✓✓	2
67	✓	1
68	✓	1
69	✓✓	2
70	✓✓✓✓✓	5
71	✓	1

Mode: 70

2. Give a reason for the difference between the mean, median, and mode for the fern sori data:

____

____

____

____

3. Calculate the mean, median, and mode for the data on ladybird masses below. Draw up a tally chart and show all calculations:

Ladybird mass (mg)		
10.1	8.2	7.7
8.0	8.8	7.8
6.7	7.7	8.8
9.8	8.8	8.9
6.2	8.8	8.4

____

____

____

____

ISBN: 978-1-877462-96-2

Interpreting Sample Variability

Measures of central tendency, such as mean, attempt to identify the most representative value in a set of data, but the description of a data set also requires that we know something about how far the data values are spread around that central measure. As we have seen in the previous activity, the **standard deviation** (s) gives a simple measure of the spread or **dispersion** in data. The **variance** (s^2) is also a measure of dispersion, but the standard deviation is usually preferred because it is expressed in the original units. Two data sets could have exactly the same mean values, but very different values of dispersion. If we were simply to use the central tendency to compare these data sets, the results would (incorrectly) suggest that they were alike. The assumptions we make about a population will be affected by what the sample data tell us. This is why it is important that sample data are unbiased (e.g. collected by **random sampling**) and that the sample set is as large as practicable. This exercise will help to illustrate how the inferences we make about a population are influenced by the information provided by the sample data.

Random Sampling, Sample Size, and Dispersion in Data

Sample size and sampling bias can both affect the information we obtain when we sample a population. In this exercise you will calculate some descriptive statistics for some sample data.

The complete set of sample data we are working with comprises 689 length measurements of year zero (young of the year) perch (column left). Basic descriptive statistics for the data have bee calculated for you below and the frequency histogram has also been plotted.

Look at this data set and then complete the exercise to calculate the same statistics from each of two smaller data sets (tabulated right) drawn from the same population. This exercise shows how random sampling, large sample size, and sampling bias affect our statistical assessment of variation in a population.

Complete sample set
n = 689 (random)

Length in mm	*Freq*
25	1
26	0
27	0
28	0
29	0
30	0
31	0
32	2
33	3
34	3
35	4
36	5
37	10
38	23
39	22
40	33
41	39
42	41
43	41
44	36
45	49
46	32
47	14
48	32
49	27
50	25
51	24
52	17
53	18
54	27
55	21
56	20
57	11
58	18
59	16
60	22
61	13
62	8
63	10
64	5
65	7
66	2
67	3
68	3
69	1
70	0
71	1
	689

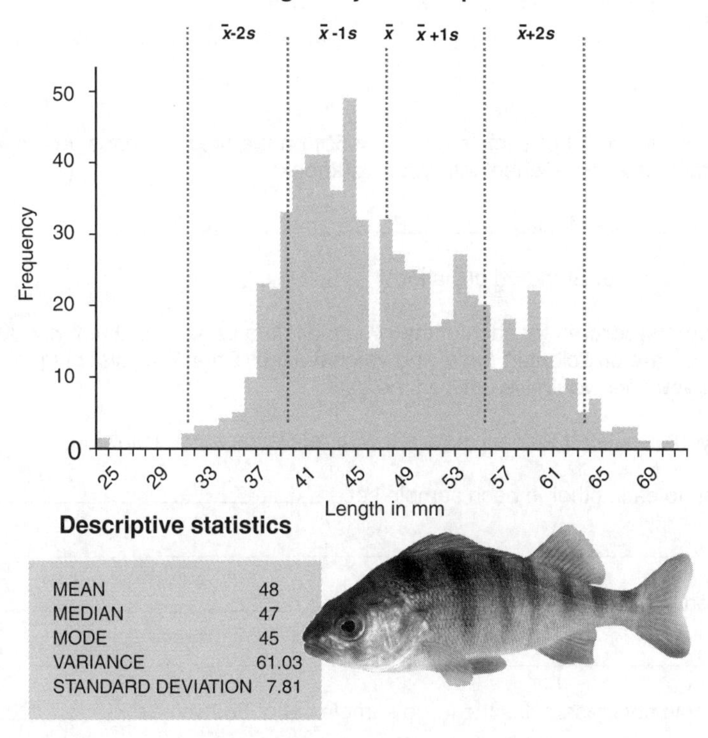

Descriptive statistics

MEAN	48
MEDIAN	47
MODE	45
VARIANCE	61.03
STANDARD DEVIATION	7.81

Small sample set
n = 30 (random)

Length in mm	*Freq*
25	1
26	0
27	0
28	0
29	0
30	0
31	0
32	0
33	0
34	0
35	2
36	0
37	0
38	3
39	2
40	1
41	3
42	0
43	0
44	0
45	0
46	1
47	0
48	2
49	0
50	0
51	1
52	3
53	0
54	0
55	0
56	0
57	1
58	0
59	3
60	2
61	2
62	0
63	0
64	0
65	0
66	0
67	2
68	1
	30

This population was sampled randomly to obtain this data set

This column records the number of fish of each size

Number of fish in the sample

Small sample set
n = 50 (bias)

Length in mm	*Freq*
46	1
47	0
48	0
49	1
50	0
51	0
52	1
53	1
54	1
55	1
56	0
57	2
58	2
59	4
60	1
61	0
62	8
63	10
64	13
65	2
66	0
67	2
	50

The person gathering this set of data was biased towards selecting larger fish because the mesh size on the net was too large to retain small fish

1. For the complete data set (n = 689) calculate the percentage of data falling within:

   (a) ± one standard deviation of the mean: ______________________

   (b) ± two standard deviations of the mean: ______________________

   (c) Explain what this information tells you about the distribution of year zero perch from this site: ______________________

   ____

2. Give another reason why you might reach the same conclusion about the distribution: ______________________

   ____

Karori age zero perch 12-15 F

	A	B	C
1		LENGTH	WEIGHT
2		25	0.15
3		35	0.44
4		35	0.44
5		38	0.57
6		38	0.57
7		38	0.57
8		39	0.61
9		39	0.61
10		40	0.67
11		41	0.72
12		41	0.72
13		41	0.72
14		46	1.03
15		48	1.18
16		48	1.18
17		51	1.43
18		[illegible]	1.52
19		[illegible]	1.52
20		[illegible]	1.52
21		[illegible]	2.04
22		[illegible]	2.27
23		[illegible]	2.27
24		[illegible]	2.27
25		60	2.39
26		60	2.39
27		61	2.52
28		61	2.52
29		67	3.39
30		67	3.39
31		68	3.56
32			
33			
34	N		=COUNT(B2:B31)
35	MEAN		=AVERAGE(B2:B31)
36	MEDIAN		=MEDIAN(B2:B31)
37	MODE		=MODE(B2:B31)
38	VARIANCE		=VAR(B2:B31)
39	STANDARD DEVIATION		=STDEV(B2:B31)
40			
41			

Enter the data values in separate cells under an appropriate descriptor

The variables being measured. Both length and weight were measured, but here we are working with only the length data.

Ignore this WEIGHT column. Sometimes the data we are interested in is part of larger data set.

The cells for the calculations below are B2 to B31

Type in the name of the statistic Excel will calculate. This gives you a reference for the row of values.

Type the formula into the cell beside its label. When you press return, the cell will contain the calculated value.

Calculating Descriptive Statistics Using *Excel*

You can use *Microsoft Excel* or other similar spreadsheet program to easily calculate descriptive statistics for sample data.

In this first example, the smaller data set (n = 30) is shown as it would appear on an *Excel* spreadsheet, ready for the calculations to be made. Use this guide to enter your data into a spreadsheet and calculate the descriptive statistics as described.

When using formulae in *Excel*, = indicates that a formula follows. The cursor will become active and you will be able to select the cells containing the data you are interested in, or you can type the location of the data using the format shown. The data in this case are located in the cells B2 through to B31 (B2:B31).

3. For this set of data, use a spreadsheet to calculate:

   (a) Mean: ____________________

   (b) Median: ____________________

   (c) Mode: ____________________

   (d) Sample variance: ____________________

   (e) Standard deviation: ____________________

   Staple the spreadsheet into your workbook.

4. Repeat the calculations for the second small set of sample data (n = 50) on the previous page. Again, calculate the statistics as indicated below and staple the spreadsheet into your workbook:

   (a) Mean: ____________________ (b) Median: ____________________ (c) Mode:

   (d) Variance: ____________________ (e) Standard deviation: ____________

5. On a separate sheet, plot **frequency histograms** for each of the two small data sets. Label them n = 30 and n = 50. Staple them into your workbook. If you are proficient in *Excel* and you have the "Data Analysis" plug in loaded, you can use *Excel* to plot the histograms for you once you have entered the data.

6. Compare the descriptive statistics you calculated for each data set with reference to the following:

   (a) How close the median and mean to each other in each sample set: ____________________

   (b) The size of the standard deviation in each case: ____________________

   (c) How close each small of the sample sets resembles the large sample set of 689 values: ____________________

7. (a) Compare the two frequency histograms you have plotted for the two smaller sample data sets: ____________________

   (b) Why do you think two histograms look so different? ____________________

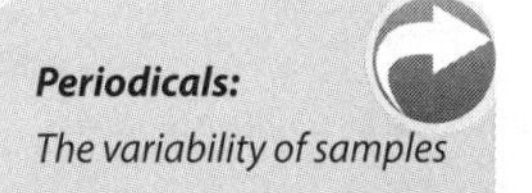

ISBN: 978-1-877462-96-2

The Reliability of the Mean

You have already seen how to use the **standard deviation** (s) to quantify the spread or **dispersion** in your data. Usually, you will also want to know how good your sample mean ($\bar{x}$) is as an estimate of the true population mean (μ). This can be indicated by the standard error of the mean (or just **standard error** or SE). **SE** is often used as an error measurement because it allows you calculate the **95% confidence interval (95% CI)**. 95% CIs are a key part of inferential statistics, i.e. you are using your sample data to make inferences about an entire population. The calculation and use of 95% CIs is outlined in this activity. By the time you have completed it, you should be able to:

- Enter data and calculate descriptive statistics using a spreadsheet program such as *Microsoft Excel*. You can follow this procedure for any set of data.
- Calculate standard error and 95% confidence intervals for sample data and plot these data appropriately with error bars.
- Interpret the graphically presented data and reach tentative conclusions about the findings of an experiment.

When we measure a particular attribute from a sample of a larger population and calculate a mean for that attribute, we can calculate how closely our sample mean (the statistic) is to the true population mean for that attribute (the parameter). **Example:** If we calculated the mean number of carapace spots from a sample of six ladybird beetles, how reliable is this statistic as an indicator of the mean number of carapace spots in the whole population? We can find out by calculating the **95% confidence interval**.

Reliability of the Sample Mean

When we take measurements from samples of a larger population, we are using those samples as indicators of the trends in the whole population. Therefore, when we calculate a sample mean, it is useful to know how close that value is to the true population mean (μ). This is not merely an academic exercise; it will enable you to make inferences about the aspect of the population in which you are interested. For this reason, statistics based on samples and used to estimate population parameters are called **inferential statistics**.

The Standard Error (SE)

The standard error (SE) is simple to calculate and is usually a small value. Standard error is given by:

$$SE = \frac{s}{\sqrt{n}}$$

where s = the standard deviation, and n = sample size.

Standard errors are sometimes plotted as error bars on graphs, but it is more meaningful to plot the **95% confidence intervals** (see box below). All calculations are easily made using a spreadsheet (see opposite).

The 95% Confidence Interval

SE is required to calculate the 95% confidence interval (CI) of the mean. This is given by:

$$95\%\ CI = SE \times t_{P(n-1)}$$

Do not be alarmed by this calculation; once you have calculated the value of the SE, it is a simple matter to multiply this value by the value of t at P = 0.05 (from the t table) for the appropriate degrees of freedom (df) for your sample (n – 1).

For example: where the SE = 0.6 and the sample size is 10, the calculation of the 95% CI is:

$$95\%\ CI = 0.6 \times 2.262 = \boxed{1.36}$$

Part of the t table is given to the right for P = 0.05. Note that, as the sample becomes very large, the value of t becomes smaller. For very large samples, t is fixed at 1.96, so the 95% CI is slightly less than twice the SE

All these statistics, including a plot of the data with Y error bars, can be calculated using a program such as *Microsoft Excel.*

Critical values of Student's t distribution at P = 0.05.

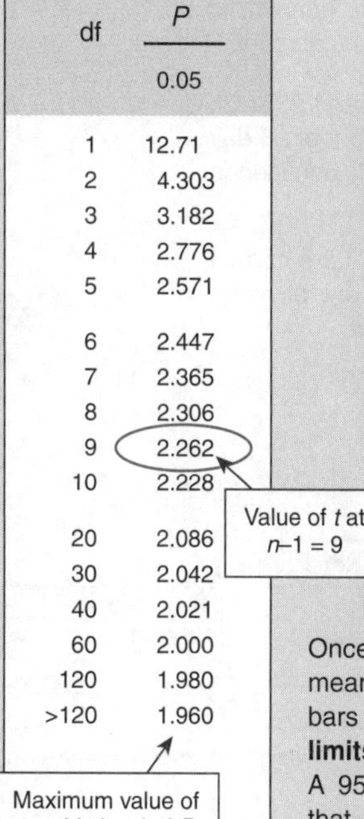

df	P 0.05
1	12.71
2	4.303
3	3.182
4	2.776
5	2.571
6	2.447
7	2.365
8	2.306
9	2.262
10	2.228
20	2.086
30	2.042
40	2.021
60	2.000
120	1.980
>120	1.960

Relationship of Y against X (± 95% confidence intervals, n = 10)

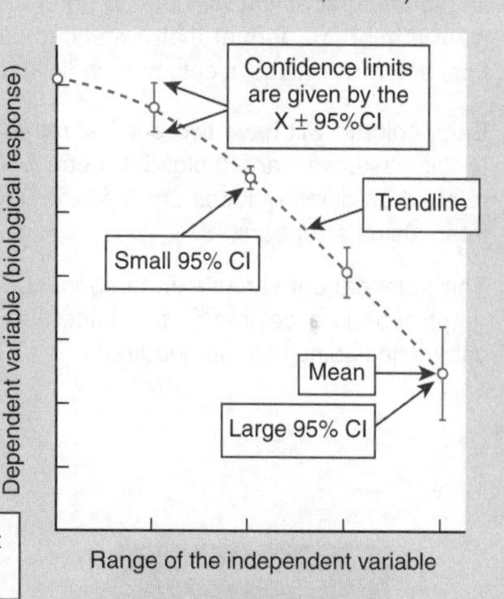

Plotting your confidence intervals

Once you have calculated the 95% CI for the means in your data set, you can plot them as error bars on your graph. Note that the **95% confidence limits** are given by the value of the **mean ± 95%CI**. A 95% confidence limit (i.e. P = 0.05) tells you that, on average, 95 times out of 100, the limits will contain the true population mean.

ISBN: 978-1-877462-96-2

Periodicals: *Estimating the mean and standard deviation*

Related activities: *Descriptive Statistics, Taking the Next Step*

Weblinks: *Introduction to Descriptive Statistics*

Comparing Treatments Using Descriptive Statistics

In an experiment, the growth of newborn rats on four different feeds was compared by weighing young rats after 28 days on each of four feeding regimes. The suitability of each food type for maximizing growth in the first month of life was evaluated by comparing the means of the four experimental groups. Each group comprised 10 individual rats. All 40 newborns were born to sibling mothers with the same feeding history. For this activity, follow the steps outlined below and reproduce them yourself.

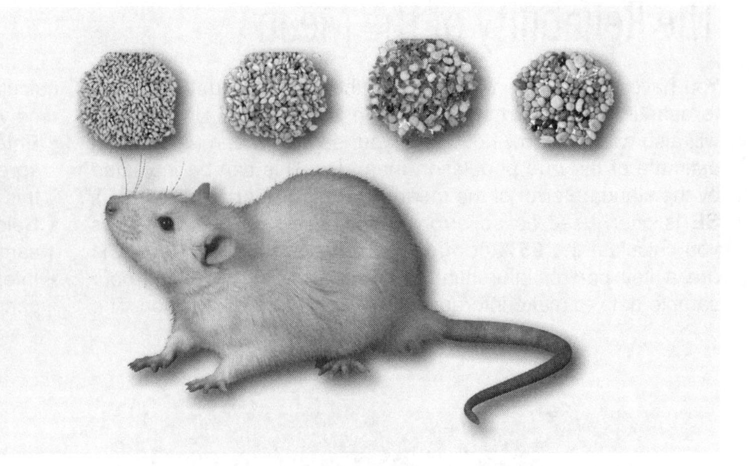

1 Calculating Descriptive Statistics

Entering your data and calculating descriptive statistics.

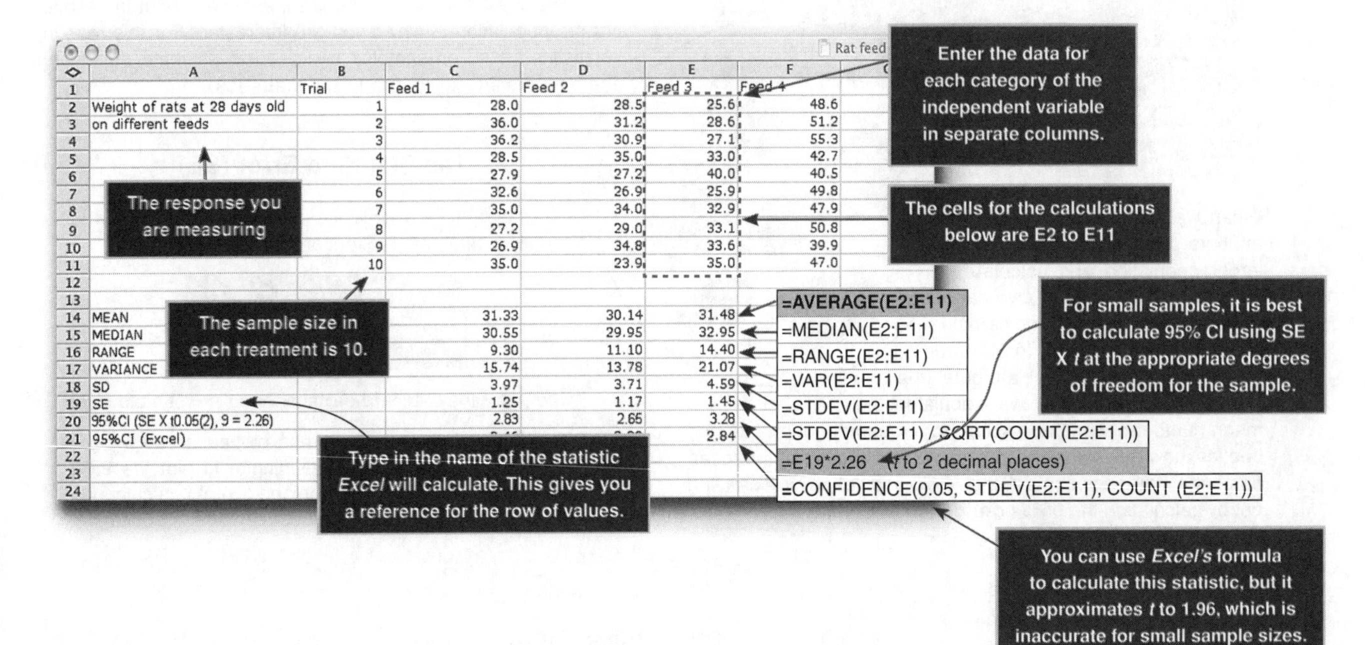

	A	B	C	D	E	F
1		Trial	Feed 1	Feed 2	Feed 3	Feed 4
2	Weight of rats at 28 days old	1	28.0	28.5	25.6	48.6
3	on different feeds	2	36.0	31.2	28.6	51.2
4		3	36.2	30.9	27.1	55.3
5		4	28.5	35.0	33.0	42.7
6		5	27.9	27.2	40.0	40.5
7		6	32.6	26.9	25.9	49.8
8		7	35.0	34.0	32.9	47.9
9		8	27.2	29.0	33.1	50.8
10		9	26.9	34.8	33.6	39.9
11		10	35.0	23.9	35.0	47.0
12						
13						
14	MEAN		31.33	30.14	31.48	
15	MEDIAN		30.55	29.95	32.95	
16	RANGE		9.30	11.10	14.40	
17	VARIANCE		15.74	13.78	21.07	
18	SD		3.97	3.71	4.59	
19	SE		1.25	1.17	1.45	
20	95%CI (SE X t0.05(2), 9 = 2.26)		2.83	2.65	3.28	
21	95%CI (Excel)		[illegible]	[illegible]	2.84	
22						
23						
24						

2 Drawing the Graph

To plot the graph, you will need to enter the data values you want to plot in a format that *Excel* can use (above). To do this, enter the values in columns under each category.

- Each column will have two entries: mean and 95% CI. In this case, we want to plot the mean weight of 28 day rats fed on different foods and add the 95% confidence intervals as error bars.
- The independent variable is categorical, so the correct graph type is a column chart. Select the row of mean values (including column headings).

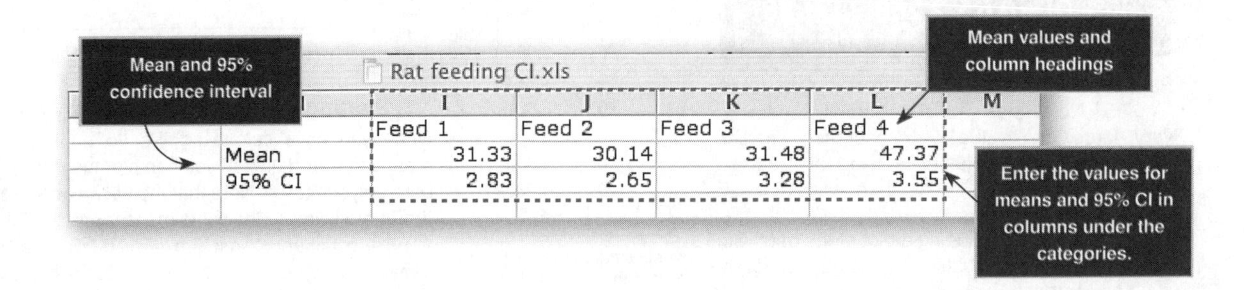

	I	J	K	L
	Feed 1	Feed 2	Feed 3	Feed 4
Mean	31.33	30.14	31.48	47.37
95% CI	2.83	2.65	3.28	3.55

ISBN: 978-1-877462-96-2

STEP 1:
From the menu bar choose: **Insert > Chart > Column**. This is **Step 1** in the Chart Wizard. Click **Next**.

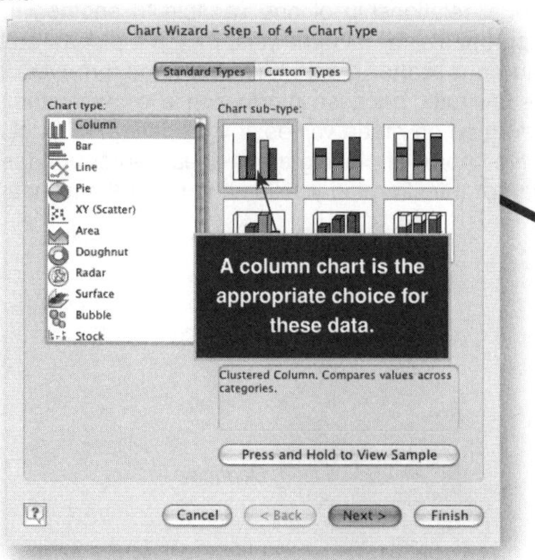

STEP 2:
Click **Next**.

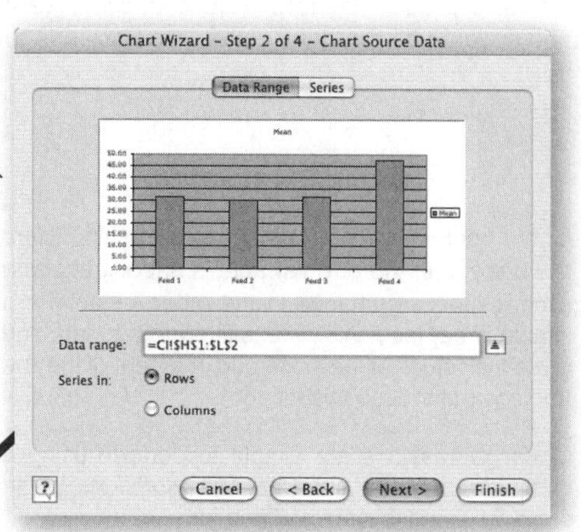

STEP 3:
You have the option to add a title, labels for your X and Y axes, turn off gridlines, and add (or remove) a legend (key). When you have added all the information, click **Next**.

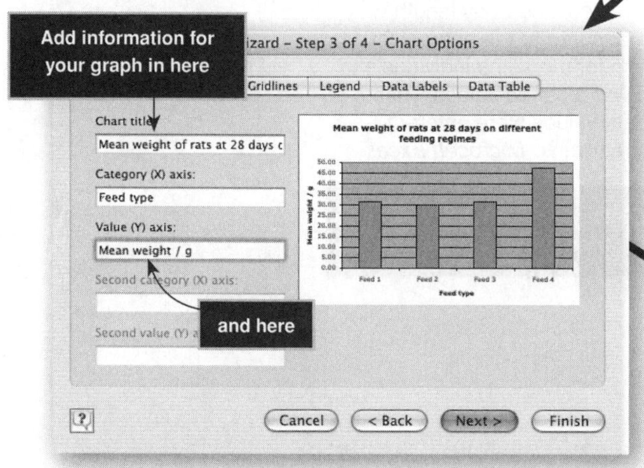

STEP 4:
Specify the chart location. It should appear "as object in" Sheet 1 by default. Click on the chart and move it to reveal the data.

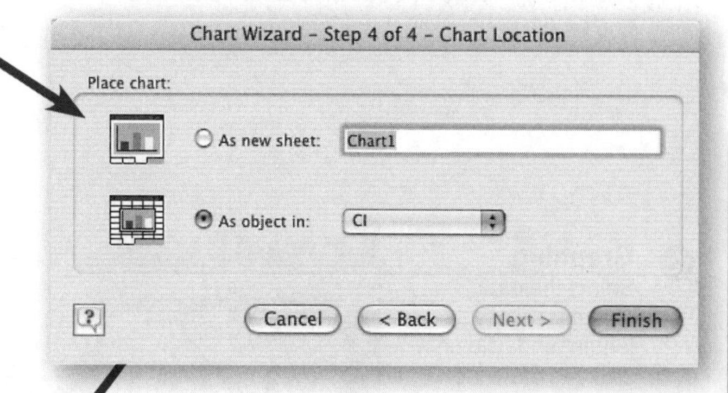

3 Formatting the graph

A chart will appear on the screen. Right click (Ctrl-click on Mac) on any part of any column and choose **Format data series**. To add error bars, select the Y error bars tab, and click on the symbol that shows Display both. Click on Custom, and use the data selection window to select the row of 95% CI data for "+" and "–" fields.

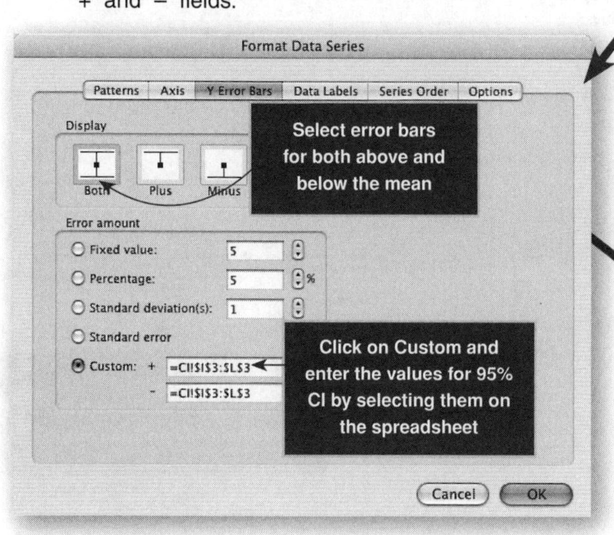

Click on OK and your chart will plot with error bars.

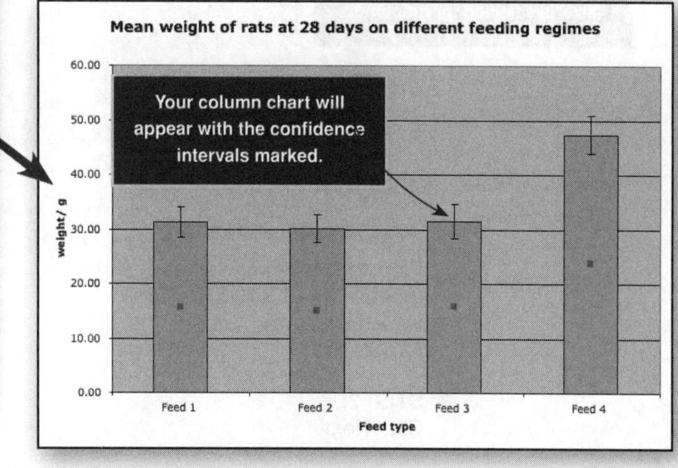

ISBN: 978-1-877462-96-2

Linear Regression

Regression is a test for an association, relationship, or trend between two variables. It is suitable for continuous data when you have a reason to believe that the changes in one variable cause changes in the other, i.e. regression assumes a cause and effect. A regression is also predictive; the **regression equation** will be able to predict unknown values of the Y variable within the range covered by the data. Linear regression is the simplest functional relationship of one variable to another. If your data are appropriate for this analysis, they will plot as a straight line spread on a scatter graph. It is best to perform your regression on the raw data, because information is lost when the calculation is performed on mean values. If your data plot is not linear, you have the choice of plotting a non-linear regression (see the next activity) or transforming your data to make them linear.

Linear Regression

Linear regression is a simple relationship where the change in the one variable is associated with a corresponding change in the other variable in a simple linear fashion. A line is fitted to the data and gives the values of the slope and intercept of the line (the computer does this for you).

Linear regressions are simple to perform using a computer program such as *Microsoft Excel*. The steps for doing this are outlined here.

Clutch Size vs Body Size in *Daphnia*

Daphnia is a small, freshwater crustacean common in water bodies throughout the world. In *Daphnia*, body size largely determines how many eggs are carried (the clutch size). This is because the eggs are carried in a brood pouch, which physically limits the size of the clutch. Larger animals can also process more food. The relationship between body size and clutch size can be described with a regression.

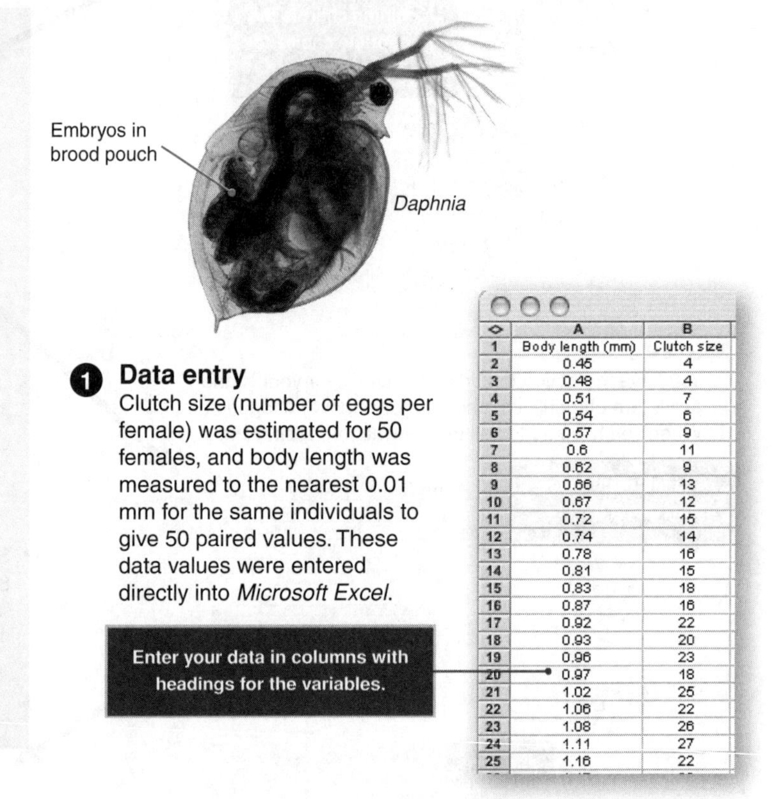

	A	B
1	Body length (mm)	Clutch size
2	0.45	4
3	0.48	4
4	0.51	7
5	0.54	6
6	0.57	9
7	0.6	11
8	0.62	9
9	0.66	13
10	0.67	12
11	0.72	15
12	0.74	14
13	0.78	16
14	0.81	15
15	0.83	18
16	0.87	16
17	0.92	22
18	0.93	20
19	0.96	23
20	0.97	18
21	1.02	25
22	1.06	22
23	1.08	26
24	1.11	27
25	1.16	22

1 Data entry

Clutch size (number of eggs per female) was estimated for 50 females, and body length was measured to the nearest 0.01 mm for the same individuals to give 50 paired values. These data values were entered directly into *Microsoft Excel*.

Enter your data in columns with headings for the variables.

2 Graphing

Select the data columns: "Body length" and "Clutch size". To draw the graph, follow the four **Chart Wizard** steps outlined below and on the following page.

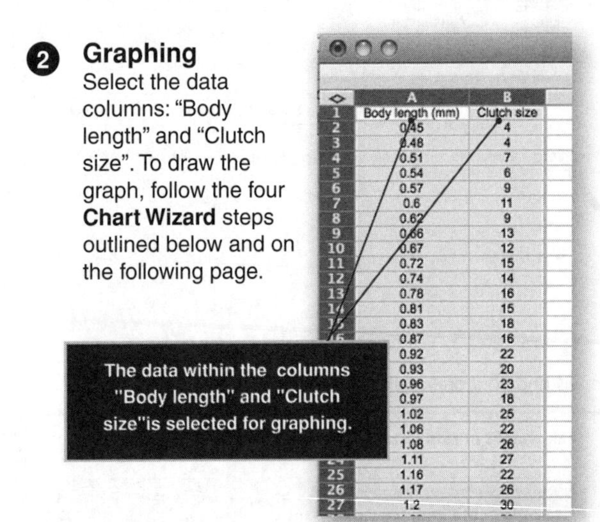

	A	B
1	Body length (mm)	Clutch size
2	0.45	4
3	0.48	4
4	0.51	7
5	0.54	6
6	0.57	9
7	0.6	11
8	0.62	9
9	0.66	13
10	0.67	12
11	0.72	15
12	0.74	14
13	0.78	16
14	0.81	15
15	0.83	18
16	0.87	16
17	0.92	22
18	0.93	20
19	0.96	23
20	0.97	18
21	1.02	25
22	1.06	22
23	1.08	26
24	1.11	27
25	1.16	22
26	1.17	26
27	1.2	30

The data within the columns "Body length" and "Clutch size" is selected for graphing.

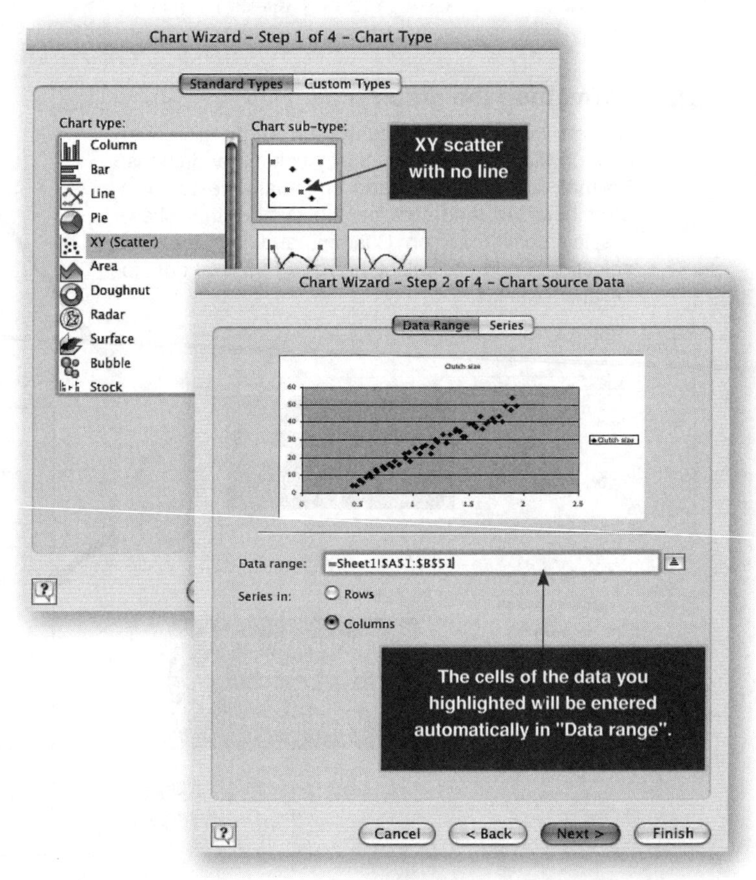

▶ **STEP 1**:
From the menu bar choose **Insert** > **Chart** > **XY (Scatter)**. Click on the option with no line. Click **Next**.

▶ **STEP 2**:
Click **Next**.

Related activities: Further Data Transformations, Drawing Scatter Plots, Descriptive Statistics, Non-Linear Regression

ISBN: 978-1-877462-96-2

▶ **STEP 3**:
You will have the option to add a title, labels for your X and Y axes, turn off gridlines, and add a legend (key). You may wish to do this in *Excel* (now or after drawing the graph), or add them yourself, by hand, later.
Click **Next**.

▶ **STEP 4**:
Specify the chart location. It should appear "as object in" Sheet 1 by default. You can choose to have the chart appear in another worksheet if you wish.
Click **Finish**.

Adjust chart axes, gridlines, legend, labels.

Chart Wizard - Step 3 of 4 - Chart Options

Titles | Axes | Gridlines | Legend | Data Labels

Chart title: Clutch size vs body size in Daph

Value (X) Axis: Body size (mm)

Value (Y) axis: Number of eggs

Second category (X) axis:

Second value (Y) axis:

Add information for your graph in here

Cancel | < Back | Next >

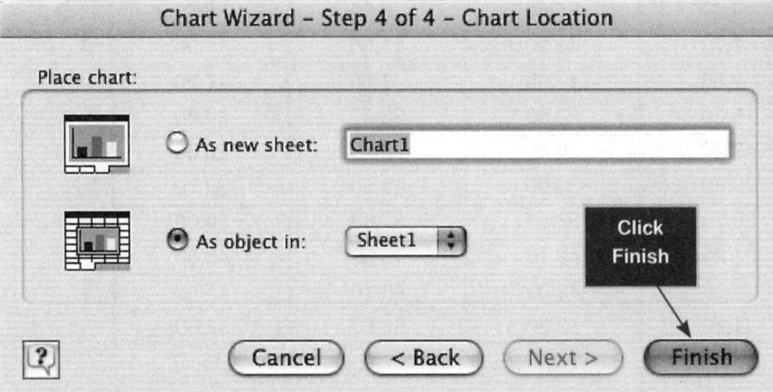

3 Fitting the regression line

A chart will appear on the screen. If necessary, click on the chart and move it slightly to reveal the data.

To add the trendline, **right click** (Ctrl-click on Mac) on any data point on the graph, choose:
Add Trendline
Choose **Type** > **Linear**.

Click on the Options tab and click on the check boxes for **Display equation on chart** and **Display R2 value on chart**. **Click OK**.
The equation is a text box that can be moved by clicking and dragging with the mouse.

Labels for the X and Y axes are added by right clicking within the plot area, and choosing Chart Options and the Titles tab.

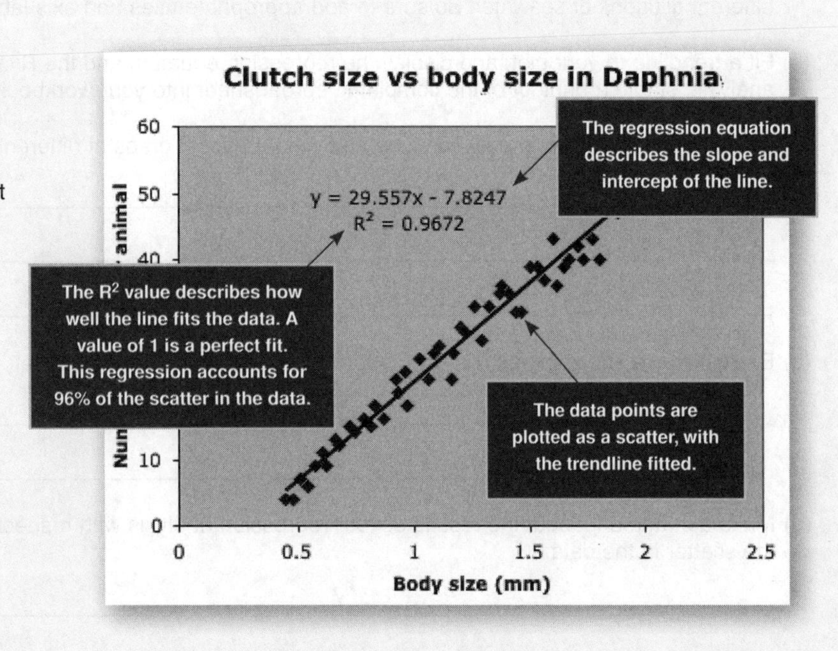

1. Explain why the data for clutch size and body size in *Daphnia* are appropriate for analysis with a linear regression:

ISBN: 978-1-877462-96-2

2. A student's experiment, investigated the effect of increasing seawater dilution on cumulative weight gain (as an indication of osmoregulatory ability) of a common shore crab. Six crabs in total were used in the experiment. Three were placed in seawater dilution of 75:25 (75% seawater) and three were placed in a seawater dilution of 50:50 (50% seawater). Cumulative weight gain in each of the six crabs was measured at regular intervals over a period of 30 minutes. The results are tabulated below:

Time (min)	Crab weight gain at 75% seawater (mg)			Crab weight gain at 50% seawater (mg)		
	Crab number			Crab number		
	1	2	3	4	5	6
3	3.80	4.00	4.00	5.60	6.20	5.80
6	8.00	8.30	7.70	11.20	11.60	11.90
9	11.50	11.00	9.50	17.00	17.60	17.20
12	14.80	15.10	15.20	23.50	23.60	24.00
15	18.90	19.50	19.70	29.00	28.20	28.60
18	23.50	22.90	23.80	33.00	32.50	32.70
21	26.50	26.90	26.70	37.50	37.60	39.00
24	31.50	32.00	31.20	43.10	43.50	43.60
27	35.00	35.50	35.50	48.00	48.10	47.50
30	40.00	40.10	41.20	53.00	52.60	52.80

(a) Following the steps outlined on the previous pages, enter these data in an appropriate way on a spreadsheet (e.g. *Microsoft Excel*) and plot a scatter plot to show the relationship between time and weight gain in crabs held at two different dilutions of seawater. Be sure to add appropriate titles and axis labels to your graph as you proceed.

(b) Fit a trendline to your plot, and display the regression equation and the R^2 value. When you have finished your analysis, staple a printout of the completed spreadsheet into your workbook.

(c) Describe the relationship between time and weight gain in crabs at different seawater dilutions: ______

(d) Explain why a linear regression is an appropriate analysis for this data set: ______

(e) Make a statement about the results of your regression analysis with respect to how well the regression accounts for the scatter in the data:

(f) Discuss the limitations of this experimental design: ______

(g) Suggest ways in which the experimental design could be improved: ______

ISBN: 978-1-877462-96-2

Non-linear Regression

The degree to which organisms respond physiologically to their environment depends on the type of organism and how tolerant they are of environmental changes. Biological responses are often not described by a simple linear relationship (although they may be linear when transformed). Many metabolic relationships are non-linear because organisms function most efficiently within certain environmental limits. When you plot the data for these kinds of relationships, they will plot out as something other than a straight line. An example of non-linear regression is described below for egg development time in *Daphnia*.

1 Data entry

Create a table in your spreadsheet with your summary data in columns, as shown below. Your raw data may already be entered in the spreadsheet and you can use the spreadsheet to calculate the **summary statistics**. See the activity on the Analysis of Variance for guidance on how to do this.

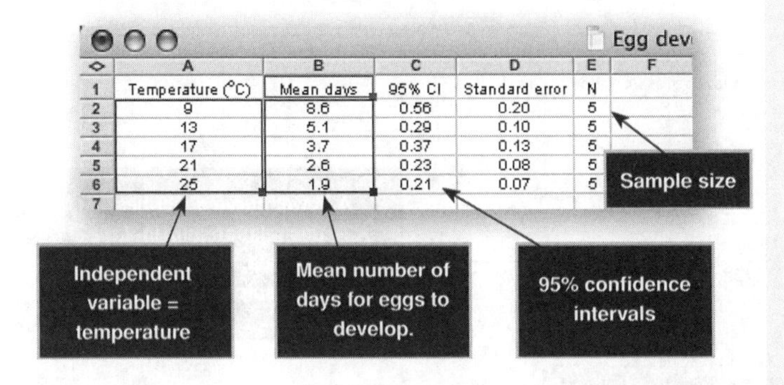

	A	B	C	D	E	F
1	Temperature (°C)	Mean days	95% CI	Standard error	N	
2	9	8.6	0.56	0.20	5	
3	13	5.1	0.29	0.10	5	
4	17	3.7	0.37	0.13	5	
5	21	2.6	0.23	0.08	5	
6	25	1.9	0.21	0.07	5	
7						

Egg Development Time in *Daphnia*

In *Daphnia*, the **egg development time** (EDT) is the time from egg deposition to release of the young from the brood pouch. From an experiment that measured EDT at controlled temperatures, means and 95% confidence intervals were calculated from a sample size of five animals at each of five temperatures between 9 and 25°C. The aim of this activity is to demonstrate an analysis of a non-linear metabolic relationship by:

- Plotting egg development time (in days) against water temperature (in °C).
- Adding error bars for the means.
- Fitting a nonlinear regression and showing the line equation and the R^2 value, which is a measure of appropriateness of the model describing the line. Here, we have used a power model, but if you have a non-linear relationship, you could also try a polynomial as a model (another choice in Chart Wizard).

2 Graphing

To perform this regression, follow the same sequence of steps to those in the earlier activity (linear regression).

▶ **STEP 1**:
First, highlight the data columns: **Temperature** and **Mean days**. From the menu bar choose **Insert > Chart > XY (Scatter)**, and click on the option with no line. This is **Step 1** of 4 in the Chart Wizard. Click **Next**.

▶ **STEP 2:**
Click **Next**.

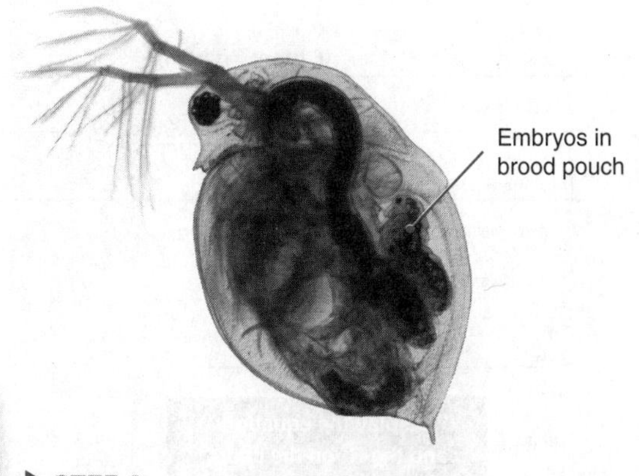

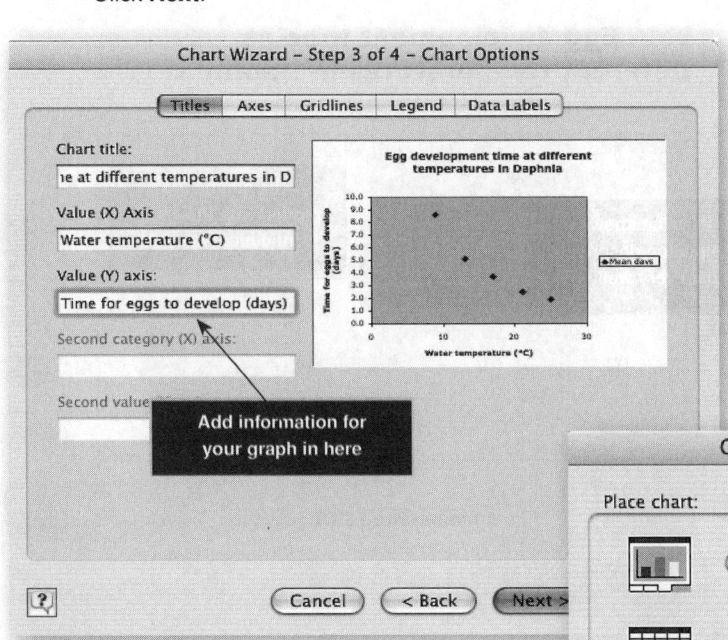

▶ **STEP 3**:
You have the option to add a title, labels for your X and Y axes, turn off gridlines, and add (or remove) a legend (key). When you have added all the information you want, click **Next**.

▶ **STEP 4**:
Specify the chart location. It should appear "as object in" Sheet 1 by default. Click on the chart and move it to reveal the data.

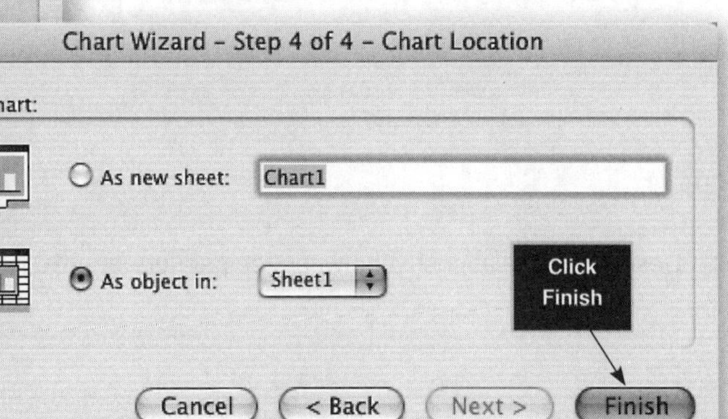

ISBN: 978-1-877462-96-2

Related activities: *Descriptive Statistics, The Reliability of the Mean, Linear Regression*

3 Fitting the regression line

A chart will appear on the screen. **Right click** (Ctrl-click on Mac) on any data point on the graph and choose **Format data series**. To add error bars, select the **Y error bars** tab, and click on the symbol that shows Display both.

Click on Custom, and use the data selection window to select the data under the 95% CI column label.

To add **trendline, right click** (Ctrl-click on Mac) on any data point on the graph, and choose **Add Trendline** and **Power**. Click on the Options tab to display the regression equation and the R^2 value.

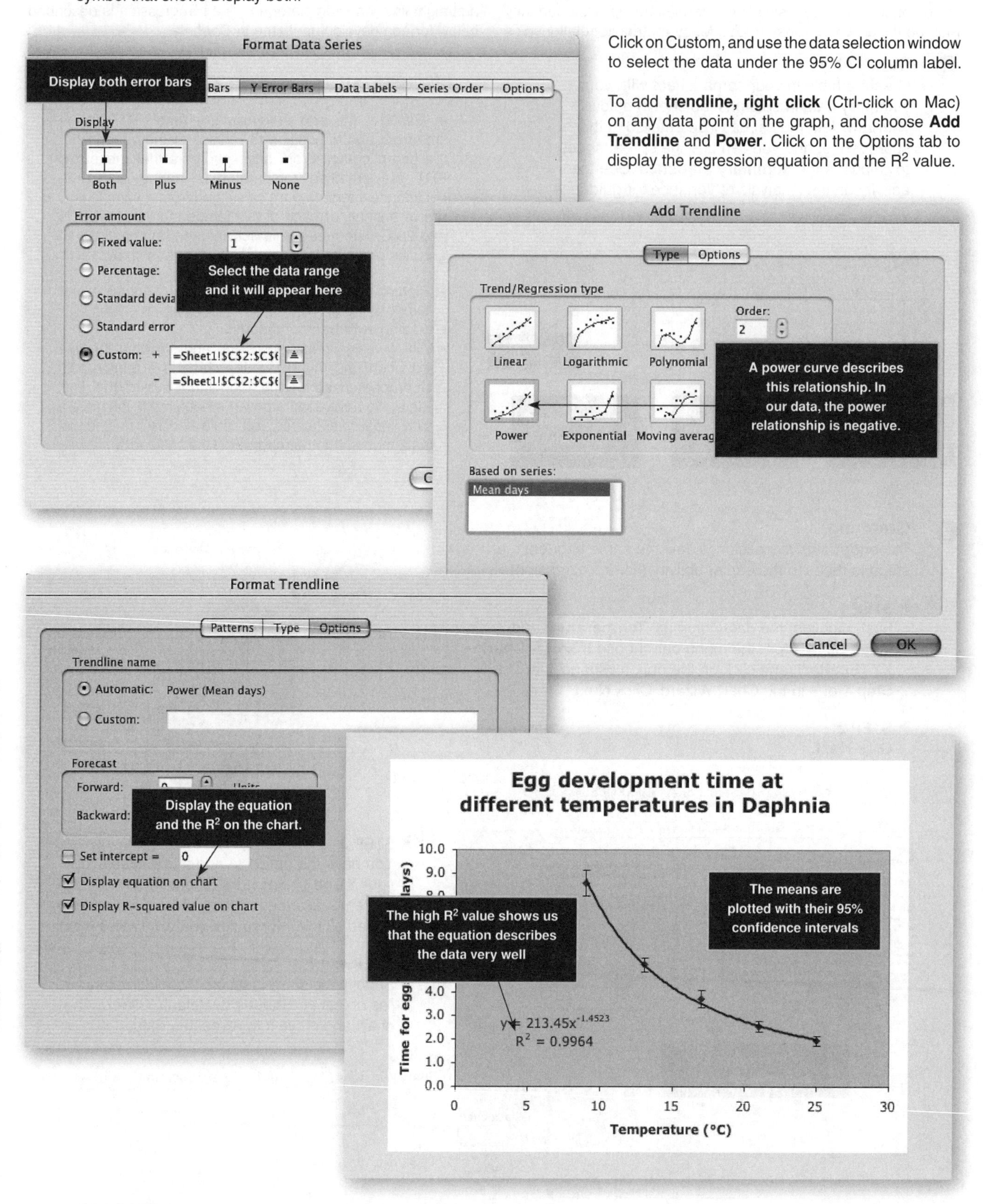

1. Describe the relationship between temperature and EDT in *Daphnia*: ______________________

____

____

____

ISBN: 978-1-877462-96-2

The Student's *t* Test

The Student's *t* test is a commonly used test when comparing two sample means, e.g. means for a treatment and a control in an experiment, or the means of some measured characteristic between two animal or plant populations. The test is a powerful one, i.e. it is a good test for distinguishing real but marginal differences between samples. The *t* test is a simple test to apply, but it is only valid for certain situations. It is a two-group test and is not appropriate for multiple use i.e. sample 1 vs 2, then sample 1 vs 3. *You must have only two sample means to compare.* You are also assuming that the data have a normal (not skewed) distribution, and the scatter (standard deviations) of the data points is similar for both samples. You may wish to exclude obvious outliers from your data set for this reason. Below is a simple example outlining the general steps involved in the Student's *t* test. The following is a simple example using a set of data from a fictitious experiment involving a treatment and a control (the units are not relevant in this case, only the values). A portion of the Student's *t* table is provided, sufficient to carry out the test. Follow the example through, making sure that you understand what is being done at each step.

Steps in performing a Student's *t* test

Explanatory notes

Step 1 ***Calculate basic summary statistics for your two data sets***

Control (A): 6.6, 5.5, 6.8, 5.8, 6.1, 5.9 $n_A = 6$, $\bar{x}_A = 6.12$, $s_A = 0.496$

Treatment (B): 6.3, 7.2, 6.5, 7.1, 7.5, 7.3 $n_B = 6$, $\bar{x}_B = 6.98$, $s_B = 0.475$

n_A and n_B are the number of values in the first and second data sets respectively (these need not be the same). $\bar{x}$ is the mean. ***s*** is the standard deviation (a measure of scatter in the data).

Step 2 ***Set up and state your null hypothesis (H_0)***

H_0: there is no treatment effect. The differences in the data sets are the result of chance variation only and they are not really different

The alternative hypothesis is that there is a treatment effect and the two sets of data are truly different.

Step 3 ***Decide if your test is one or two tailed***

This tells you what section of the t table to consult. Most biological tests are two-tailed. Very few are one-tailed.

A one-tailed test looks for a difference only in one particular direction. A two-tailed test looks for any difference (+ or –).

Step 4 ***Calculate the t statistic***

For our sample data above the calculated value of t is –3.09. The degrees of freedom (df) are $n_1 + n_2 - 2 = 10$.

Calculation of the *t* value uses the variance which is simply the square of the standard deviation (s^2). You may compute the *t* value by entering your data onto a computer and using a simple statistical program.

It does not matter if your calculated *t* value is a positive or negative (the sign is irrelevant). If you do not have access to a statistical program, computation of *t* is not difficult. Step 4 (calculating *t*) is described in the following *t* test exercises.

Step 5 ***Consult the t table of critical values***

Selected critical values for Student's t statistic (two-tailed test)

Degrees of freedom	$P = 0.05$	$P = 0.01$	$P = 0.001$
5	2.57	4.03	6.87
10	2.23	3.17	4.59
15	2.13	2.95	4.07
20	2.09	2.85	3.85

Critical value of *t* for 10 degrees of freedom. The calculated *t* value must exceed this

The absolute value of the *t* statistic (3.09) well exceeds the critical value for $P = 0.05$ at 10 degrees of freedom.

We can reject H_0 and conclude that the means are different at the 5% level of significance.

If the calculated absolute value of *t* had been less than 2.23, we could not have rejected H_0.

1. (a) In an experiment, data values were obtained from four plants in experimental conditions and three plants in control conditions. The mean values for each data set (control and experimental conditions) were calculated. The *t* value was calculated to be 2.16. The null hypothesis was: "The plants in the control and experimental conditions are not different". State whether the calculated *t* value supports the null hypothesis or its alternative (consult *t* table above):

   (b) The experiment was repeated, but this time using 6 control and 6 "experimental" plants. The new *t* value was 2.54. State whether the calculated *t* value supports the null hypothesis or its alternative now:

2. Explain why, in terms of applying Student's *t* test, extreme data values (outliers) are often excluded from the data set(s):

3. Explain what you understand by statistical significance (for any statistical test):

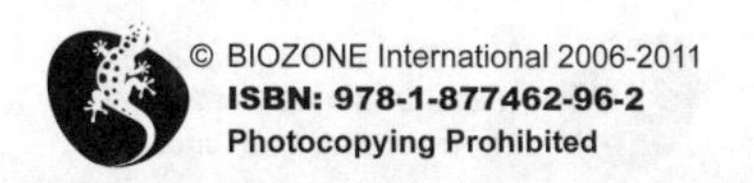

ISBN: 978-1-877462-96-2

Related activities: *Descriptive Statistics, The Reliability of the Mean*
Weblinks: *Student's t-tests*

Student's *t* Test Exercise

Data from two flour beetle populations are given below. Ten samples were taken from each population and the number of beetles in each sample were counted. The student's *t* test is used to determine if the densities of the two populations were significantly different. The exercise below uses a workbook computation to determine a *t* value. Follow the steps to complete the test. The calculations are also very simple yo do using a spreadsheet programme such as Excel (see the following page).

1. (a) Complete the calculations to perform the *t* test for these two populations. Some calculations are provided for you.

x (counts)		$x - \bar{x}$ (deviation from the mean)		$(x - \bar{x})^2$ (deviation from mean)^2	
Popn A	**Popn B**	**Popn A**	**Popn B**	**Popn A**	**Popn B**
465	310	9.3	−10.6	86.5	112.4
475	310	19.3	−10.6	372.5	112.4
415	290				
480	355				
436	350				
435	335				
445	295				
460	315				
471	316				
475	330				
$n_A = 10$	$n_B = 10$			$\Sigma(x - \bar{x})^2$	$\Sigma(x - \bar{x})^2$

The number of samples in each data set

The sum of each column is called the sum of squares

(b) The variance for population A: s^2_A =

The variance for population B: s^2_B =

(c) The difference between the population means

$(\bar{x}_A - \bar{x}_B)$ =

(d) $t_{(calculated)}$ =

(e) Determine the degrees of freedom (d.f.)

d.f. $(n_A + n_B - 2)$ =

(f) P =

$t_{(critical\ value)}$ =

(g) Your decision is:

Step 1: Summary statistics

Tabulate the data as shown in the first 2 columns of the table (left). Calculate the mean and give the n value for each data set. Compute the standard deviation if you wish.

Popn A $\bar{x}_A = 455.7$, $n_A = 10$, $s_A = 21.76$

Popn B $\bar{x}_B = 320.6$, $n_B = 10$, $s_B = 21.64$

Step 2: State your null hypothesis

Step 3: Decide if your test is one or two tailed

Calculating the t value

Step 4a: Calculate sums of squares

Complete the computations outlined in the table left. The sum of each of the final two columns (left) is called the sum of squares.

Step 4b: Calculate the variances

Calculate the variance (s^2) for each set of data. This is the sum of squares divided by $n - 1$ (number of samples in each data set − 1). In this case the n values are the same, but they need not be.

$$s^2_A = \frac{\Sigma(x - \bar{x})^2_{(A)}}{n_A - 1} \qquad s^2_B = \frac{\Sigma(x - \bar{x})^2_{(B)}}{n_B - 1}$$

Step 4c: Differences between means

Calculate the *actual* difference between the means

$$(\bar{x}_A - \bar{x}_B)$$

Step 4d: Calculate t

Calculate the *t* value. Ask for assistance if you find interpreting the lower part of the equation difficult

$$t = \frac{(\bar{x}_A - \bar{x}_B)}{\sqrt{\frac{s^2_A}{n_A} + \frac{s^2_B}{n_B}}}$$

Step 4e: Determine the degrees of freedom

Degrees of freedom (d.f.) are defined by the number of samples (e.g. counts) taken: d.f. = $n_A + n_B - 2$ where n_A and n_B are the number of counts in each of populations A and B.

Step 5: Consult the t table

Consult the *t*-tables (opposite page) for the critical *t* value at the appropriate degrees of freedom and the acceptable probability level (e.g. P = 0.05).

Step 5a: Make your decision

Make your decision whether or not to reject H_0. If your *t* value is large enough you may be able to reject H_0 at a lower *P* value (e.g. 0.001), increasing your confidence in the alternative hypothesis.

ISBN: 978-1-877462-96-2

2. The previous example (manual calculation for two beetle populations) is outlined below in a spreadsheet (created in *Microsoft Excel*). The spreadsheet has been shown in a special mode with the formulae displayed. Normally, when using a spreadsheet, the calculated values will appear as the calculation is completed (entered) and a formula is visible only when you click into an individual cell. When setting up a spreadsheet, you can arrange your calculating cells wherever you wish. What is important is that you accurately identify the cells being used for each calculation. Also provided below is a summary of the spreadsheet notations used and a table of critical values of t at different levels of P. Note that, for brevity, only some probability values have been shown. To be significant at the appropriate level of probability, calculated values must be greater than those in the table for the appropriate degrees of freedom.

   (a) Using the data in question 1, set up a spreadsheet as indicated below to calculate t. Save your spreadsheet. Print it out and staple the print-out into your workbook.

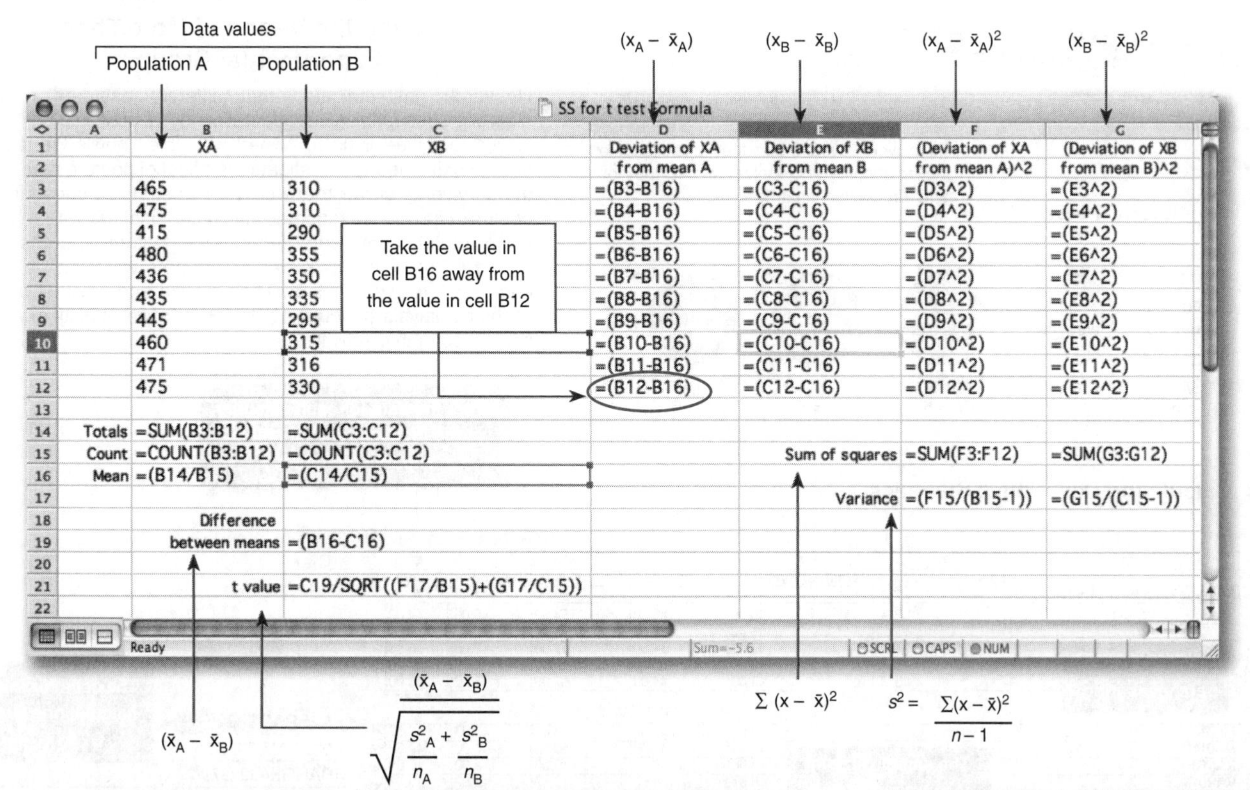

Notation	Meaning
Columns and rows	Columns are denoted A, B, C ... at the top of the spreadsheet, rows are 1, 2, 3, ... on the left. Using this notation a cell can be located e.g. C3
=	An "equals" sign before other entries in a cell denotes a formula.
( )	Parentheses are used to group together terms for a single calculation. This is important for larger calculations (see cell C21 above)
C3:C12	Cell locations are separated by a colon. C3:C12 means "every cell between and including C3 and C12"
SUM	Denotes that what follows is added up. =SUM(C3:C12) means "add up the values in cells C3 down to C12"
COUNT	Denotes that the number of values is counted =COUNT(C3:C12) means "count up the number of values in cells C3 down to C12"
SQRT	Denotes "take the square root of what follows"
^2	Denotes an exponent e.g. x^2 means that value x is squared.

Above is a table explaining some of the spreadsheet notations used for the calculation of the t value for the exercise on the previous page. It is not meant to be an exhaustive list for all spreadsheet work, but it should help you to become familiar with some of the terms and how they are used. This list applies to *Microsoft Excel*. Different spreadsheets may use different notations. These will be described in the spreadsheet manual.

Table of critical values of t at different levels of P.

Degrees of freedom	Level of Probability 0.05	0.01	0.001
1	12.71	63.66	636.6
2	4.303	9.925	31.60
3	3.182	5.841	12.92
4	2.776	4.604	8.610
5	2.571	4.032	6.869
6	2.447	3.707	5.959
7	2.365	3.499	5.408
8	2.306	3.355	5.041
9	2.262	3.250	4.781
10	2.228	3.169	4.587
11	2.201	3.106	4.437
12	2.179	3.055	4.318
13	2.160	3.012	4.221
14	2.145	2.977	4.140
15	2.131	2.947	4.073
16	2.120	2.921	4.015
17	2.110	2.898	3.965
18	2.101	2.878	3.922
19	2.093	2.861	3.883
20	2.086	2.845	3.850

   (b) Save your spreadsheet under a different name and enter the following new data values for population B: **425, 478, 428, 465, 439, 475, 469, 445, 421, 438**. Notice that, as you enter the new values, the calculations are updated over the entire spreadsheet. Re-run the t-test using the new t value. State your decision for the two populations now:

   New t value: ____________________ Decision on null hypothesis (delete one): Reject / Do not reject

ISBN: 978-1-877462-96-2

Comparing More Than Two Groups

The Student's t test is limited to comparing two groups of data. To compare more than two groups at once you need to use a test that is appropriate to this aim. One such test, appropriate for normally distributed data, is an analysis of variance (**ANOVA**), as described in the next activity. However such an analysis may not be necessary if there is a clear difference between treatments in an experiment. You can go a long way in your analysis by plotting your data, together with some measure of the spread around the central tendency. For normally distributed data, this is likely to be the mean and the 95% confidence interval (95% CI). In the example described below, students recorded the survival of weevil larvae on five different pasture types and calculated descriptive statistics for the data. After you have worked through the analysis, you should be able to enter your own data and calculate descriptive statistics using *Microsoft Excel®*. The plot of the experiment is provided in the next page of this activity.

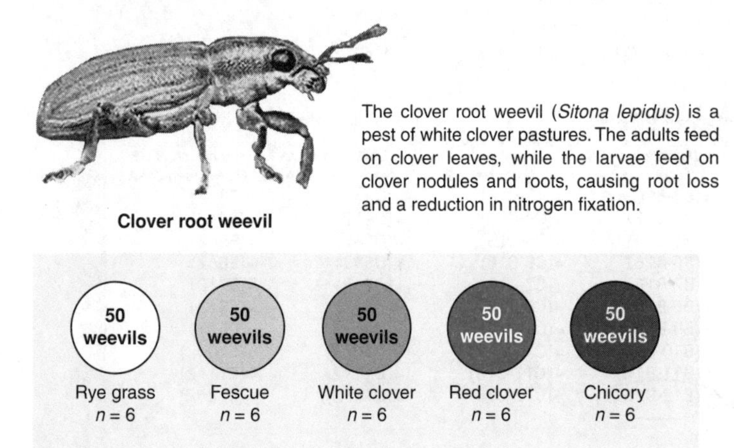

Clover root weevil

The clover root weevil (*Sitona lepidus*) is a pest of white clover pastures. The adults feed on clover leaves, while the larvae feed on clover nodules and roots, causing root loss and a reduction in nitrogen fixation.

Comparing the Means of More Than Two Experimental Groups

Research has indicated that different pastures have different susceptibility to infestation by a pest insect, the clover root weevil (left). Armed with this knowledge, two students decided to investigate the effect of pasture type on the survival of clover root weevils. The students chose five pasture types, and recorded the number of weevil larvae (from a total of 50) surviving in each pasture type after a period of 14 days. Six experimental pots were set up for each pasture type (n = 6). Their results and the first part of their analysis (calculating the descriptive statistics) are presented in this activity.

1 Calculating Descriptive Statistics

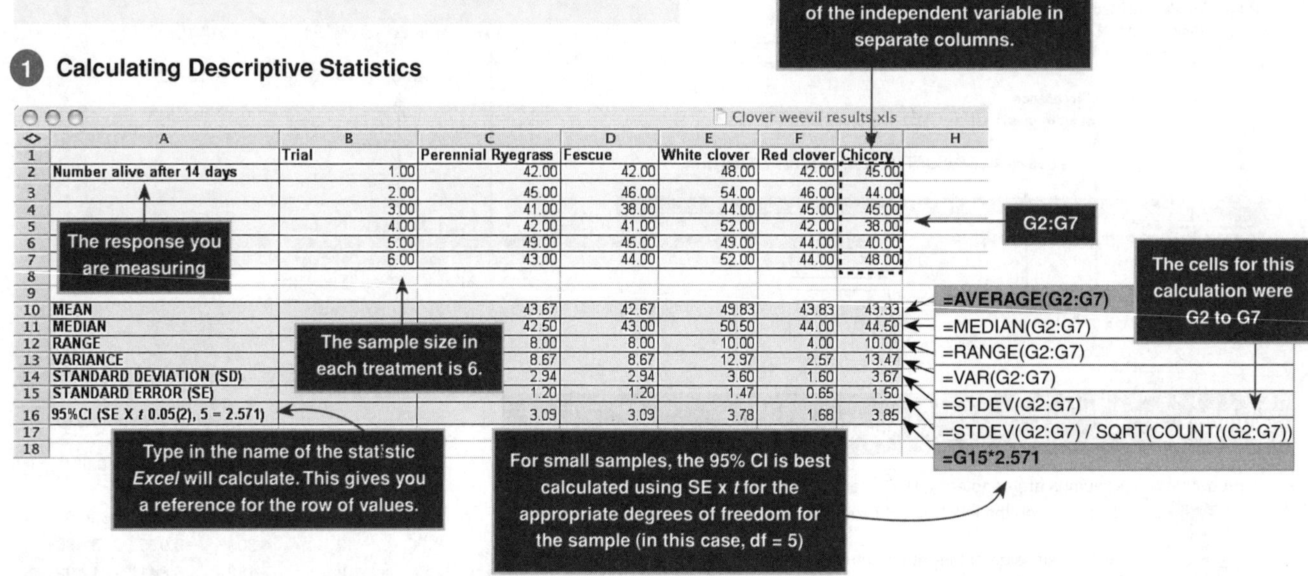

Clover weevil results.xls

	A	B	C	D	E	F	G
1		Trial	Perennial Ryegrass	Fescue	White clover	Red clover	Chicory
2	Number alive after 14 days	1.00	42.00	42.00	48.00	42.00	45.00
3		2.00	45.00	46.00	54.00	46.00	44.00
4		3.00	41.00	38.00	44.00	45.00	45.00
5		4.00	42.00	41.00	52.00	42.00	38.00
6		5.00	49.00	45.00	49.00	44.00	40.00
7		6.00	43.00	44.00	52.00	44.00	48.00
8							
9							
10	MEAN		43.67	42.67	49.83	43.83	43.33
11	MEDIAN		42.50	43.00	50.50	44.00	44.50
12	RANGE		8.00	8.00	10.00	4.00	10.00
13	VARIANCE		8.67	8.67	12.97	2.57	13.47
14	STANDARD DEVIATION (SD)		2.94	2.94	3.60	1.60	3.67
15	STANDARD ERROR (SE)		1.20	1.20	1.47	0.65	1.50
16	95%CI (SE X t 0.05(2), 5 = 2.571)		3.09	3.09	3.78	1.68	3.85

	J	K	L	M	N
	nial Ryegrass	Fescue	White clover	Red clover	Chicory
Mean	43.67	42.67	49.83	43.83	43.33
95% CI	3.09	3.09	3.78	1.68	3.85

Enter the values for means and 95% CI in columns under the categories.

2 To plot a graph in *Excel*, you will need to enter the values for the data you want to plot in a format that *Excel* can use. To do this, enter the values in columns under each category (left). Each column will have two entries: mean and 95% CI. In this case, we want to plot the mean survival of weevils in different pasture types and add the 95% CI as error bars. You are now ready to plot the data set. Recall the design of this experiment. The independent variable is categorical, so the correct graph type is a **column chart**.

1. Identify the number of treatments in this experimental design: ______________________

2. Identify the independent variable for this experiment: ______________________

3. Identify the dependent variable for this experiment: ______________________

4. Identify the type of graph you would use to plot this data set and explain your choice: ______________________

____

5. Explain what the 95% confidence interval tells you about the means for each treatment: ______________________

____

____

ISBN: 978-1-877462-96-2

Related activities: Analysis of Variance

3 Drawing the Graph

Recall the design of this experiment. The independent variable is categorical, so the correct graph type is a column chart. To plot the graph, select the row of mean values (including column headings) from the small table of results you constructed (screen, right).

▶ **STEP 1**:
From the menu bar choose:
Insert > Chart > Column. Click **Next**.

▶ **STEP 2**:
The data range you have selected (the source data for the chart) will appear in the "Data range" window. Click **Next**.

▶ **STEP 3**:
You have the option to add a title, labels for your X and Y axes, turn off grid lines, and add or remove a legend (a legend or key is useful when you have two or more columns, such as males and females, for each treatment). When you have added all the information you want, click **Next**.

▶ **STEP 4**:
Specify the chart location. It should appear in the active sheet by default. Click on the chart and move it to reveal the data.

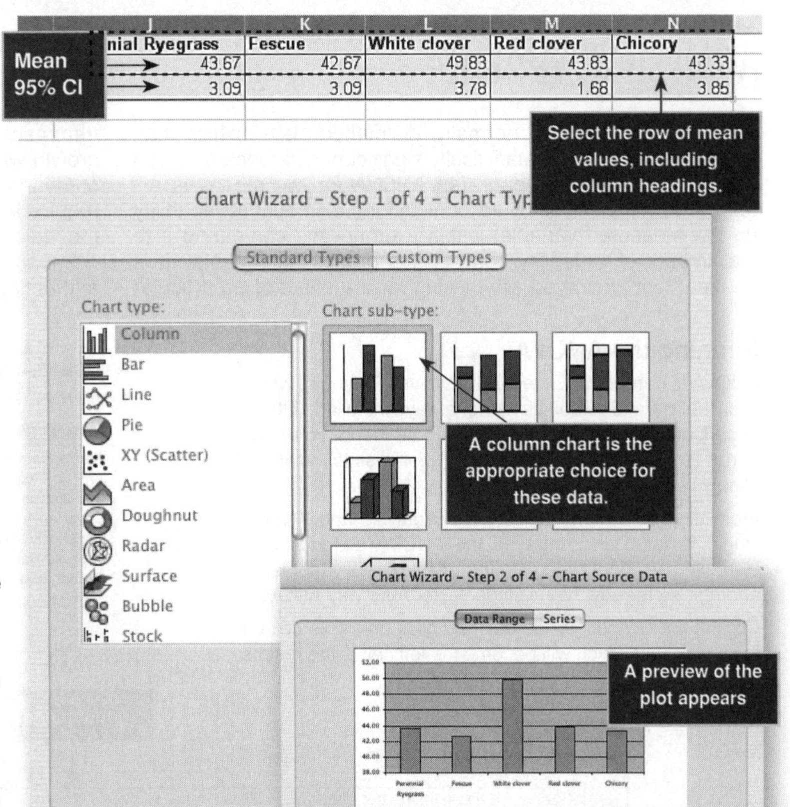

	nial Ryegrass	Fescue	White clover	Red clover	Chicory
Mean	43.67	42.67	49.83	43.83	43.33
95% CI	3.09	3.09	3.78	1.68	3.85

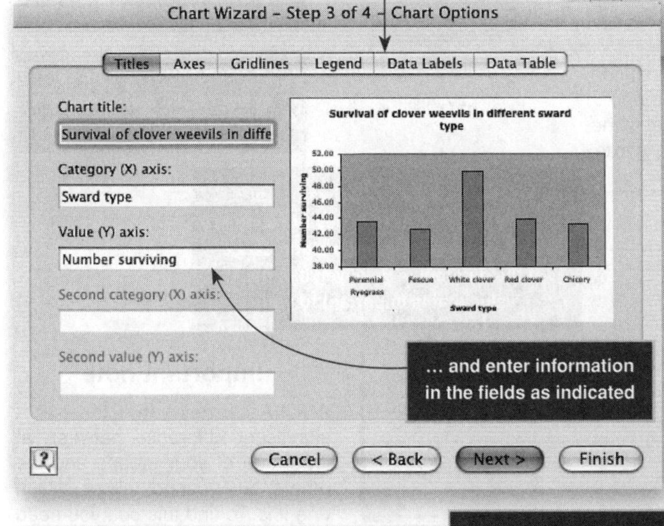

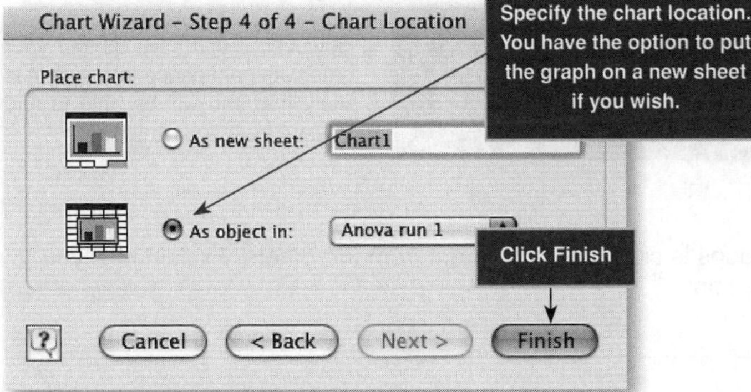

4 Formatting the Graph

A chart will appear. Right click on any part of any column and choose **Format data series**. To add error bars, select the Y error bars tab, and click on the symbol that shows Display both (below). Click on Custom, and use the data selection window to select the row of 95% CI data. Click **OK**.

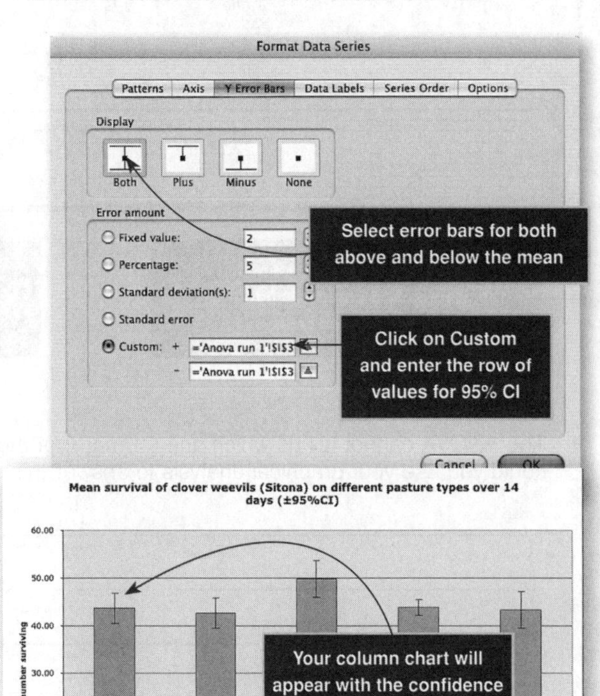

After you have added error bars using the "Format data series" option, your chart will plot with error bars. These error bars represent the 95% confidence intervals for the mean of each treatment. The completed plot gives you a visual representation of your data and an immediate idea as to how confident you can be about the differences between the five treatments. From this data we can see that the white clover offers significantly different survival for larvae than the other treatments. Can you explain why?

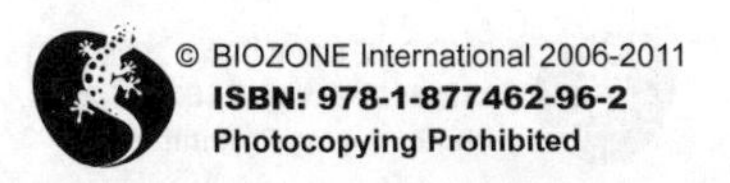

ISBN: 978-1-877462-96-2

Analysis of Variance

ANOVA is a test for normally distributed data, which can determine if there is a statistically significant difference between two or more sample means (an ANOVA for two means is a *t* test). ANOVA does this by accounting for the amount of variability (in the measured variable) within a group and comparing it to the amount of variability between the groups (treatments). It is an ideal test when you are looking for the effect of a particular treatment on some kind of biological response, e.g. plant growth with different fertilizers. ANOVA is a very useful test for comparing multiple samples because, like the *t* test, it does not require large sample sizes. The ANOVA described below tests the data on weevil survival provided in the previous activity *Comparing More Than Two Groups*. Review that activity before attempting this final stage of the analysis.

Running the ANOVA

ANOVA is part of the *Excel* "Data Analysis Toolpak", which is part of normal *Excel*, but is not always installed. If there is no Data Analysis option on the Tools menu, you need to run *Excel* from the original installation disk to install the "Analysis Toolpak add-in".

From the Tools menu select Data Analysis and ANOVA single factor. This brings up the ANOVA dialogue box. Here we are concerned with the effect of one variable on another, so the ANOVA is single factor (one way ANOVA).

Click in the Output Range box and click on a free cell on the worksheet which will become the left cell of the results table. Click OK.

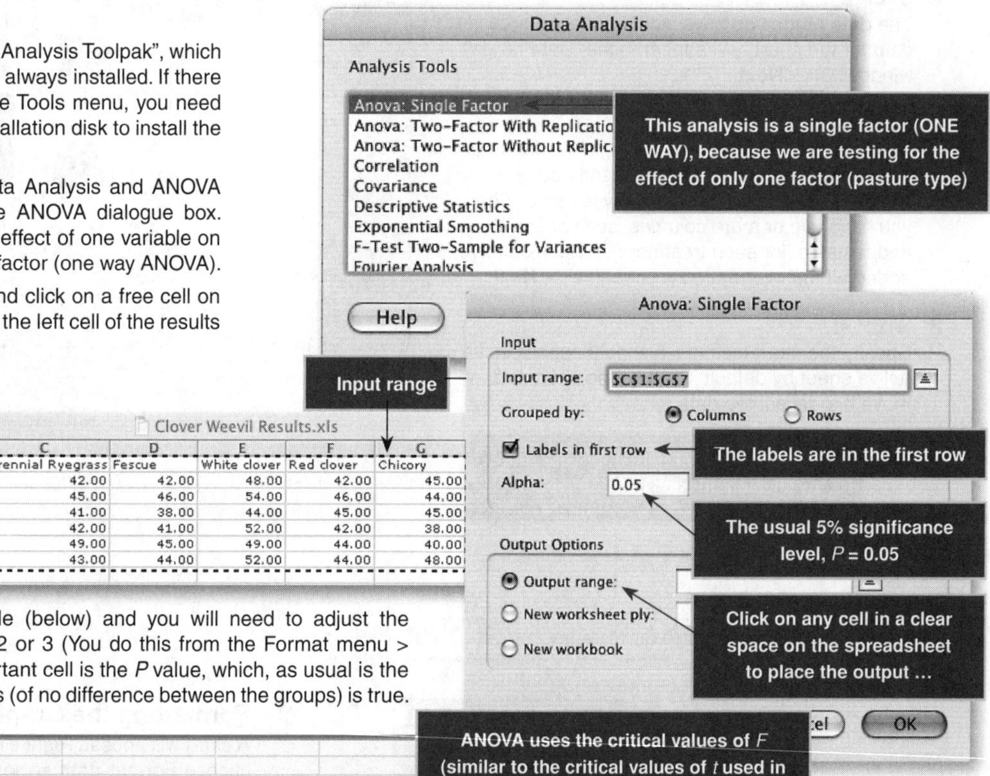

A	B	C	D	E	F	G
	Trial	Perennial Ryegrass	Fescue	White clover	Red clover	Chicory
Number alive after 14 days	1.00	42.00	42.00	48.00	42.00	45.00
	2.00	45.00	46.00	54.00	46.00	44.00
	3.00	41.00	38.00	44.00	45.00	45.00
	4.00	42.00	41.00	52.00	42.00	38.00
	5.00	49.00	45.00	49.00	44.00	40.00
	6.00	43.00	44.00	52.00	44.00	48.00

The output is a large data table (below) and you will need to adjust the number of significant figures to 2 or 3 (You do this from the Format menu > Cells > Number). The most important cell is the *P* value, which, as usual is the probability that the null hypothesis (of no difference between the groups) is true.

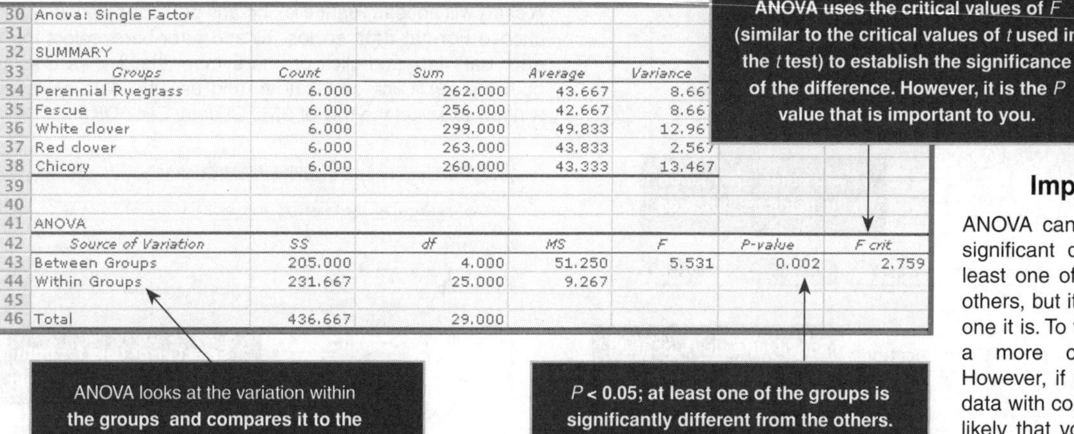

30	Anova: Single Factor						
31							
32	SUMMARY						
33	*Groups*	*Count*	*Sum*	*Average*	*Variance*		
34	Perennial Ryegrass	6.000	262.000	43.667	8.667		
35	Fescue	6.000	256.000	42.667	8.667		
36	White clover	6.000	299.000	49.833	12.967		
37	Red clover	6.000	263.000	43.833	2.567		
38	Chicory	6.000	260.000	43.333	13.467		
39							
40							
41	ANOVA						
42	*Source of Variation*	*SS*	*df*	*MS*	*F*	*P-value*	*F crit*
43	Between Groups	205.000	4.000	51.250	5.531	0.002	2.759
44	Within Groups	231.667	25.000	9.267			
45							
46	Total	436.667	29.000				

Important note

ANOVA can tell you if there is a significant difference between at least one of your groups and the others, but it cannot tell you which one it is. To find this out, you need a more complicated analysis. However, if you have plotted your data with confidence intervals, it is likely that you will be able to find this out from your graph.

1. The ANOVA cannot tell us which one (or more) of the groups is significantly different from the others. Explain how you could you use your graphical analysis to answer this question:

ISBN: 978-1-877462-96-2

Related activities: *Comparing More Than Two Groups*

Using the Chi-Squared Test in Ecology

The **chi-squared test** (χ^2), like the student's *t* test, is a test for difference between data sets, but it is used when you are working with frequencies (counts) rather than measurements. It is a simple test to perform but the data must meet the requirements of the test. These are as follows:

- It can only be used for data that are raw counts (not measurements or derived data such as percentages).
- It is used to compare an experimental result with an expected theoretical outcome (e.g. an expected Mendelian ratio or a theoretical value indicating "no preference" or "no difference" between groups in a response such as habitat preference).
- It is not a valid test when sample sizes are small (<20).

Like all statistical tests, it aims to test the null hypothesis; the hypothesis of no difference between groups of data. The following exercise is a worked example using chi-squared for testing an ecological study of habitat preference. As with most of these simple statistical tests, chi-squared is easily calculated using a spreadsheet.

Using χ^2 in Ecology

In an investigation of the ecological niche of the mangrove, *Avicennia marina var. resinifera*, the density of pneumatophores was measured in regions with different substrate. The mangrove trees were selected from four different areas: mostly sand, some sand, mostly mud, and some mud. Note that the variable, substrate type, is categorical in this case. Quadrats (1 m by 1 m) were placed around a large number of trees in each of these four areas and the numbers of pneumatophores were counted. Chi-squared was used to compare the observed results for pneumatophore density (as follows) to an expected outcome of no difference in density between substrates.

Mangrove pneumatophore density in different substrate areas

Mostly sand	**85**	Mostly mud	**130**
Some sand	**102**	Some mud	**123**

Using χ^2, the probability of this result being consistent with the expected result could be tested. Worked example as follows:

Step 1: Calculate the expected value (E)

In this case, this is the sum of the observed values divided by the number of categories.

$$\frac{440}{4} = 110$$

Step 2: Calculate O – E

The difference between the observed and expected values is calculated as a measure of the deviation from a predicted result. Since some deviations are negative, they are all squared to give positive values. This step is usually performed as part of a tabulation (right, darker blue column).

Step 3: Calculate the value of χ^2

$$\chi^2 = \sum \frac{(O - E)^2}{E}$$

Where: O = the observed result
E = the expected result
Σ = sum of

The calculated χ^2 value is given at the bottom right of the last column in the tabulation.

Step 4: Calculating degrees of freedom

The probability that any particular χ^2 value could be exceeded by chance depends on the number of degrees of freedom. This is simply ***one less than the total number of categories*** (this is the number that could vary independently without affecting the last value). ***In this case: 4–1 = 3.***

Category	O	E	O–E	$(O-E)^2$	$\frac{(O-E)^2}{E}$
Mostly sand	85	110	-25	625	5.68
Some sand	102	110	-8	64	0.58
Mostly sand	130	110	20	400	3.64
Some sand	123	110	13	169	1.54
	Total = 440				χ^2 → Σ = 11.44

Step 5a: Using the χ^2 table

On the χ^2 table (part reproduced in Table 1 below) with 3 degrees of freedom, the calculated value for χ^2 of 11.44 corresponds to a probability of between 0.01 and 0.001 (see arrow). *This means that by chance alone a χ^2 value of 11.44 could be expected between 1% and 0.1% of the time.*

Step 5b: Using the χ^2 table

The probability of between 0.1 and 0.01 is lower than the 0.05 value which is generally regarded as significant. The null hypothesis can be rejected and we have reason to believe that the observed results differ significantly from the expected (at P = 0.05).

Table 1: Critical values of χ^2 at different levels of probability. By convention, the critical probability for rejecting the null hypothesis (H_0) is 5%. If the test statistic is less than the tabulated critical value for P = 0.05 we cannot reject H_0 and the result is not significant. If the test statistic is greater than the tabulated value for P = 0.05 we reject H_0 in favour of the alternative hypothesis.

Degrees of freedom	Level of probability (*P*)									
	0.98	**0.95**	**0.80**	**0.50**	**0.20**	**0.10**	**0.05**	**0.02**	**0.01**	**0.001**
1	0.001	0.004	0.064	0.455	1.64	2.71	3.84	5.41	6.64	χ^2 10.83
2	0.040	0.103	0.466	1.386	3.22	4.61	5.99	7.82	9.21	13.82
3	0.185	0.352	1.005	2.366	4.64	6.25	7.82	9.84	11.35	16.27
4	0.429	0.711	1.649	3.357	5.99	7.78	9.49	11.67	13.28	18.47
5	0.752	0.145	2.343	4.351	7.29	9.24	11.07	13.39	15.09	20.52
	← ***Do not reject H_0***							***Reject H_0*** →		

ISBN: 978-1-877462-96-2

Chi-Squared Exercise in Ecology

The following exercise illustrates the use of chi-squared (χ^2) in ecological studies of habitat preference. In the first example, it is used for determining if the flat periwinkle *(Littorina littoralis)* shows significant preference for any of the four species of seaweeds with which it is found. Using quadrats, the numbers of periwinkles associated with each seaweed species were recorded. The data from this investigation are provided for you in Table 1. In the second example, the results of an investigation into habitat preference in woodlice (also called pillbugs, sowbugs, or slaters) are presented for analysis (Table 2).

1. (a) State your null hypothesis for this investigation (H_0):

____

____

____

(b) State the alternative hypothesis (H_A): ______________________________

____

____

Table 1: Number of periwinkles associated with different seaweed species

Seaweed species	Number of periwinkles
Spiral wrack	9
Bladder wrack	28
Toothed wrack	19
Knotted wrack	64

2. Use the chi-squared test to determine if the differences observed between the samples are significant or if they can be attributed to chance alone. The table of critical values of χ^2 is provided in "*Using The Chi-Squared Test in Ecology*".

(a) Enter the observed values (no. of periwinkles) and complete the table to calculate the χ^2 value:

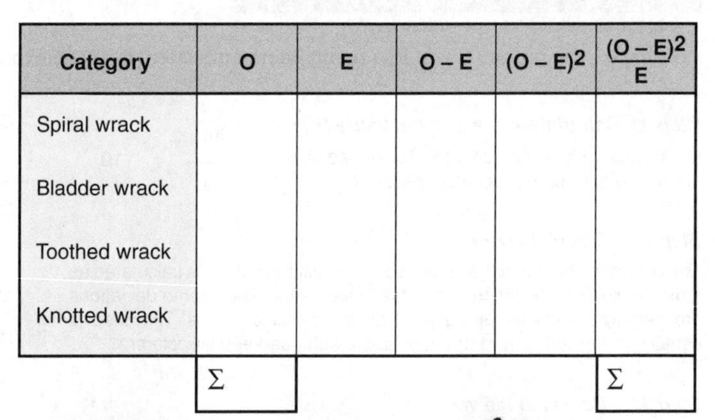

Category	O	E	O – E	$(O-E)^2$	$\frac{(O-E)^2}{E}$
Spiral wrack					
Bladder wrack					
Toothed wrack					
Knotted wrack					
	Σ				Σ

(b) Calculate χ^2 value using the equation:

$$\chi^2 = \sum \frac{(O-E)^2}{E} \qquad \chi^2 = \_\_\_\_\_\_\_\_$$

(c) Calculate the degrees of freedom: ______

(d) Using the χ^2, state the *P* value corresponding to your calculated χ^2 value:

____

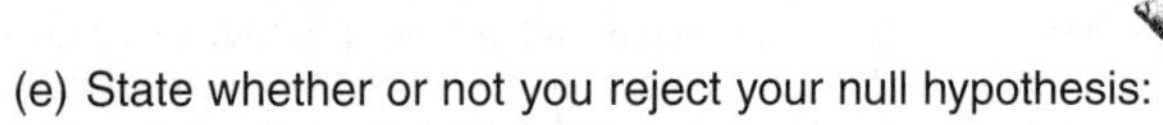

(e) State whether or not you reject your null hypothesis:

reject H_0 / do not reject H_0 (*circle one*)

3. Students carried out an investigation into habitat preference in woodlice. In particular, they were wanting to know if the woodlice preferred a humid atmosphere to a dry one, as this may play a part in their choice of habitat. They designed a simple investigation to test this idea. The woodlice were randomly placed into a choice chamber for 5 minutes where they could choose between dry and humid conditions (atmosphere). The investigation consisted of five trials with ten woodlice used in each trial. Their results are shown on Table 2 (right):

(a) State the null and alternative hypotheses (H_0 and H_A) :

____

____

Table 2: Habitat preference in woodlice

Trial	Atmosphere	
	Dry	Humid
1	2	8
2	3	7
3	4	6
4	1	9
5	5	5

Use a separate piece of paper (or a spreadsheet) to calculate the chi-squared value and summarize your answers below:

(b) Calculate χ^2 value: ____________

(c) Calculate the degrees of freedom and state the *P* value corresponding to your calculated χ^2 value: ____________

(d) State whether or not you reject your null hypothesis: reject H_0 / do not reject H_0 (*circle one*)

ISBN: 978-1-877462-96-2

Using the Chi-Squared Test in Genetics

The **chi-squared test**, χ^2, is frequently used for testing the outcome of dihybrid crosses against an expected (predicted) Mendelian ratio, and it is appropriate for use in this way. When using the chi-squared test for this purpose, the null hypothesis predicts the ratio of offspring of different phenotypes according to the expected Mendelian ratio for the cross, assuming independent assortment of alleles (no linkage). Significant departures from the predicted Mendelian ratio indicate linkage of the alleles in question. Raw counts should be used and a large sample size is required for the test to be valid.

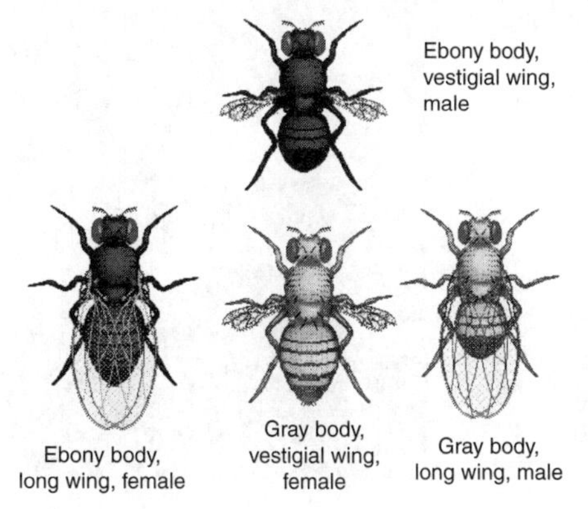

Images of *Drosophila* courtesy of **Newbyte Educational Software**: *Drosophila* Genetics Lab (**www.newbyte.com**)

Using χ^2 in Mendelian Genetics

In a *Drosophila* genetics experiment, two individuals were crossed (the details of the cross are not relevant here). The predicted Mendelian ratios for the offspring of this cross were 1:1:1:1 for each of the four following phenotypes: gray body-long wing, gray body-vestigial wing, ebony body-long wing, ebony body-vestigial wing. The observed results of the cross were not exactly as predicted. The following numbers for each phenotype were observed in the offspring of the cross:

Observed results of the example *Drosophila* cross

Gray body, long wing	**98**	Ebony body, long wing	**102**
Gray body, vestigial wing	**88**	Ebony body, vestigial wing	**112**

Using χ^2, the probability of this result being consistent with a 1:1:1:1 ratio could be tested. Worked example as follows:

Step 1: Calculate the expected value (E)

In this case, this is the sum of the observed values divided by the number of categories (see note below)

$$\frac{400}{4} = 100$$

Step 2: Calculate O – E

The difference between the observed and expected values is calculated as a measure of the deviation from a predicted result. Since some deviations are negative, they are all squared to give positive values. This step is usually performed as part of a tabulation (right, darker blue column).

Step 3: Calculate the value of χ^2

$$\chi^2 = \sum \frac{(O - E)^2}{E}$$

Where: O = the observed result
E = the expected result
$\sum$ = sum of

The calculated χ^2 value is given at the bottom right of the last column in the tabulation.

Step 4: Calculating degrees of freedom

The probability that any particular χ^2 value could be exceeded by chance depends on the number of degrees of freedom. This is simply ***one less than the total number of categories*** (this is the number that could vary independently without affecting the last value). ***In this case: 4–1 = 3.***

Category	O	E	O – E	$(O - E)^2$	$\frac{(O - E)^2}{E}$
Gray, long wing	98	100	–2	4	0.04
Gray, vestigial wing	88	100	–12	144	1.44
Ebony, long wing	102	100	2	4	0.04
Ebony, vestigial wing	112	100	12	144	1.44
	Total = 400			χ^2	$\sum$ = 2.96

Step 5a: Using the χ^2 table

On the χ^2 table (part reproduced in Table 1 below) with 3 degrees of freedom, the calculated value for χ^2 of 2.96 corresponds to a probability of between 0.2 and 0.5 (see arrow). *This means that by chance alone a χ^2 value of 2.96 could be expected between 20% and 50% of the time.*

Step 5b: Using the χ^2 table

The probability of between 0.2 and 0.5 is higher than the 0.05 value which is generally regarded as significant. The null hypothesis cannot be rejected and we have no reason to believe that the observed results differ significantly from the expected (at $P = 0.05$).

Footnote: Many Mendelian crosses involve ratios other than 1:1. For these, calculation of the expected values is not simply a division of the total by the number of categories. Instead, the total must be apportioned according to the ratio. For example, for a total of 400 as above, in a predicted 9:3:3:1 ratio, the total count must be divided by 16 (9+3+3+1) and the expected values will be 225: 75: 75: 25 in each category.

Table 1: Critical values of χ^2 at different levels of probability. By convention, the critical probability for rejecting the null hypothesis (H_0) is 5%. If the test statistic is less than the tabulated critical value for $P = 0.05$ we cannot reject H_0 and the result is not significant. If the test statistic is greater than the tabulated value for $P = 0.05$ we reject H_0 in favor of the alternative hypothesis.

Degrees of freedom	Level of probability (*P*)									
	0.98	0.95	0.80	0.50	0.20	0.10	0.05	0.02	0.01	0.001
1	0.001	0.004	0.064	0.455	χ^2 1.64	2.71	3.84	5.41	6.64	10.83
2	0.040	0.103	0.466	1.386	3.22	4.61	5.99	7.82	9.21	13.82
3	0.185	0.352	1.005	2.366	4.64	6.25	7.82	9.84	11.35	16.27
4	0.429	0.711	1.649	3.357	5.99	7.78	9.49	11.67	13.28	18.47
5	0.752	0.145	2.343	4.351	7.29	9.24	11.07	13.39	15.09	20.52
	←				*Do not reject H_0*			*Reject H_0* →		

ISBN: 978-1-877462-96-2

Chi-Squared Exercise in Genetics

The following problems examine the use of the chi-squared (χ^2) test in genetics. A worked example illustrating the use of the chi-squared test for a genetic cross is provided on the previous page.

1. In a tomato plant experiment, two heterozygous individuals were crossed (the details of the cross are not relevant here). The predicted Mendelian ratios for the offspring of this cross were **9:3:3:1** for each of the **four following phenotypes**: purple stem-jagged leaf edge, purple stem-smooth leaf edge, green stem-jagged leaf edge, green stem-smooth leaf edge.

   The observed results of the cross were not exactly as predicted.
   The numbers of offspring with each phenotype are provided below:

Observed results of the tomato plant cross			
Purple stem-jagged leaf edge	12	Green stem-jagged leaf edge	8
Purple stem-smooth leaf edge	9	Green stem-smooth leaf edge	0

   (a) State your null hypothesis for this investigation (Ho): ____________

   (b) State the alternative hypothesis (HA): ____________

2. Use the chi-squared (χ^2) test to determine if the differences observed between the phenotypes are significant. The table of critical values of χ^2 at different P values is provided on the previous page.

   (a) Enter the observed values (number of individuals) and complete the table to calculate the χ^2 value:

Category	O	E	O — E	$(O - E)^2$	$\frac{(O-E)^2}{E}$
Purple stem, jagged leaf					
Purple stem, smooth leaf					
Green stem, jagged leaf					
Green stem, smooth leaf					
	Σ				Σ

   (b) Calculate χ^2 value using the equation:

$$\chi^2 = \sum \frac{(O-E)^2}{E} \qquad \chi^2 = \_\_\_\_\_\_$$

   (c) Calculate the degrees of freedom: ____________

   (d) Using the χ^2 table, state the P value corresponding to your calculated χ^2 value:

   ____

   (e) State your decision: *(circle one)*
   reject Ho / do not reject Ho

3. Students carried out a pea plant experiment, where two heterozygous individuals were crossed. The predicted Mendelian ratios for the offspring were **9:3:3:1** for each of the **four following phenotypes**: round-yellow seed, round-green seed, wrinkled-yellow seed, wrinkled-green seed.

   The observed results were as follows:

Round-yellow seed	**441**	Wrinkled-yellow seed	**143**
Round-green seed	**159**	Wrinkled-green seed	**57**

   Use a separate piece of paper to complete the following:

   (a) State the null and alternative hypotheses (Ho and HA).

   (b) Calculate the χ^2 value.

   (c) Calculate the degrees of freedom and state the P value corresponding to your calculated χ^2 value.

   (d) State whether or not you reject your null hypothesis: reject Ho / do not reject Ho (circle one)

4. Comment on the whether the χ^2 values obtained above are similar. Suggest a reason for any difference:

   ____

ISBN: 978-1-877462-96-2

Related activities: *Using the Chi-Squared Test in Genetics*

Spearman Rank Correlation

The Spearman rank correlation is a test used to determine if there is a statistical dependence (correlation) between two variables. The test is appropriate for data that have a non-normal distribution (or where the distribution is not known) and assesses the degree of association between the X and Y variables. For the test to work, the values used must be **monotonic** i.e. the values must increase or decrease together or one increases while the other decreases. A value of 1 indicates a perfect correlation; a value of 0 indicates no correlation between the variables. The example below examines the relationship between the frequency of the drumming sound made by male frigatebirds (Y) and the volume of their throat pouch (X).

Spearman's Rank Data for Frigate Bird Pouch Volume and Drumming Frequency

Bird	Volume of pouch (cm^3)	Rank (R_1)	Frequency of drumming sound (Hz)	Rank (R_2)	Difference (D) (R_1-R_2)	D^2
1	2550		461			
2	2440	1	473	6	-5	25
3	2740		532			
4	2730		465			
5	3010		485			
6	3370		488			
7	3080		527			
8	4910		478			
9	3740		485			
10	5090		434			
11	5090		468			
12	5380		449			
				Σ(Sum)		

Based on Madsen et al 2004

r_s value

Analyzing the Data

Step one: Rank the data for each variable. For each variable, the numbers are ranked in descending order, e.g. for the variable, volume, the highest value 5380 cm^3 is given the rank of 12 while its corresponding frequency value is given the rank of 2. Fill in the rank columns in the table above in the same way. If two numbers have the same rank value, then use the mean rank of the two values (e.g. 1+2 = 3. 3/2= 1.5).

Step two: Calculate the difference (D) between each pair of ranks (R_1-R_2) and enter the value in the table (as a check, the sum of all differences should be 0).

Step three: Square the differences and enter them into the table above (this removes any negative values).

Step four: Sum all the D^2 values and enter the total into the table.

Step five: Use the formula below to calculate the Spearman Rank Correlation Coefficient (r_s). Enter the r_s value in the box above.

$$r_s = 1 - \left(\frac{6\Sigma D^2}{n(n^2-1)}\right)$$

Spearman Rank Correlation Coefficient

Step six: Compare the r_s value to the table of critical values (right) for the appropriate number of pairs. If the r_s value (ignoring sign) is greater than or equal to the critical value then there is a significant correlation. If r_s is positive then there is a positive correlation. If r_s is negative then there is a negative value correlation.

Number of pairs of measurements	Critical value
5	1.00
6	0.89
7	0.79
8	0.74
9	0.68
10	0.65
12	0.59
14	0.54
16	0.51
18	0.48
20	0.45

Analysis and Reporting

1. State the null hypothesis for the data set. ______________________________

2 (a) Identify the critical value for the frigate bird data: ______________________________

(b) State is the correlation is positive of negative: ______________________________

(c) State whether the correlation is significant: ______________________________

3. Explain why the data collected must be monotonic if a Spearman rank correlation is to be used: ______________________________

ISBN: 978-1-877462-96-2

The Structure of a Report

Once you have collected and analysed your data, you can write your report. You may wish to present your findings as a written report, a poster, or an oral presentation. The structure of a scientific report is described below for a poster (which is necessarily very concise) as an example. When writing your report, it is useful to write the methods or the results first, followed by the discussion and conclusion. The introduction should be one of the last sections that you write. Writing the other sections first gives you a better understanding of your investigation within the context of other work in the same area.

To view this and other examples of posters, see the excellent NC State University web site listed below

1. Title (and author)
Provides a clear and concise description of the project.

2. Introduction
Includes the aim, hypothesis, and background to the study

3. Materials and Methods
A description of the materials and procedures used.

4. Results
An account of results including tables and graphs. This section should not discuss the result, just present them.

5. Discussion
An discussion of the findings in light of the biological concepts involved. It should include comments on any limitations of the study.

6. Conclusion
A clear statement of whether tor not the findings support the hypothesis. In abbreviated poster presentations, these sections may be combined.

7. References & acknowledgements
An organised list of all sources of information. Entries should be consistent within your report. Your teacher will advise you as to the preferred format.

NC STATE UNIVERSITY

…n Flounder Exhibit Temperature-Dependent Sex Determination

J. Adam Luckenbach*, John Godwin and Russell Borski
Department of Zoology, Box 7617, North Carolina State University, Raleigh, NC 27695

Introduction

Southern flounder (*Paralichthys lethostigma*) support valuable fisheries and show great promise for aquaculture. Female flounder … grow faster and reach larger adult … Therefore, information on sex dete… might increase the ratio of female … important for aquaculture.

Objective

This study was conducted to determine whether southern flounder exhibit temperature-dependent sex determination (TSD), and if growth is affected by rearing temperature.

Methods

- Southern flounder broodstock were strip spawned to collect eggs and sperm for *in vitro* fertilization.
- Hatched larvae were weaned from a natural diet (rotifers/*Artemia*) to high protein pelleted feed and fed until satiation at least twice daily.
- Upon reaching a mean total length of 40 mm, the juvenile flounder were stocked at equal densities into one of three temperatures 18, 23, or 28°C for 245 days.
- Gonads were preserved and later sectioned at 2-6 microns.
- Sex-distinguishing markers were used to distinguish males (spermatogenesis) from females (oogenesis).

Histological Analysis

Male Differentiation

Female Differe…

Temperature Affects Sex Determination

% Fe… ; 0, 10, 20 ; 18, 23, 28 ; 64, 53, 49 ; ***

…dy Weight ; 40

Growth Does Not Differ by Sex

0 ; 31, 6 ; 28, 23 ; 31, 6 ; 18, 23, 28 ; Temperature (°C)

Results

- Sex was discernible in most fish greater than 120 mm long.
- High (28°C) temperature produced 4% females.
- Low (18°C) temperature produced 22% females.
- Mid-range (23°C) temperature produced 44% females.
- Fish raised at high or low temperatures showed reduced growth compared to those at the mid-range temperature.
- Up to 245 days, no differences in growth existed between sexes.

Conclusions

- These findings indicate that sex determination in southern flounder is temperature-sensitive and temperature has a profound effect on growth.
- A mid-range rearing temperature (23°C) appears to maximize the number of females and promote better growth in young southern flounder.
- Although adult females are known to grow larger than males, no difference in growth between sexes occurred in age-0 (< 1 year) southern flounder.

Acknowledgements

The authors acknowledge the Salstonstall-Kennedy Program of the National Marine Fisheries Service and the University of North Carolina Sea Grant College Program for funding this research. Special thanks to Lea Ware and Beth Shimps for help with the work.

Image courtesy: Adam Luckenbach, NC State University

1. Explain the purpose of each of the following sections of a report. The first has one been completed for you:
   (a) Introduction: Provides the reader with the background to the topic and the rationale for the study
   (b) Methods: ___
   (c) Results: ___
   (d) Discussion: ___
   (e) References and acknowledgements: ___

2. Posters are a highly visual method of presenting the findings of a study. Describe the positive features of this format:

Related activities: *Hypotheses and Predictions*
Web links: *NC State University: Creating Effective Poster Presentations*

ISBN: 978-1-877462-96-2

Writing the Methods

The methods section of a report should include enough detail to enable the study to be repeated, but should omit the details of standard procedures (e.g. how to use a balance). Details of statistical analyses can be included, as well as the rationale for these. If your methodology includes complicated preparations (e.g. culture media) it is appropriate to include these as an appendix or refer to the original information source. The diagram below describes the information that should be included in the methods of a field or laboratory based study. It is not exhaustive, but indicates the sort of information that should be presented.

Field Studies

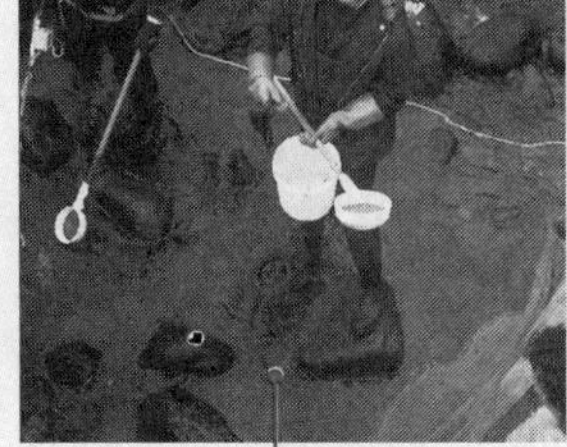

Study site & organisms
- Site location and features
- Why that site was chosen
- Species involved

Specialized equipment
- pH and oxygen meters
- Thermometers
- Nets and traps

Data collection
- Number and timing of observations/collections
- Time of day or year
- Sample sizes and size of the sampling unit
- Temperature at time of sampling
- Methods of sample preservation or staining
- Weather conditions on the day(s) of sampling
- Methods of measurement/sampling
- Methods of recording

Laboratory Based Studies

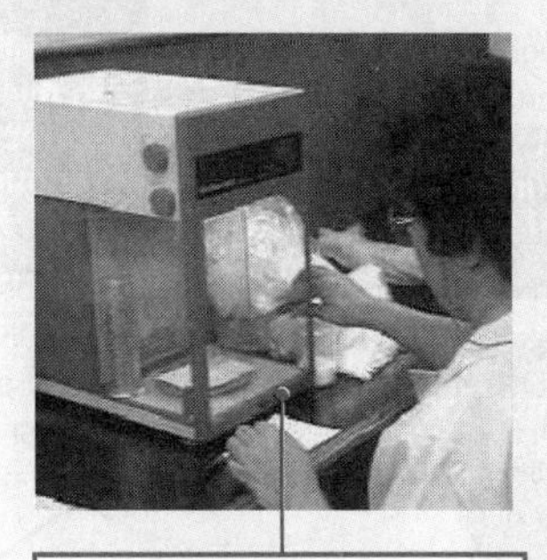

Data collection
- Details of treatments and controls
- Duration and timing of observations
- Temperature
- Sample sizes
- Repeats of the entire investigation
- Methods of measurement or sampling
- Methods of recording

Experimental organisms
- Species or strain
- Age and sex
- Number of individuals used

Specialized equipment
- pH meters
- Water baths & incubators
- Spectrophotometers
- Centrifuges
- Aquaria & choice chambers
- Microscopes and videos

Special preparations
- Techniques for the preparation of material (staining, grinding)
- Indicators, salt solutions, buffers, special dilutions

1. Why would researchers:

 (a) Increase the sample size (n)? ______________________________

 (b) Repeat (replicate) the entire experiment? ______________________________

2. Why is it important to state the time of day or time of year samples were collected? ______________________________

3. Why is it important to make sure experimental organisms are as similar as possible (e.g. the same gender):

____

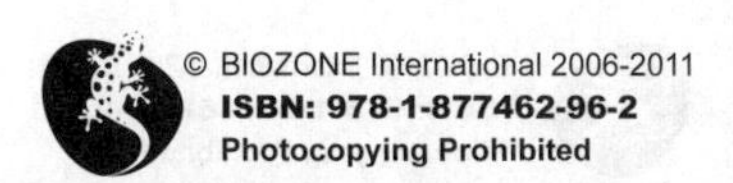

ISBN: 978-1-877462-96-2

Related activities: The Structure of a Report

Writing Your Results

The results section is arguably the most important part of any research report; it is the place where you can bring together and present your findings. When properly constructed, this section will present your results clearly and in a way that shows you have organized your data and carefully considered the appropriate analysis. A portion of the results section from a scientific paper on the habitat preference of New Zealand black mudfish is presented below (Hicks, B. and Barrier, R. (1996), NZJMFR. 30, 135-151). It highlights some important features of the results section and shows you how you can present information concisely, even if your results are relatively lengthy. Use it as a guide for content when you write up this section.

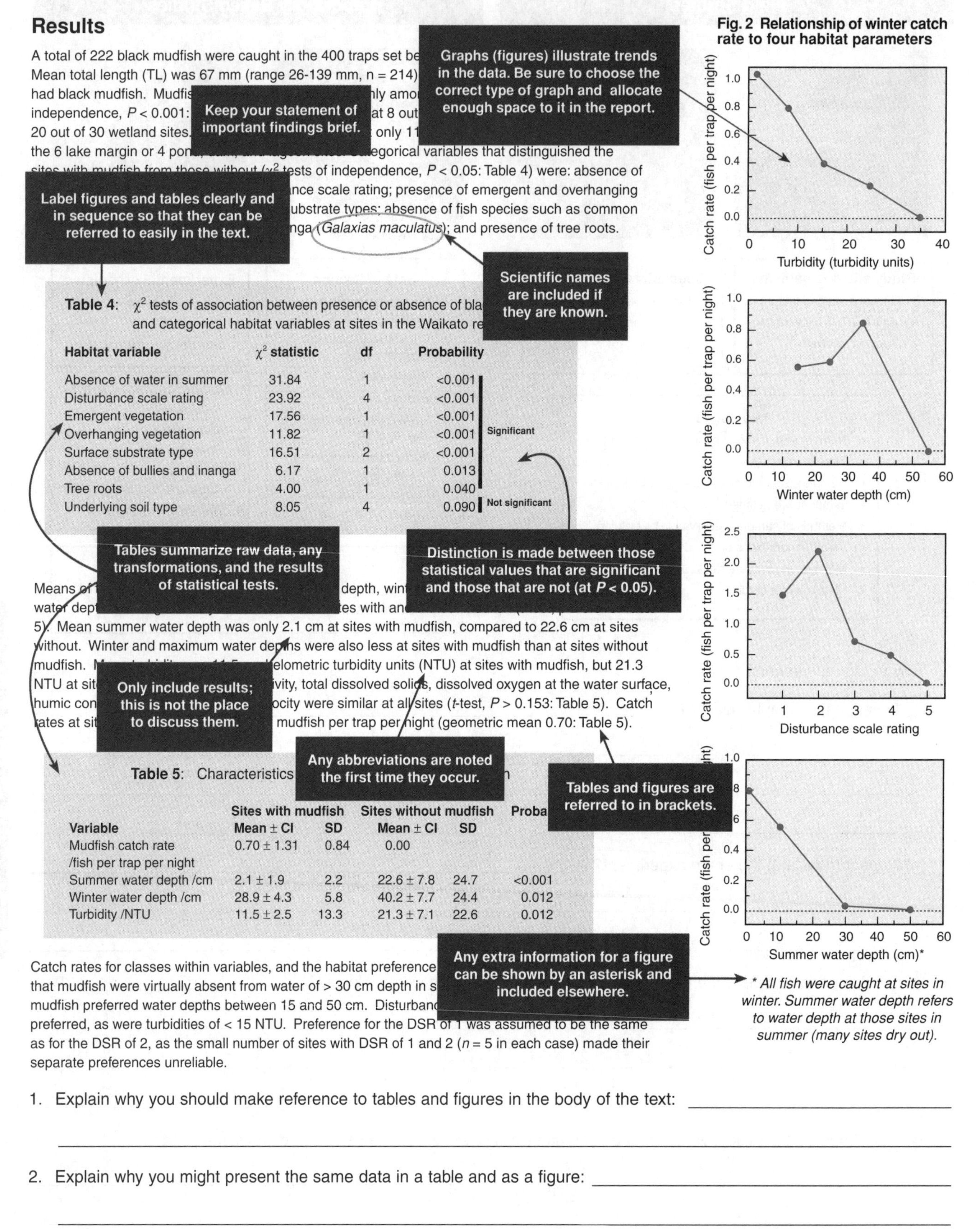

Results

A total of 222 black mudfish were caught in the 400 traps set be... Mean total length (TL) was 67 mm (range 26-139 mm, n = 214)... had black mudfish. Mudfis...nly amo... independence, $P < 0.001$: ...at 8 out... 20 out of 30 wetland sites... only 11... the 6 lake margin or 4 pon...egorical variables that distinguished the sites with mudfish from those without (χ^2 tests of independence, $P < 0.05$: Table 4) were: absence of ...nce scale rating; presence of emergent and overhanging ...ubstrate types; absence of fish species such as common ...nga (*Galaxias maculatus*); and presence of tree roots.

Table 4: χ^2 tests of association between presence or absence of bla... and categorical habitat variables at sites in the Waikato re...

Habitat variable	χ^2 statistic	df	Probability	
Absence of water in summer	31.84	1	<0.001	Significant
Disturbance scale rating	23.92	4	<0.001	
Emergent vegetation	17.56	1	<0.001	
Overhanging vegetation	11.82	1	<0.001	
Surface substrate type	16.51	2	<0.001	
Absence of bullies and inanga	6.17	1	0.013	
Tree roots	4.00	1	0.040	
Underlying soil type	8.05	4	0.090	Not significant

Means of ... depth, win... water dep... ...es with an... 5). Mean summer water depth was only 2.1 cm at sites with mudfish, compared to 22.6 cm at sites without. Winter and maximum water depths were also less at sites with mudfish than at sites without mudfish. M... ...elometric turbidity units (NTU) at sites with mudfish, but 21.3 NTU at sit... ...ivity, total dissolved solids, dissolved oxygen at the water surface, humic con... ...ocity were similar at all sites (*t*-test, $P > 0.153$: Table 5). Catch rates at si... mudfish per trap per night (geometric mean 0.70: Table 5).

Table 5: Characteristics ...

Variable	Sites with mudfish Mean ± CI	Sites with mudfish SD	Sites without mudfish Mean ± CI	Sites without mudfish SD	Proba...
Mudfish catch rate /fish per trap per night	0.70 ± 1.31	0.84	0.00		
Summer water depth /cm	2.1 ± 1.9	2.2	22.6 ± 7.8	24.7	<0.001
Winter water depth /cm	28.9 ± 4.3	5.8	40.2 ± 7.7	24.4	0.012
Turbidity /NTU	11.5 ± 2.5	13.3	21.3 ± 7.1	22.6	0.012

Catch rates for classes within variables, and the habitat preference... that mudfish were virtually absent from water of > 30 cm depth in s... mudfish preferred water depths between 15 and 50 cm. Disturban... preferred, as were turbidities of < 15 NTU. Preference for the DSR of 1 was assumed to be the same as for the DSR of 2, as the small number of sites with DSR of 1 and 2 (*n* = 5 in each case) made their separate preferences unreliable.

Fig. 2 Relationship of winter catch rate to four habitat parameters

* All fish were caught at sites in winter. Summer water depth refers to water depth at those sites in summer (many sites dry out).

1. Explain why you should make reference to tables and figures in the body of the text: ______

2. Explain why you might present the same data in a table and as a figure: ______

Related activities: Transforming Raw Data, Constructing Tables, Constructing Graphs, The Structure of a Report

ISBN: 978-1-877462-96-2

Writing Your Discussion

In the discussion section of your report, you must interpret your results in the context of the specific questions you set out to answer in the investigation. You should also place your findings in the context of any broader relevant issues. If your results coincide exactly with what you expected, then your discussion will be relatively brief. However, be prepared to discuss any unexpected or conflicting results and critically evaluate any problems with your study design. The Discussion section may (and should) refer to the findings in the Results section, but it is not the place to introduce new results. Try to work towards a point in your discussion where the reader is lead naturally to the conclusion. The conclusion may be presented within the discussion or it may be included separately after the discussion as a separate section.

Discussion:

Black mudfish habitat in the Waikato region can be ad ... ses by four variables that are easy to measure: summer water depth, winter wat ... cated by vegetation), and turbidity. Catch rates of black mudfish can be extreme ... s ranged from 0.2 to 8.4 mudfish per trap per night (mean 0.70) between May ... those of Dean (1995) in September 1993 and October 1994 in the Whangamarino Wetland complex (0.0-2.0 mudfish per trap per night). The highest mean catch rate in our study, 8.4 mudfish per trap per night, was at Site 24 (Table 1, Figure 1). The second highest (6.4 mudfish per trap per night) was at Site 32, in a drain about 4 km east of Hamilton. Black mudfish in the Waikato region were most commonly found at sites in wetlands with absence of water in summer, moderate depth of water in winter, limited modification of the vegetation (low DSR), and low turbidity (Fig. 2). There are similarities between the habitat requirements of black mudfish and those of brown mudfish and the common river galaxias (*Galaxias vulgaris*). Brown mudfish inhabited shallow water, sometimes at the edges of deeper water bodies, but were usually absent from water deeper than about 30-50 cm (Eldon 1978). The common river galaxias also has a preference for shallow water, occupying river margins < 20 cm deep (Jowett and Richardson 1995).

Support your statements with reference to Tables and Figures from the Results section.

The discussion describes the relevance of the results of the investigation.

Sites where black mudfish were found were not just shallow or dry i ... easonal variation in water depth. A weakness of this study is the fact that site ... e traps were spread relatively widely at each site to maximise the chance of ... ver was important for bl ... or overhanging vegetation, or tree roots. The significance of cover in determining t ... fish is predictable, considering the shallow nature of their habitats. Mudfish, though ... y to require cover during the to protect them from avian predators, such as bitterns ... kingfishers (*Halcyon sancta vagans*). Predation of black mudfish by a swamp bitt ... e 1981). Cover is also important for brown mudfish (Eldon 1978). Black mudfish were found at sites with the predatory mosquitofish and juvenile eels, and the seasonal drying of their habitats may be a key to the successful coexistence of mudfish with their predators. Mosquitofish are known predators of mudfish fry (Barrier & Hicks 1994), and eels would presumably also prey on black mu ... ury mudfish (Eldon 1979b). If, however, black mudfish are relatively uncompetitive and vuln ... tion remains as to how they manage to coexist with juvenile eels and mosquitofish. The ha ... this study can be used to classify the suitability of sites for black mudfish in future. The adaptability of black mudfish allows them to survive in some altered habitats, such as farm or roadside drains. From this study, we can conclude that the continued existence of suitable habitats appears to be more important to black mudfish than the presence of predators and competitors. This study has also improved methods of identifying suitable mudfish habitats in the Waikato region.

State any limitations of your approach in carrying out the investigation and what further studies might be appropriate.

Reference is made to the work of others.

Further research is suggested

A clear conclusion is made towards the end of the discussion.

1. Explain why it is important to discuss any weaknesses in your study design: ____________________

2. Explain why you should **critically evaluate** your results in the discussion: ____________________

3. Describe the purpose of the conclusion: ____________________

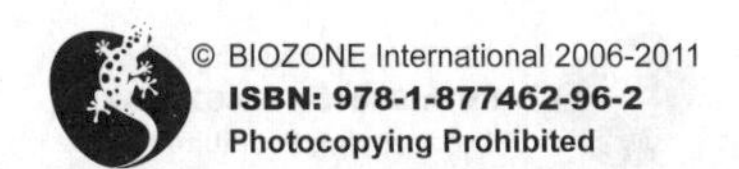

ISBN: 978-1-877462-96-2

Citing and Listing References

Proper referencing of sources of information is an important aspect of report writing. It shows that you have explored the topic and recognise and respect the work of others. There are two aspects to consider: **citing sources** within the text (making reference to other work to support a statement or compare results) and **compiling a reference list** at the end of the report. A **bibliography** lists all sources of information, but these may not necessarily appear as citations in the report. In contrast, a reference list should contain only those texts cited in the report.

Citations in the main body of the report should include only the authors' surnames, publication date, and page numbers (or internet site) and the citation should be relevant to the statement it claims to support. Accepted methods for referencing vary, but your reference list should provide all the information necessary to locate the source material, it should be consistently presented, and it should contain only the references that you have *yourself* read (not those cited by others). A suggested format using the **APA** referencing system is described below.

Preparing a Reference List

When teachers ask students to write in "APA style", they are referring to the editorial style established by the **American Psychological Association** (APA). These guidelines for citing **electronic (online) resources** differ only slightly from the **print sources**.

For the Internet

Where you use information from the internet, you must provide the following:

- The website address (URL), the person or organization who is in charge of the web site and the date you accessed the web page.

This is written in the form: URL (person or organization's name, day, month, and year retrieved)

This goes together as follows:

http://www.scientificamerican.com (Scientific American, 17.12.03)

For Periodicals (or Journals)

This is written in the form: author(s), date of publication, article title, periodical title, and publication information.
Example: Author's family name, A. A. (author's initials only), Author, B. B., & Author, C. C. (xxxx = year of publication in brackets). Title of article. Title of Periodical, volume number, page numbers (Note, only use "pp." before the page numbers in newspapers and magazines).

This goes together as follows:

Bamshad M. J., & Olson S. E. (2003). Does Race Exist? Scientific American, 289(6), 50-57.

For Online Periodicals based on a Print Source

At present, the majority of periodicals retrieved from online publications are exact duplicates of those in their print versions and although they are unlikely to have additional analyses and data attached to them, this is likely to change in the future.

- If the article that is to be referenced has been viewed only in electronic form and not in print form, then you must add in brackets, "Electronic version", after the title.

  This goes together as follows:

  Bamshad M. J., & Olson S. E. (2003). Does Race Exist? (Electronic version). Scientific American, 289(6), 50-57.

- If you have reason to believe the article has changed in its electronic form, then you will need to add the date you retrieved the document and the URL.

  This goes together as follows:

  Bamshad M. J., & Olson S. E. (2003). Does Race Exist? (Electronic version). Scientific American, 289(6), 50-57. Retrieved December 17, 2003, from http://www.scientificamerican.com

For Books

This is written in the form: author(s), date of publication, title, and publication information.
Example: Author, A. A., Author, B. B., & Author, C. C. (xxxx). Title (any additional information to enable identification is given in brackets). City of publication: publishers name.

This goes together as follows:

Martin, R.A. (2004). Missing Links Evolutionary Concepts & Transitions Through Time. Sudbury, MA: Jones and Bartlett

For Citation in the Text of References

This is written in the form: authors' surname(s), date of publication, page number(s) (abbreviated p.), chapter (abbreviated chap.), figure, table, equation, or internet site, in brackets at the appropriate point in text.

This goes together as follows:

(Bamshad & Olson, 2003, p. 51) or (Bamshad & Olson, 2003, http://www.scientificamerican.com)

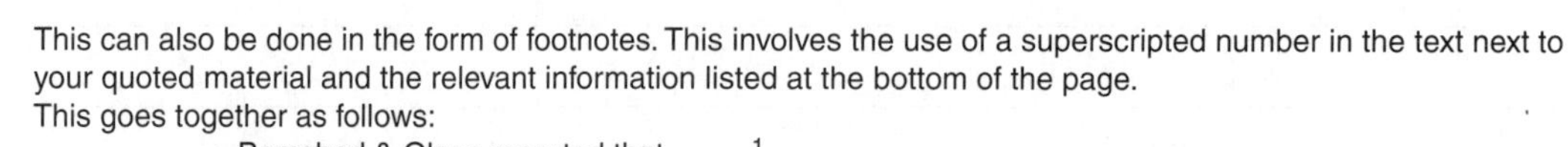

This can also be done in the form of footnotes. This involves the use of a superscripted number in the text next to your quoted material and the relevant information listed at the bottom of the page.

This goes together as follows:

.... Bamshad & Olson reported that ....[1]

---

[1]Bamshad & Olson, 2003, p. 51

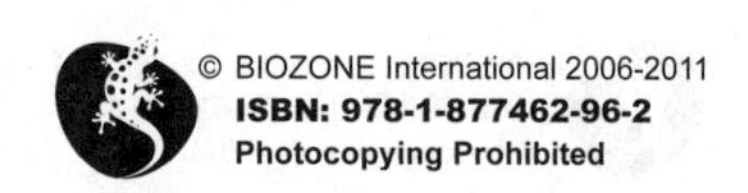

ISBN: 978-1-877462-96-2

Related activities: *The structure of a Report*

Example of a Reference List

Lab notes can be listed according to title if the author is unknown. → Advanced biology laboratory manual (2000). Cell membranes. pp. 16-18. Sunhigh College.

References are listed alphabetically according to the author's surname.

Cooper, G.M. (1997). *The cell: A molecular approach* (2nd ed.). Washington D.C.: ASM Press

Book title in italics (or underlined) | Place of publication: Publisher

Davis, P (1996). Cellular factories. *New Scientist* 2057: Inside science supplement.

Publication date | Journal title in italics | A supplement may not need page references

If a single author appears more than once, then list the publications from oldest to most recent.

Indge, B. (2001). Diarrhea, digestion and dehydration. *Biological Sciences Review*, 14(1), 7-9.

Indge, B. (2002). Experiments. *Biological Sciences Review*, 14(3), 11-13.

Article title follows date

Kingsland, J. (2000). Border control. *New Scientist* 2247: Inside science supplement.

Laver, H. (1995). Osmosis and water retention in plants. *Biological Sciences Review*, 7(3), 14-18.

Volume (Issue number), Pages

Spell out only the last name of authors. Use initials for first and middle names. → Steward, M. (1996). Water channels in the cell membrane. *Biological Sciences Review*, 9(2), 18-22.

Internet sites change often so the date accessed is included. The person or organization in charge of the site is also included. → http://www.cbc.umn.edu/~mwd/cell_intro.html (Dalton, M. "Introduction to cell biology" 12.02.03)

1. Distinguish between a **reference list** and a **bibliography**:

2. Explain why internet articles based on a print source are likely to have additional analyses and data attached in the future, and why this point should be noted in a reference list:

3. Following are the details of references and source material used by a student in preparing a report on enzymes and their uses in biotechnology. He provided his reference list in prose. From it, compile a correctly formatted reference list:

Pages 18-23 in the sixth edition of the textbook "Biology" by Neil Campbell. Published by Benjamin/Cummings in California (2002). New Scientist article by Peter Moore called "Fuelled for life" (January 1996, volume 2012, supplement). "Food biotechnology" published in the journal Biological Sciences Review, page 25, volume 8 (number 3) 1996, by Liam and Katherine O'Hare. An article called "Living factories" by Philip Ball in New Scientist, volume 2015 1996, pages 28-31. Pages 75-85 in the book "The cell: a molecular approach" by Geoffrey Cooper, published in 1997 by ASM Press, Washington D.C. An article called "Development of a procedure for purification of a recombinant therapeutic protein" in the journal "Australasian Biotechnology", by I Roberts and S. Taylor, pages 93-99 in volume 6, number 2, 1996.

REFERENCE LIST

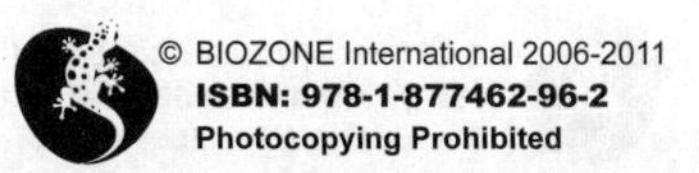

ISBN: 978-1-877462-96-2

Analysis and Reporting

KEY TERMS: Mix and Match

INSTRUCTIONS: Test your vocabulary by matching each term to its definition, as identified by its preceding letter code.

- 95% CONFIDENCE INTERVAL ....
- ANOVA ....
- BIBLIOGRAPHY ....
- CHI-SQUARED TEST ....
- CITATION ....
- CONCLUSION ....
- DATA ....
- DISCUSSION ....
- MEAN ....
- MEDIAN ....
- METHODS ....
- MODE ....
- RAW DATA ....
- REPORT ....
- RESULTS ....
- SAMPLE MEAN ....
- SIGNIFICANCE (STATISTICAL) ....
- SPEARMAN RANK CORRELATION ....
- STANDARD DEVIATION ....
- STANDARD ERROR ....
- STATISTIC ....
- STATISTICAL TEST ....
- STUDENT'S T-TEST ....
- TRANSFORMATION (OF DATA) ....
- TREND (OF DATA) ....

A A pattern observed in processed data showing that data values may be linked.

B A calculated measure of some attribute of a sample (e.g. the arithmetic mean).

C A calculation used to determine if the null hypothesis is to be accepted or rejected. The greater the significance level of the test the greater the likelihood the outcome of the calculation will represent the true situation.

D A series of systematic and orderly steps used when carrying out scientific procedures.

E The value that occurs most often in a data set.

F The sum of the data divided by the number of data points (n).

G The process of changing raw data into a form that makes it easier to identify important features of the data (e.g. trends).

H The decisions reached after carefully and thoroughly analyzing the data produced from a scientific experiment or observation.

I A calculated statistic used to express the variability of a population about the mean.

J Facts collected for analysis.

K A test to determine the statistical dependence between two variables in non-normal data.

L A statistical test for determining the significance of departures of observed data from an expected result.

M Data that has not been processed or summarized in any way.

N The completed study including methods, results and discussion of the data obtained.

O A list displaying the titles and publication information of resources used in the gathering of information.

P A calculated statistic giving a range that encompasses 95% of the values.

Q Note normally appearing directly after a new fact or data that states the author of the information and the date it was published.

R Estimate of the true population mean based upon data collected by random sampling. Valid for population data that are normally distributed.

S The probability that the result of an experiment is not caused by chance events.

T The central value in a sorted set of data.

U The consequences or outcomes resulting from a particular action or event. Can be expressed qualitatively or quantitatively.

V The standard deviation of the mean calculated for each sample.

W A statistical test used to analyze more than two groups of normally distributed data.

X A calculated measure of some attribute of a sample (e.g. the arithmetic mean).

Y A test used to determine if the difference between two sample means is significant.

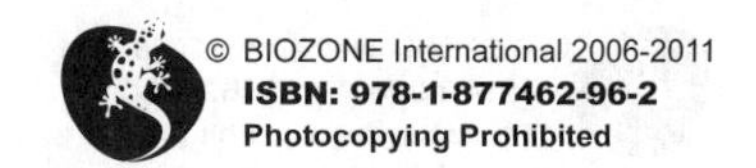

ISBN: 978-1-877462-96-2

Field Studies

Key concepts

- Populations are too usually too large to assess without sampling.
- Population distribution and abundance can be quantified based on data from random samples.
- Common sampling methods include quadrats, transects, mark and recapture, and netting and trapping.
- Information about the physical environment is important in field studies.

Key terms

abiotic (physical) factor
abundance
belt transect
community
density
distribution
diversity index
indirect sampling
line transect
mark and recapture
n
percentage cover
population
quadrat
radio-tracking
random sample
sample
sample size
sampling accuracy
sampling effort
species evenness
species richness
transect

Objectives

☐ 1. Use the **KEY TERMS** to help you understand and complete these objectives.

Designing A Field Study pages 79-80

☐ 2. Formulate a working hypothesis from which you can generate predictions about the outcome of your investigation.

☐ 3. Explain the need for reliable, representative data when sampling populations. Explain how and why **sample size** affects the accuracy of population estimates. Explain how you would decide on a suitable sample size, and its importance in obtaining representative results.

Sampling Populations pages 76-78, 81-98

☐ 4. Explain the term **sampling** as it relates to populations and communities.

☐ 5. Distinguish between **species richness** and **species evenness**.

☐ 6. Explain the need for precise, representative data when sampling populations.

☐ 7. Explain how **diversity indices** (e.g. Simpson's index) can be used to estimate community diversity.

☐ 8. Describe and explain the use of **quadrats** to sample ecological communities. Explain how the size of quadrat is determined.

☐ 9. Describe and explain the use of **transects**, including line and belt transects, to sample communities. Explain when transect use is most appropriate.

☐ 10. Describe and explain the use of **mark-and-recapture** for sampling populations of mobile species. Explain how population size is calculated.

☐ 11. Explain the value of **radio-tracking** and **indirect sampling** methods.

☐ 12. Explain how aspects of the physical (**abiotic**) environment can be measured in a field study.

Periodicals:
Listings for this chapter are on page 153

Weblinks:
www.thebiozone.com/weblink/Skills-2962.html

Sampling Populations

In most ecological studies, it is not possible to measure or count all the members of a population. Instead, information is obtained through **sampling** in a manner that provides a fair (unbiased) representation of the organisms present and their distribution. This is usually achieved through **random sampling**, a technique in which every possible sample of a given size has the same chance of selection. Most practical exercises in community ecology involve the collection or census of living organisms, with a view to identifying the species and quantifying their abundance and other population features of interest. Sampling techniques must be appropriate to the community being studied and the information you wish to obtain. Any field study must also consider the time and equipment available, the organisms involved, and the impact of the sampling method on the environment. Often indicator species and **species diversity indices** are used as a way of quantifying biodiversity and ecosystem "health". Such indicators can be particularly useful when monitoring ecosystem change and looking for causative factors in species loss.

Quantifying the Diversity of Ecosystems

Reef community:
high density, clumped distribution

The methods we use to sample communities and their constituent populations must be appropriate to the ecosystem being investigated. Communities in which the populations are at low density and have a random or clumped distribution will require a different sampling strategy to those where the populations are uniformly distributed and at higher density. There are many sampling options, each with advantages and drawbacks for particular communities. How would you assess aspects (e.g. species richness, abundance, or distribution) of the reef community above?

Types of Sampling

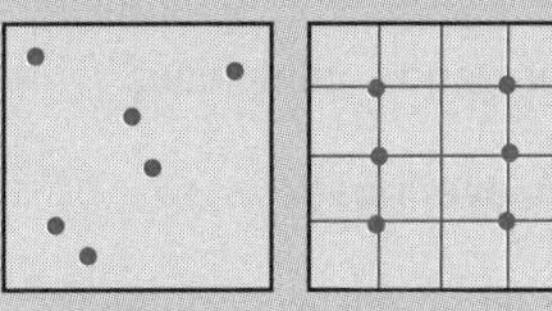

Random Systematic (grid)

Point sampling: Individual points are chosen on a map (using a grid reference or random numbers applied to a map grid) and the organisms are sampled at those points. Mobile organisms may be sampled using traps, nets etc.

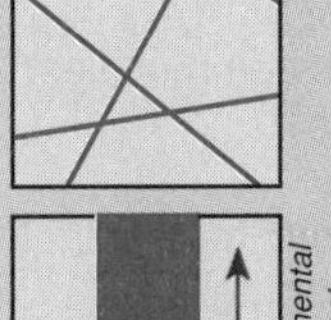

Line transects: Tape or rope marks the line. The species occurring on the line are recorded (all along the line or, more usually, at regular intervals). Lines can be chosen randomly (left) or may follow an environmental gradient.

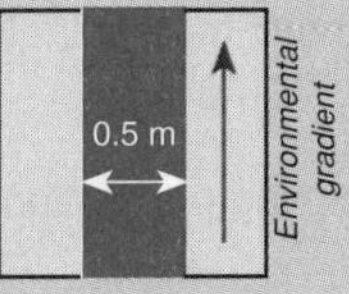

Belt transects: A measured strip is located across the study area to highlight any transitions. Quadrats are used to sample the plants and animals at regular intervals along the belt. Plants and immobile animals are easily recorded. Mobile or cryptic animals need to be trapped or recorded using appropriate methods.

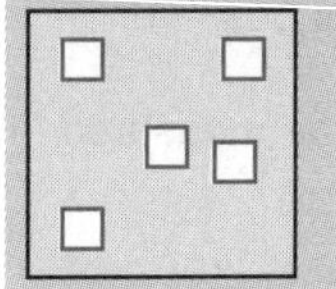

Quadrat sampling: Sampling units or quadrats are placed randomly or in a grid pattern on the sample area. The occurrence of organisms in these squares is noted. Plants and slow moving animals are easily recorded. Rapidly moving or cryptic animals need to be trapped or recorded using appropriate methods.

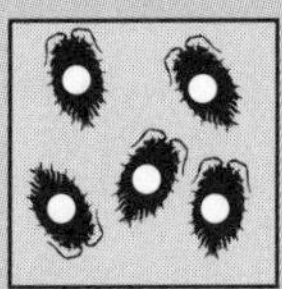

First sample: marked

Second sample: proportion recapture

Mark and recapture sampling: Animals are captured, marked, and then released. After a suitable time period, the population is resampled. The number of marked animals recaptured in a second sample is recorded as a proportion of the total.

Evenness and Richness

Species richness (S) is directly related to the number of species in a sampled area. It is a crude measure of the homogeneity of a community. It does not give any information on the relative abundance of particular species and so is relatively meaningless by itself. Thus a sample area found to have 500 daisies and 3 dandelions has as much species richness as a sample area found to have 200 daisies and 300 dandelions.

High species richness

Low species richness

Species evenness measures the proportion of individuals of each species in an area (the relative abundance). When the proportions of all species are the same, species evenness equals 1. As the proportions become less similar, the value increases.

Sample of Freshwater Invertebrates in a Stream			
Common name	Site 1 (n m^{-2})	Site 2 (n m^{-2})	Site 3 (n m^{-2})
Freshwater shrimp	67	20	5
Freshwater mite	4	15	1
Flat mayfly	23	21	0
Bighead stonefly	12	18	2
Blackfly	78	40	100
Bloodworm	21	22	43

Data for species richness and species evenness can be obtained by sampling, e.g. using quadrats. In the example above, three sites in a stream were sampled using quadrats and the species and number of individuals per m^2 recorded for each site. Using Site 1 as an example, species richness is 6, since S = n. Species evenness can be calculated using formulae, but can also be estimated from the numbers of individuals of each species. For Site 1, species evenness can be said to be greater than 1.

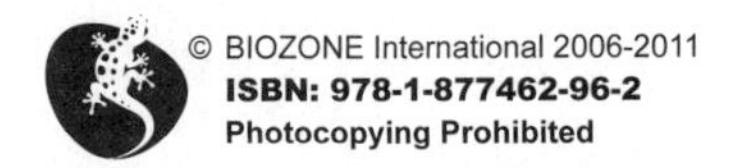

ISBN: 978-1-877462-96-2

Related activities: Quadrat Sampling, Transect Sampling, Mark and Recapture Sampling **Weblinks:** Ecological Sampling Methods

Photo: www.coastal planning.net

Marine ecologists use quadrat sampling to estimate biodiversity prior to works such as dredging.

RA

Line transects are appropriate to estimate biodiversity along an environmental gradient.

Tagging has been used for more than 30 years to follow the migration of monarch butterflies. The photograph here depicts an older tagging method, which has largely been replaced by a tag on the underside of the hindwing (inset). The newer method results in better survival and recapture rates and interferes less with flight.

Which Sampling Method?

Field biologists take a number of factors into consideration when deciding on a sampling method for a chosen population or community. The benefits and drawbacks of some common methods are outlined below:

Point sampling is time efficient and good for determining species abundance and community composition. However, organisms in low abundance may be missed.

Transects are well suited to determining changes in community composition along an environmental gradient but can be time consuming to do well.

Quadrats are also good for assessments of community diversity and composition but are largely restricted to plants and immobile animals. Quadrat size must also be appropriate for the organisms being sampled.

Mark and recapture is useful for highly mobile species which are otherwise difficult to record. However, it is time consuming to do well. **Radiotracking** offers an alternative to mark and recapture and is now widely used in conservation to study the movements of both threatened species and pests.

1. Explain why we **sample** populations: ____________________

2. Describe a sampling technique that would be appropriate for determining each of the following:

   (a) The percentage cover of a plant species in pasture: ____________________

   (b) The density and age structure of a plankton population: ____________________

   (c) Change in community composition from low to high altitude on a mountain: ____________________

3. Explain why it is common to also collect information about the physical environment when sampling populations:

   ____

4. (a) Distinguish between species richness and species evenness: ____________________

   (b) Why should both these measures be assessed when considering species conservation: ____________________

5. (a) State the species richness for each of the sites sampled in the stream on the previous page:

   Site 1: __________ Site 2: __________ Site 3: __________

   (b) Estimate the species evenness (= 1, >1, >>1) for each of the sites in the stream:

   Site 1: __________ Site 2: __________ Site 3: __________

   (c) Calculate Simpson's index for each site and the stream as a whole:

   Site 1: __________ Site 2: __________ Site 3: __________ Stream: __________

ISBN: 978-1-877462-96-2

Diversity Indices

One of the best ways to determine the health of an ecosystem is to measure the variety (rather than the absolute number) of organisms living in it. Certain species, called **indicator species**, are typical of ecosystems in a particular state (e.g. polluted or pristine). An objective evaluation of an ecosystem's biodiversity can provide valuable insight into its status, particularly if the species assemblages have changed as a result of disturbance.

Diversity can be quantified using a **diversity index** (DI). Diversity indices attempt to quantify the degree of diversity and identify indicators for environmental stress or degradation. Most indices of diversity are easy to use and they are widely used in ecological work, particularly for monitoring ecosystem change or pollution (i.e. before and after assessments).

Simpson's Index of Diversity

Simpson's Index of Diversity (below) produces values ranging between 0 and almost 1. These are more easily interpreted than some other versions of Simpson's Index because of the more limited range of values, but no single index offers the "best" measure of diversity; each is chosen on the basis of suitability to different situations.

Simpson's Index of Diversity (D) is easily calculated using the following simple formula. Communities with a wide range of species produce a higher diversity score than communities dominated by larger numbers of only a few species.

$$D = 1-(\Sigma(n/N)^2)$$

Where:
D = Diversity index
N = Total number of individuals (of all species) in the sample
n = Number of individuals of each species in the sample

This index ranges between 0 (low diversity) and 1 (high diversity). Indices are usually evaluated with reference to earlier measurement or a standard ecosystem measure to be properly interpreted.

Example of species diversity in a stream

The example describes the results from a survey of stream invertebrates. It is not necessary to know the species to calculate a diversity index as long as the different species can be distinguished. For the example below, Simpson's Index of Diversity using $D = 1 - (\Sigma(n/N)^2)$ is:

Species	n	n/N	$(n/N)^2$
A (backswimmer)	12	0.300	0.090
B (stonefly larva)	7	0.175	0.031
C (silver water beetle)	2	0.050	0.003
D (caddisfly larva)	6	0.150	0.023
E (water spider)	5	0.125	0.016
F (mayfly larva)	8	0.20	0.040
	$\Sigma n = 40$		$\Sigma(n/N)^2 = 0.201$

$$D = 1-0.201 = 0.799$$

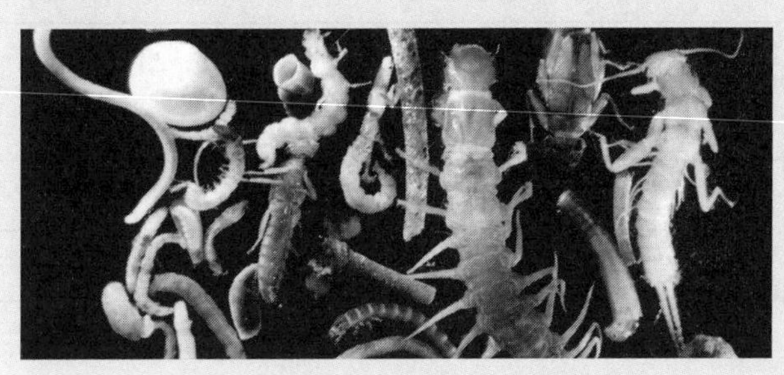

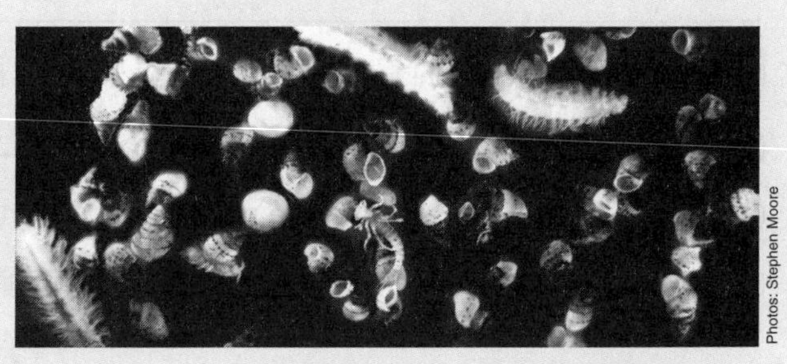

Photos: Stephen Moore

A stream community with a high macroinvertebrate diversity (left) in contrast to a low diversity stream community (right).

1. Describe two necessary considerations in attempting to make an unbiased measurement of biodiversity:

2. Explain why high biodiversity is generally associated with greater ecosystem stability:

3. Describe a situation where a species diversity index may provide useful information:

4. An area of forest floor was sampled and six invertebrate species were recorded, with counts of 7, 10, 11, 2, 4, and 3 individuals. Calculate Simpson's index of diversity for this community:

   (a) DI=

   (b) Comment on the diversity of this community:

Related activities: *Sampling Populations*

ISBN: 978-1-877462-96-2

Designing Your Field Study

The figure below provides an example and some ideas for designing a field study. It provides a framework which can be modified for most simple comparative field investigations. For reasons of space, the full methodology is not included.

Observation

A student read that a particular species of pill millipede (left) is extremely abundant in forest leaf litter, but a search in the litter of a conifer-dominated woodland near his home revealed only very low numbers of this millipede species.

Hypothesis

This millipede species is adapted to a niche in the leaf litter of oak woodlands and is abundant there. However, it is rare in the litter of coniferous woodland. The **null hypothesis** is that there is no difference between the abundance of this millipede species in oak and coniferous woodland litter.

Oak or coniferous woodland

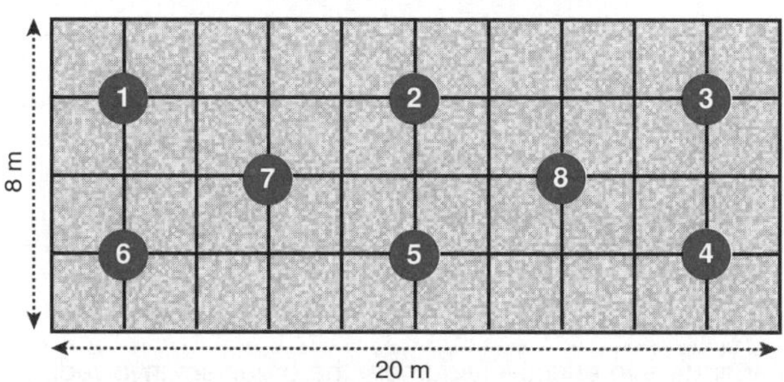

Sampling sites numbered 1-8 at evenly spaced intervals on a 2 x 2 m grid within an area of 20 m x 8 m.

Sampling equipment: leaf litter light trap

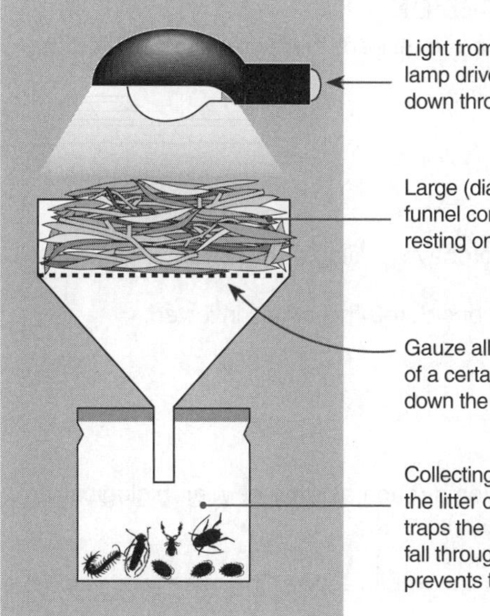

Notes on collection and analysis

- Mean millipede abundance was calculated from the counts from the eight sites. The difference in abundance at the sites was tested using a Student's *t* test.
- After counting and analysis of the samples, all the collected invertebrates were returned to the sites.

Sampling Program

A sampling program was designed to test the prediction that the millipedes would be more abundant in the leaf litter of oak woodlands than in coniferous woodlands.

Equipment and Procedure

Sites: For each of the two woodland types, an area 20 x 8 m was chosen and marked out in 2 x 2 m grids. Eight sampling sites were selected, evenly spaced along the grid as shown.

- The general area for the study chosen was selected on the basis of the large amounts of leaf litter present.
- Eight sites were chosen as the largest number feasible to collect and analyze in the time available.
- The two woodlands were sampled on sequential days.

Capture of millipedes: At each site, a 0.4 x 0.4 m quadrat was placed on the forest floor and the leaf litter within the quadrat was collected. Millipedes and other leaf litter invertebrates were captured using a simple gauze lined funnel containing the leaf litter from within the quadrat. A lamp was positioned over each funnel for two hours and the invertebrates in the litter moved down and were trapped in the collecting jar.

- After two hours each jar was labeled with the site number and returned to the lab for analysis.
- The litter in each funnel was bagged, labeled with the site number and returned to the lab for weighing.
- The number of millipedes at each site was recorded.
- The numbers of other invertebrates (classified into major taxa) were also noted for reference.

Assumptions

- The areas chosen in each woodland were representative of the woodland types in terms of millipede abundance.
- Eight sites were sufficient to adequately sample the millipede populations in each forest.
- A quadrat size of 0.4 x 0.4 m contained enough leaf litter to adequately sample the millipedes at each site.
- The millipedes were not preyed on by any of the other invertebrates captured in the collecting jar.
- All the invertebrates within the quadrat were captured.
- Millipedes moving away from the light are effectively captured by the funnel apparatus and cannot escape.
- Two hours was long enough for the millipedes to move down through the litter and fall into the trap.

  Note that these last two assumptions could be tested by examining the bagged leaf litter for millipedes after returning to the lab.

Field Studies

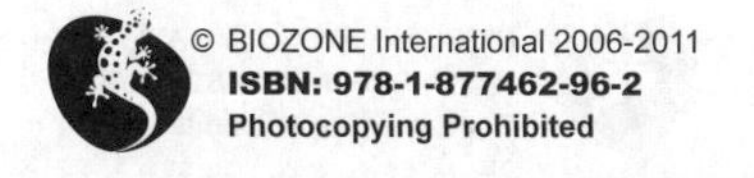

ISBN: 978-1-877462-96-2

Periodicals:
Fieldwork - sampling animals
Fieldwork - sampling plants

Related activities: *Quadrat-Based Estimates*

The Importance of Sample Size

In any field study, two of the most important considerations are the **sample size** (the number of samples you will take) and the size of the **sampling unit** (e.g. quadrat size). An appropriate choice will enable you to collect sufficient, unbiased data to confidently estimate the population parameters of interest (e.g. mean size of individuals in the population). The number of samples you take will be determined largely by the resources and time that you have available to collect and analyze your data (your **sampling effort**).

Yohan euan o4

1. Explain the importance of each of the following in field studies:

   (a) Appropriate quadrat size (or any equivalent sampling unit):

   (b) Recognizing any assumptions that you are making:

   (c) Appropriate consideration of the environment:

   (d) Return of organisms to the same place after removal:

   (e) Appropriate size of total sampling area within which the sites are located:

2. Explain how you could test whether any given quadrat size was adequate to effectively sample the organism involved:

YOUR CHECKLIST FOR FIELD STUDY DESIGN

The following provides a checklist for a field study. Check off the points when you are confident that you have satisfied the requirements in each case:

1. **Preliminary:**
   - ☐ (a) Makes a hypothesis based on observation(s).
   - ☐ (b) The hypothesis (and its predictions) are testable using the resources you have available (the study is feasible).
   - ☐ (c) The organism you have chosen is suitable for the study and you have considered the ethics involved.

2. **Assumptions and site selection:**
   - ☐ (a) You are aware of any assumptions that you are making in your study.
   - ☐ (b) You have identified aspects of your field design that could present problems (such as time of year, biological rhythms of your test organism, difficulty in identifying suitable habitats etc.).
   - ☐ (c) The study sites you have selected have the features necessary in order for you to answer the questions you have asked in your hypothesis.

3. **Data collection:**
   - ☐ (a) You are happy with the way in which you are going to take your measurements or samples.
   - ☐ (b) You have considered the size of your sampling unit and the number of samples you are going to take (and tested for these if necessary).
   - ☐ (c) You have given consideration to how you will analyze the data you collect and made sure that your study design allows you to answer the questions you wish to answer.

ISBN: 978-1-877462-96-2

Monitoring Physical Factors

Most ecological studies require us to measure the physical factors (parameters) in the environment that may influence the abundance and distribution of organisms. In recent years there have been substantial advances in the development of portable, light-weight meters and dataloggers. These enable easy collection and storage of data in the field.

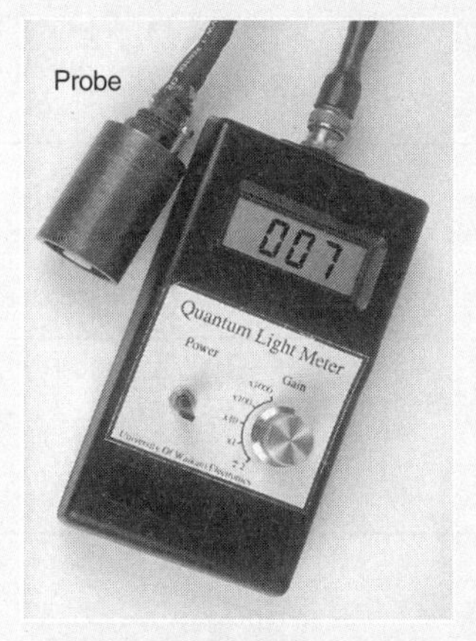

Quantum light meter: Measures light intensity levels. It is not capable of measuring light quality (wavelength).

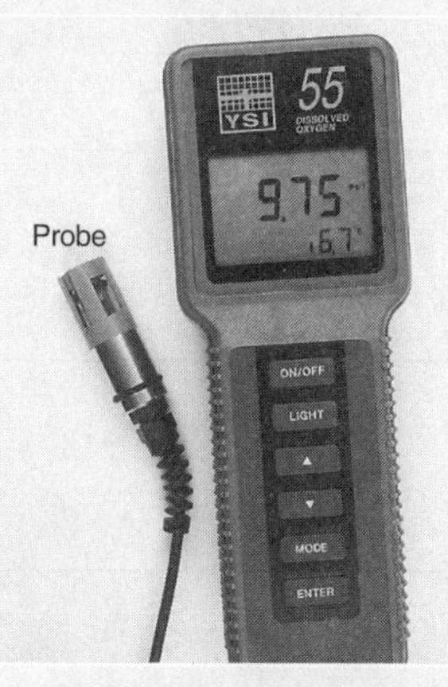

Dissolved oxygen meter: Measures the amount of oxygen dissolved in water (expressed as mg L^{-1}).

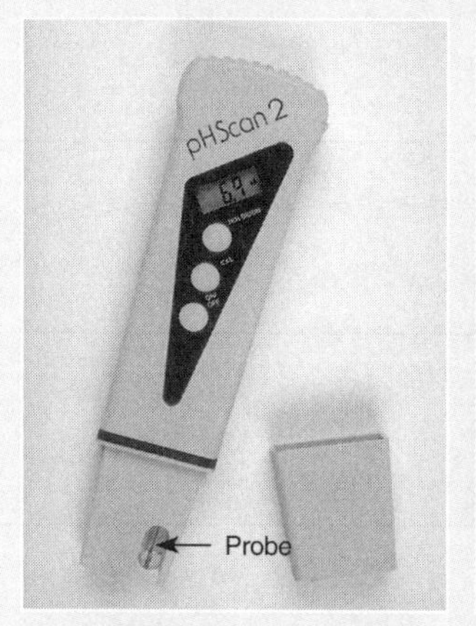

pH meter: Measures the acidity of water or soil, if it is first dissolved in pure water (pH scale 0 to 14).

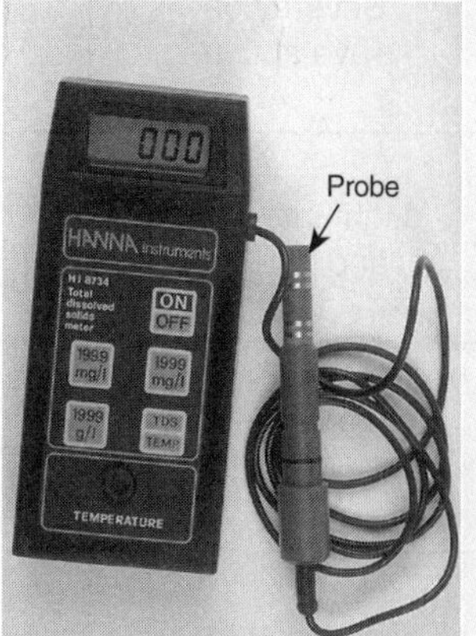

Total dissolved solids (TDS) meter: Measures content of dissolved solids (as ions) in water in mg L^{-1}.

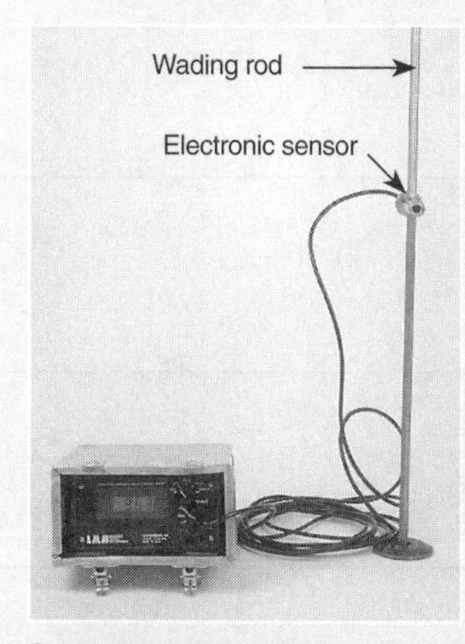

Current meter: The electronic sensor is positioned at set depths in a stream or river on the calibrated wading rod as current readings are taken.

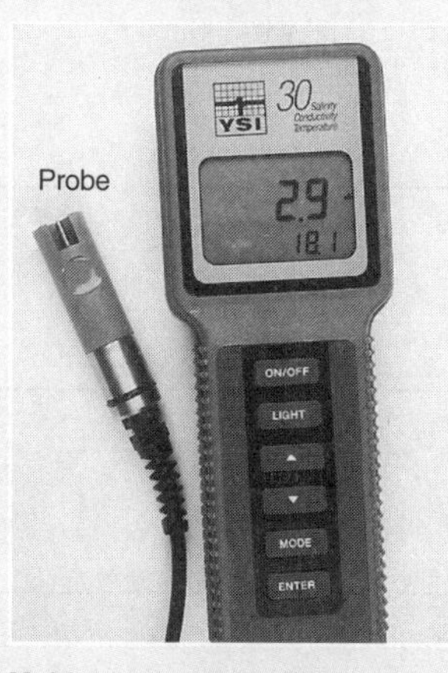

Multipurpose meter: This is a multi-functional meter, which can measure salinity, conductivity and temperature simply by pushing the MODE button.

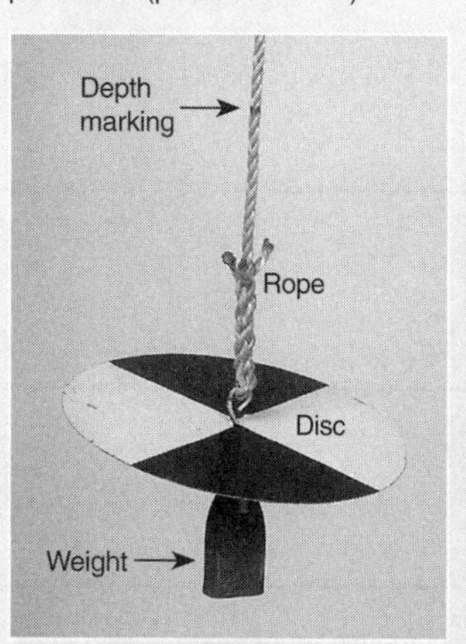

Secchi disc: This simple device is used to provide a crude measure of water clarity (the maximum depth at which the disc can just be seen).

Collecting a water sample: A Nansen bottle is used to collect water samples from a lake for lab analysis, testing for nutrients, oxygen and pH.

Dataloggers and Environmental Sensors

Dataloggers are electronic instruments that record measurements over time. They are equipped with a microprocessor, data storage facility, and sensor. Different sensors are employed to measure a range of variables in water (photos A and B) or air (photos C and D), as well as make physiological measurements. The datalogger is connected to a computer, and software is used to set the limits of operation (e.g. the sampling interval) and initiate the logger. The logger is then disconnected and used remotely to record and store data. When reconnected to the computer, the data are downloaded, viewed, and plotted. Dataloggers, such as those pictured here from PASCO, are being increasingly used in professional and school research. They make data collection quick and accurate, and they enable prompt data analysis.

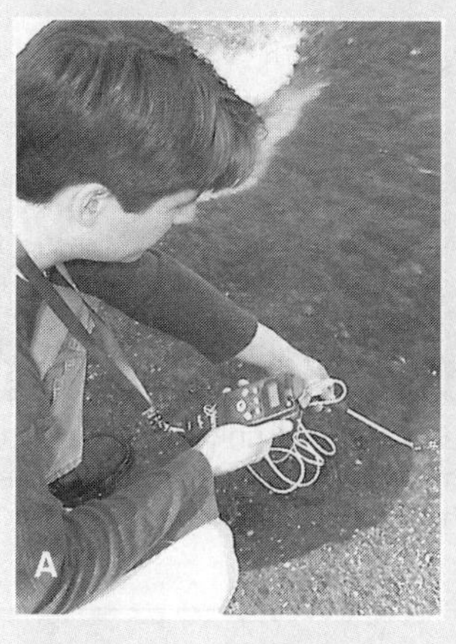

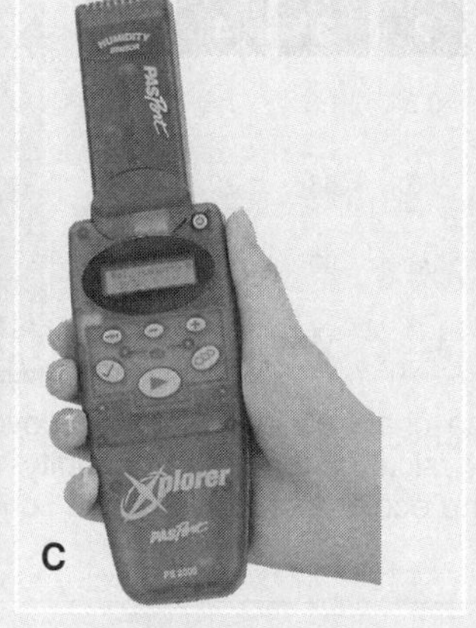

Dataloggers are now widely used to monitor conditions in aquatic environments. Different variables such as pH, temperature, conductivity, and dissolved oxygen can be measured by changing the sensor attached to the logger.

Dataloggers fitted with sensors are portable and easy to use in a wide range of terrestrial environments. They are used to measure variables such as air temperature and pressure, relative humidity, light, and carbon dioxide gas.

Field Studies

ISBN: 978-1-877462-96-2

1. The physical factors of an exposed rocky shore and a sheltered estuarine mudflat differ markedly. For each of the factors listed in the table below, briefly describe how they may differ (if at all):

Environmental parameter	Exposed rocky coastline	Estuarine mudflat
Severity of wave action		
Light intensity and quality		
Salinity/ conductivity		
Temperature change (diurnal)		
Substrate/ sediment type		
Oxygen concentration		
Exposure time to air (tide out)		

Quadrat 5
Quadrat 4
Quadrat 3
Quadrat 2
Quadrat 1

0 50 100
Percentage cover

Red stem moss
Fern moss
Snake moss
Star moss
Eye brow moss
Broad leaved star moss
Tree moss
Lichens (various species)

QUADRAT	1	2	3	4	5
Height (m)	0.4	0.8	1.2	1.6	2.0
Light (arbitrary units)	40	56	68	72	72
Humidity (percent)	99	88	80	76	78
Temperature (°C)	12.1	12.2	13	14.3	14.2

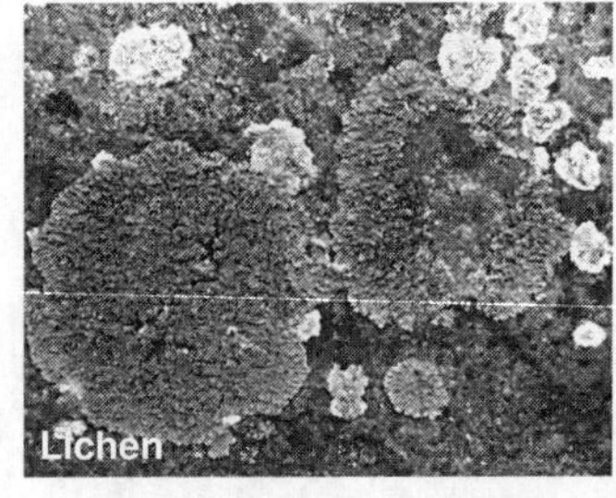
Lichen

Moss

2. The figure (above) shows the changes in vegetation cover along a 2 m vertical transect up the trunk of an oak tree (*Quercus*). Changes in the physical factors light, humidity, and temperature along the same transect were also recorded. From what you know about the ecology of mosses and lichens, account for the observed vegetation distribution:

ISBN: 978-1-877462-96-2

Indirect Sampling

If populations are small and easily recognized they may be monitored directly quite easily. However, direct measurement of elusive, or widely dispersed populations is not always feasible. In these cases, indirect methods can be used to assess population abundance, provide information on habitat use and range, and enable biologists to link habitat quality to species presence or absence. Indirect sampling methods provide less reliable measures of abundance than direct sampling methods, such as mark and recapture, but are widely used nevertheless. They rely on recording the signs of a species, e.g. scat, calls, tracks, and rubbings or markings on vegetation, and using these to assess population abundance. In Australia, the Environmental Protection Agency (EPA) provides a Frog Census Datasheet (below) on which volunteers record details about frog populations and habitat quality in their area. This program enables the EPA to gather information across Australia. Another example of an alternative method of population sampling used in New Zealand is the Kiwi Recovery Program (see following page).

INFORMATION NEEDED FOR THE FROG CENSUS

- Where you recorded frogs calling; When you made the recordings; and What frogs you recorded (if possible).

Observers Name:
Contact Address:
Post Code:
Telephone Home: Work / Mobile:
Do You Want to be involved next year?(Please Circle) Yes /
Location Description (Try to provide enough detail to enable us to find site o map.
Please use a separate datasheet for each site):
is location the same as in (CIRCLE) 1994 1995 1996 1997 New
Grid Reference of Location and Type of Map Used:
OR Street Directory Reference: Year and Edition:
Page Number: Grid Reference:
Nearest Town from Location (If known):
Date of Observation (e.g. 8 Sept 1998):
Time Range of Observation (e.g. 8.30-8.40 pm):

HABITAT ASSESSMENT

Habitat Type (please circle one): pond dam stream drain reservoir wetland spring swamp
Comments:

WATER QUALITY and WEATHER

CIRCLE to indicate the condition of the site (you can circle more than one choice).
Water Flow: Still Flowing Slowly Flowing Quickly
Water Appearance: Clear Polluted Frothy Oily Muddy
Weather Conditions: 1. Windy / Still
2. Overcast / Recent Rains / Dry (indicate for 1 AND 2)

FROGS HEARD CALLING

Please indicate your estimate of how many frogs you heard calling
(NOTE it is very important to tell us if you heard no frogs)
Number of Calls Heard (circle):
None One Few (2-9) Many (10-50) Lots (>50)
If you want to test your frog knowledge write the species you heard calling:
Species of Frog(s) Identified: 1. 2. 3. 4.
Comments:

Now we need you to return your datasheet and tape in the **postage free** post-pak addressed to REPLY PAID 6360 Mr Peter Goonan Environment Protection Agency Box 2607 ADELAIDE SA 5001. We will identify your frog calls and let you the results of your recordings.

Office use only. Please leave blank.
FROG SPECIES PRESENT.

cies Number	Species 1	Species 2	Species 3	Species 4	Species 5
cies Name					
e					
(2 - 9)					
y (10 - 50)					
(>50)					

ENVIRONMENT PROTECTION AGENCY
PARTMENT FOR ENVIRONMENT HERITAGE AND ABORIGINAL AFFAIRS

Recording a date and accurate map reference is important

Population estimates are based on the number of frog calls recorded by the observer

COD

Sam Banks

To sample nocturnal, highly mobile species, e.g. bats, electronic devices, such as the bat detector above, can be used to estimate population density. In this case, the detector is tuned to the particular frequency of the hunting clicks emitted by specific bat species. The number of calls recorded per unit time can be used to estimate numbers per area.

The analysis of animal tracks allows wildlife biologists to identify habitats in which animals live and to conduct population surveys. Interpreting tracks accurately requires considerable skill as tracks may vary in appearance even when from the same individual. Tracks are particularly useful as a way to determine habitat use and preference.

All animals leave scats (feces) which are species specific and readily identifiable. Scats can be a valuable tool by which to gather data from elusive, nocturnal, easily disturbed, or highly mobile species. Fecal analyses can provide information on diet, movements, population density, sex ratios, age structure, and even genetic diversity.

1. Describe two kinds of indirect signs that could be used to detect the presence of frogs:

   (a) ______________________ (b) ______________________

2. (a) Describe the kind of information that the EPA would gather from their Frog Census Datasheet: ______________________

   ____

   ____

   ____

   (b) Explain a use for this information: ______________________

   ____

ISBN: 978-1-877462-96-2

Periodicals: *Bowels of the beast*

Related activities: *Sampling Populations, Sampling Animal Populations*

The **Kiwi Reporting Card** is issued to trampers and conservation groups who are helping New Zealand's Department of Conservation to gather census data on kiwi. Read all parts of the card carefully and answer the questions below.

DATE:	OBSERVER'S DETAILS:
LOCATION:	NAME
	ADDRESS
MAP SERIES / SHEET / GRID REFERENCE E N	PHONE Home/Work
NUMBER OF KIWI SEEN (Other, please specify)	
NUMBER OF KIWI HEARD (Male calls / Female calls) — SIGNS OF KIWI PRESENT (eg. footprints, probeholes)	COMMENTS (Vegetation, habitat, dogs or other predators seen)
Are you 100% sure that what you saw or heard was a kiwi? YES/NO	

KIWI REPORTING CARD

Please complete this form as fully as possible and return to the Department of Conservation.

KIWI RECOVERY

NOTES

1. The call of the male kiwi is a repetitive (8-25 notes) high-pitched whistle.
2. The call of the female kiwi is a repetitive (10-20 notes) coarse rasping note.
3. Weka, moreporks and possums are often confused with kiwi calls.
4. Footprints are about the size of a domestic chicken and are often found in mud or snow.
5. Probeholes usually occur in groups and look like a screwdriver has been pushed into the ground, rotated and pulled out again. They are about 10cm deep.
6. This form may also be used to report other species of wildlife such as kaka, kokako, blue duck, bats, etc. Please ensure you clearly identify what you are recording.
7. Post this card to the Departme (address provided o with a hut warde

3. Describe three kinds of indirect signs that can be used to detect the presence of kiwi:

(a) ______________________

(b) ______________________

(c) ______________________

4. Explain why it is not easy to carry out a direct count of a kiwi population:

5. Describe the attempts that the organizers of this data collecting program have made to ensure that the people recording their observations are correctly identifying kiwi signs:

6. Explain why the comments section on the card requests information on the habitat, dogs, or other predators seen:

7. Describe one other indirect method of population sampling and outline its advantages and drawbacks:

ISBN: 978-1-877462-96-2

Sampling Animal Populations

Unlike plants, most animals are highly mobile and present special challenges in terms of sampling them **quantitatively** to estimate their distribution and abundance. The equipment available for sampling animals ranges from various types of nets and traps (below), to more complex electronic devices, such as those used for radio-tracking large mobile species.

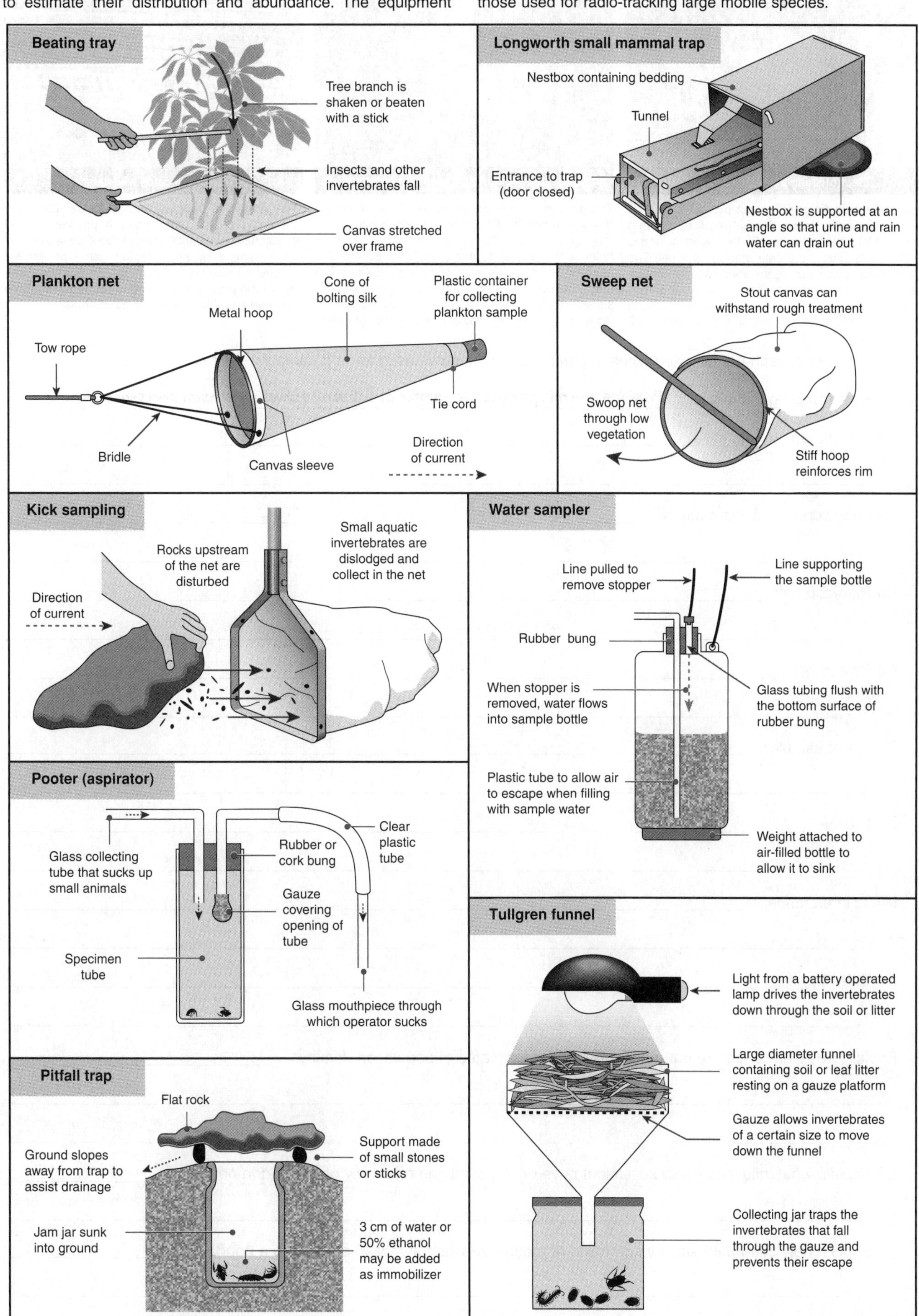

ISBN: 978-1-877462-96-2

Related activities: *Mark and Recapture Sampling, Sampling a Leaf Litter Population*
Weblinks: *Ecological Sampling Methods*

Electrofishing a stream (Sweden)

Schindler trap for sampling plankton communities

Trap set to catch wild cats

Electrofishing: An effective, but expensive method of sampling larger stream animals (e.g. fish). Wearing a portable battery backpack, the operator walks upstream holding the anode probe and a net. The electrical circuit created by the anode and the stream bed stuns the animals, which are netted and placed in a bucket to recover. After analysis (measurement, species, weights) the animals are released.

Trapping in aquatic communities: There are many designs of nets and traps for aquatic communities, ranging from those that are placed on the substrate to those that are towed through a water column. For plankton communities, a known quantity of water from a specific depth can be trapped and brought to the surface where the water is drained and the plankton in the water are trapped against a small removable filter.

Trapping: Live trapping is used for sampling and managing animal populations. It provides a way to estimate population size (of both desirable and undesirable species). Trapping can help protect threatened species by targeting their predators and controlling pest numbers, and to capture animals so they can be reintroduced into other areas.

1. Describe what each the following types of sampling equipment is used for in a sampling context:

   (a) Kick sampling technique: Provides a semi-quantitative sample of substrate-dwelling stream invertebrates

   (b) Beating tray: ______

   (c) Longworth small mammal trap: ______

   (d) Plankton net: ______

   (e) Sweep net: ______

   (f) Water sampler: ______

   (g) Pooter: ______

   (h) Tullgren funnel: ______

   (i) Pitfall trap: ______

2. Explain why pitfall traps are not recommended for estimates of population density: ______

3. (a) Explain what influence mesh size might have on the sampling efficiency of a plankton net: ______

   (b) Explain how this would affect your choice of mesh size when sampling animals in a pond: ______

ISBN: 978-1-877462-96-2

Transect Sampling

A **transect** is a line placed across a community of organisms. Transects are usually carried out to provide information on the **distribution** of species in the community. This is of particular value in situations where environmental factors change over the sampled distance. This change is called an **environmental gradient** (e.g. up a mountain or across a seashore). The usual practice for small transects is to stretch a string between two markers. The string is marked off in measured distance intervals, and the species at each marked point are noted. The sampling points along the transect may also be used for the siting of quadrats, so that changes in density and community composition can be recorded. Belt transects are essentially a form of continuous quadrat sampling. They provide more information on community composition but can be difficult to carry out. Some transects provide information on the vertical, as well as horizontal, distribution of species (e.g. tree canopies in a forest).

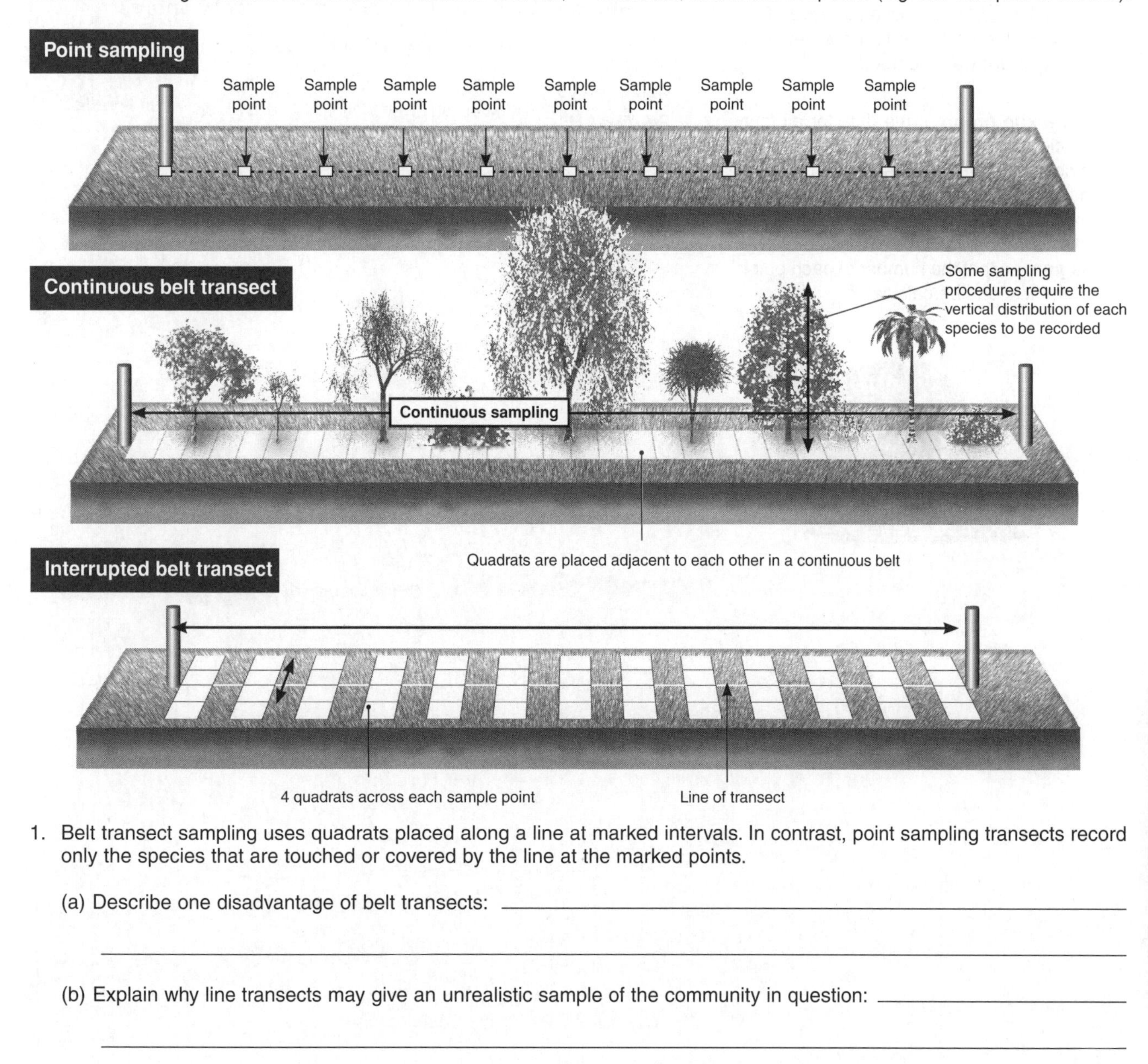

1. Belt transect sampling uses quadrats placed along a line at marked intervals. In contrast, point sampling transects record only the species that are touched or covered by the line at the marked points.

   (a) Describe one disadvantage of belt transects: ______________________

   (b) Explain why line transects may give an unrealistic sample of the community in question: ______________________

   (c) Explain how belt transects overcome this problem: ______________________

   (d) Describe a situation where the use of transects to sample the community would be inappropriate: ______________________

2. Explain how you could test whether or not a transect sampling interval was sufficient to accurately sample a community:

____

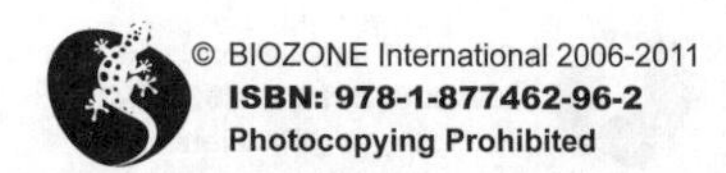

ISBN: 978-1-877462-96-2

Related activities: *Drawing Kite Graphs*

Kite graphs are an ideal way in which to present distributional data from a belt transect (e.g. abundance or percentage cover along an environmental gradient. Usually, they involve plots for more than one species. This makes them good for highlighting probable differences in habitat preference between species. Kite graphs may also be used to show changes in distribution with time (e.g. with daily or seasonal cycles).

3. The data on the right were collected from a rocky shore field trip. Periwinkles from four common species of the genus *Littorina* were sampled in a continuous belt transect from the low water mark, to a height of 10 m above that level. The number of each of the four species in a 1 m^2 quadrat was recorded.

   Plot a **kite graph** of the data for all four species on the grid below. Be sure to choose a scale that takes account of the maximum number found at any one point and allows you to include all the species on the one plot. Include the scale on the diagram so that the number at each point on the kite can be calculated.

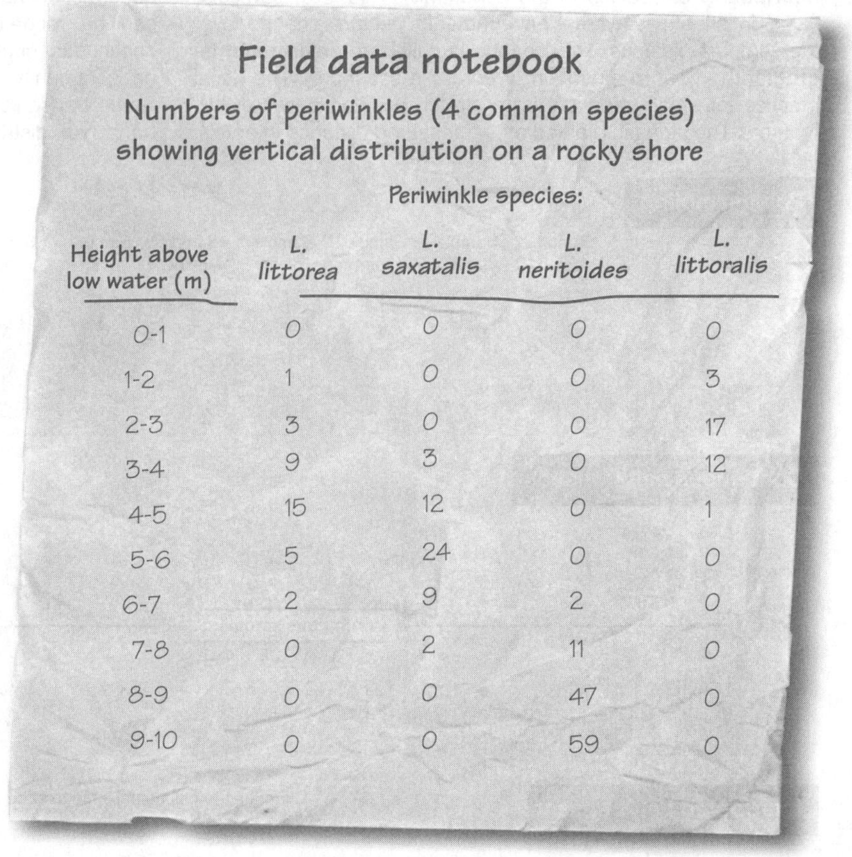

Field data notebook

Numbers of periwinkles (4 common species) showing vertical distribution on a rocky shore

Height above low water (m)	*L. littorea*	*L. saxatalis*	*L. neritoides*	*L. littoralis*
0-1	0	0	0	0
1-2	1	0	0	3
2-3	3	0	0	17
3-4	9	3	0	12
4-5	15	12	0	1
5-6	5	24	0	0
6-7	2	9	2	0
7-8	0	2	11	0
8-9	0	0	47	0
9-10	0	0	59	0

(Periwinkle species: column headings)

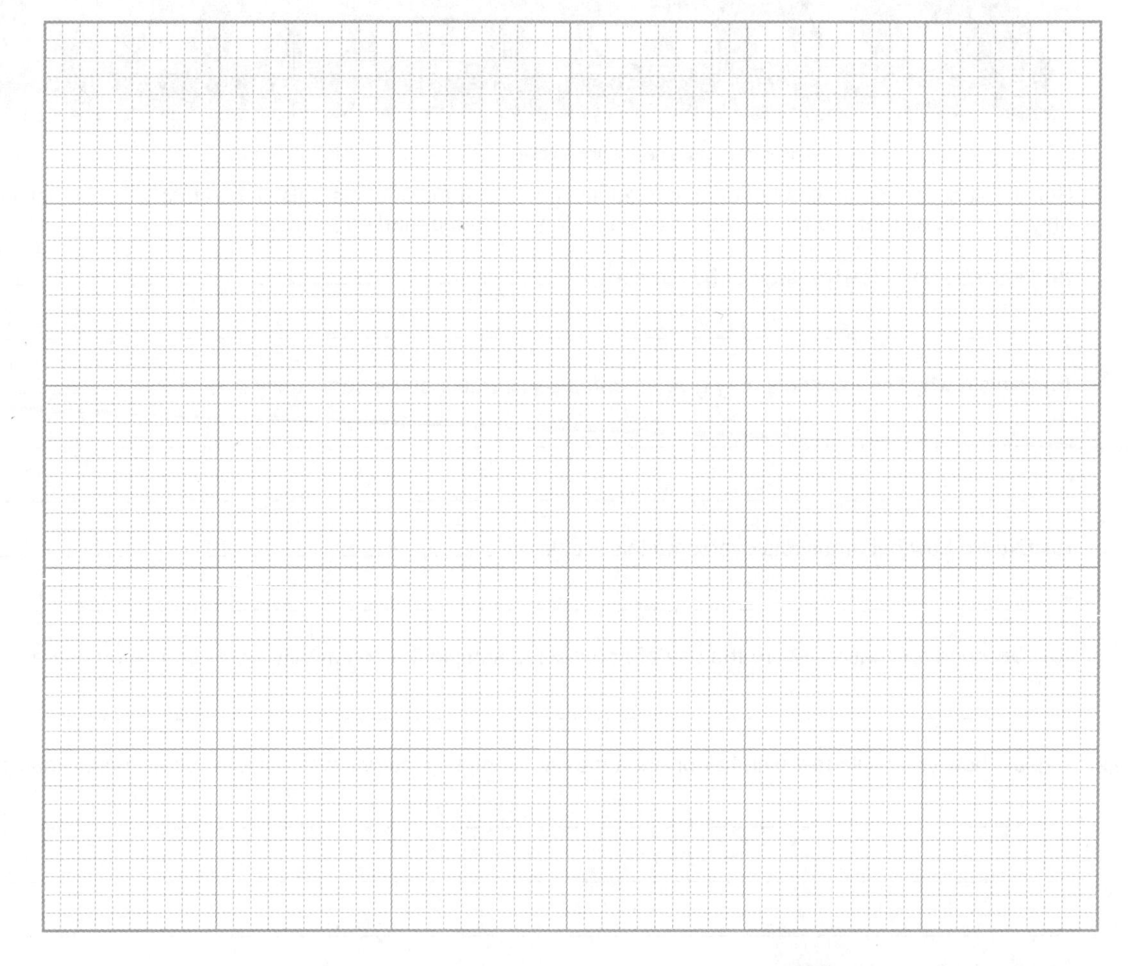

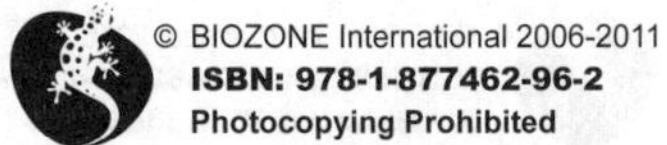

ISBN: 978-1-877462-96-2

Mark and Recapture Sampling

The mark and recapture method of estimating population size is used in the study of animal populations where individuals are highly mobile. It is of no value where animals do not move or move very little. The number of animals caught in each sample must be large enough to be valid. The technique is outlined in the diagram below.

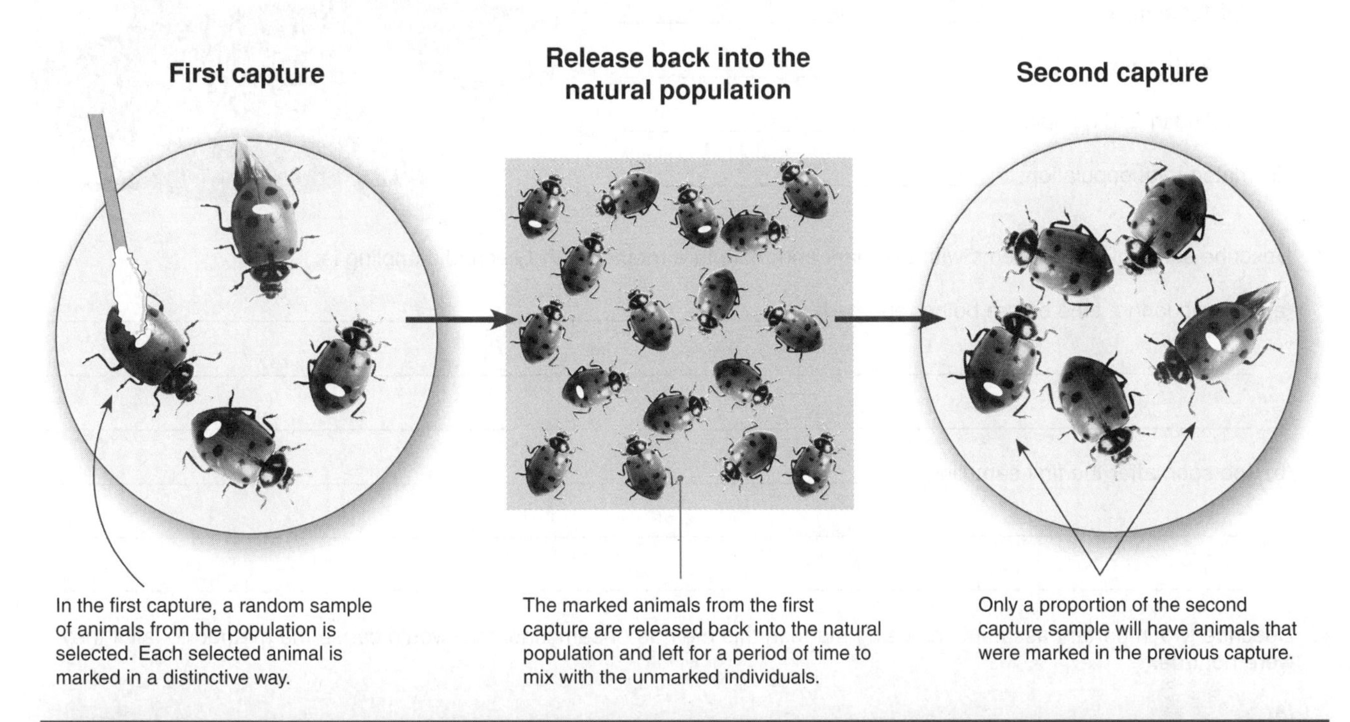

The Lincoln Index

$$\text{Total population} = \frac{\text{No. of animals in 1st sample (all marked)} \times \text{Total no. of animals in 2nd sample}}{\text{Number of marked animals in the second sample (recaptured)}}$$

The mark and recapture technique comprises a number of simple steps:

1. The population is sampled by capturing as many of the individuals as possible and practical.
2. Each animal is marked in a way to distinguish it from unmarked animals (unique mark for each individual not required).
3. Return the animals to their habitat and leave them for a long enough period for complete mixing with the rest of the population to take place
4. Take another sample of the population (this does not need to be the same sample size as the first sample, but it does have to be large enough to be valid).
5. Determine the numbers of marked to unmarked animals in this second sample. Use the equation above to estimate the size of the overall population.

Field Studies

1. For this exercise you will need several boxes of matches and a pen. Work in a group of 2-3 students to 'sample' the population of matches in the full box by using the mark and recapture method. Each match will represent one animal.

   (a) Take out 10 matches from the box and mark them on 4 sides with a pen so that you will be able to recognize them from the other unmarked matches later.
   (b) Return the marked matches to the box and shake the box to mix the matches.
   (c) Take a sample of 20 matches from the same box and record the number of marked matches and unmarked matches.
   (d) Determine the total population size by using the equation above.
   (e) Repeat the sampling 4 more times (steps b–d above) and record your results:

	Sample 1	Sample 2	Sample 3	Sample 4	Sample 5
Estimated population					

   (f) Count the actual number of matches in the matchbox : ______________________

   (g) Compare the actual number to your estimates. By how much does it differ: ______________________

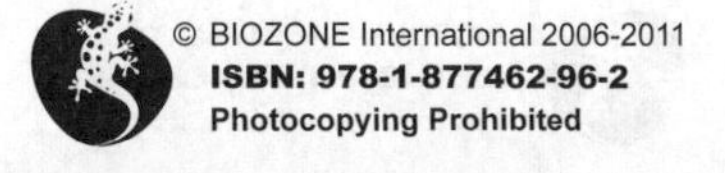

ISBN: 978-1-877462-96-2

2. In 1919 a researcher by the name of Dahl wanted to estimate the number of trout in a Norwegian lake. The trout were subject to fishing so it was important to know how big the population was in order to manage the fish stock. He captured and marked 109 trout in his first sample. A few days later, he caught 177 trout in his second sample, of which 57 were marked. Use the **Lincoln index** to estimate the total population size:

   Size of 1st sample: ____________________

   Size of 2nd sample: ____________________

   No. marked in 2nd sample: ____________________

   Estimated total population: ____________________

3. Describe some of the problems with the mark and recapture method if the second sampling is:

   (a) Left too long a time before being repeated: ____________________

   (b) Too soon after the first sampling: ____________________

4. Describe two important assumptions being made in this method of sampling, that would cause the method to fail if they were not true:

   (a) ____________________

   (b) ____________________

5. Some types of animal would be unsuitable for this method of population estimation (i.e. the method would not work).

   (a) Name an animal for which this method of sampling would not be effective: ____________________

   (b) Explain your answer above: ____________________

6. Describe three methods for marking animals for mark and recapture sampling. Take into account the possibility of animals shedding their skin, or being difficult to get close to again:

   (a) ____________________

   (b) ____________________

   (c) ____________________

7. Scientists in the UK and Canada have, at various times since the 1950s, been involved in computerized tagging programs for Northern cod (a species once abundant in Northern Hemisphere waters but now severely depleted). Describe the type of information that could be obtained through such tagging programs:

   ____

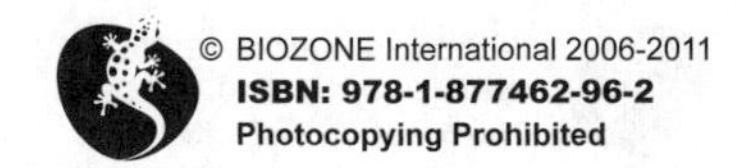

ISBN: 978-1-877462-96-2

Sampling Using Radio-tracking

Field work involving difficult terrain, aquatic environments, or highly mobile, secretive, or easily disturbed species, has been greatly assisted in recent years by the use of radio-transmitter technology. Radio-tracking can be used to quickly obtain accurate information about an animal's home range and can provide information about dispersal, distribution, habitat use, and competitive relationships. Radio-tracking is particularly suited to population studies of threatened species (because it is relatively non-invasive) and of pests (because their dispersal and habitat use can be monitored). The information can be used to manage an endangered species effectively or to plan more efficient pest control operations. Satellite transmitters can be used to study migratory movements of large animals and marine species, which are more difficult to follow.

Radio-tracking technology is widely used in conservation work to study animal movements and habitat use. The information allows conservation organizations to develop better strategies for the management of species in the wild or follow the progress of reintroduced captive-bred animals.

A tracking antenna and receiver can be used to pinpoint the location of an animal. Antennae are directional and so can accurately fix an animal's position. They can be mounted on to light aircraft or off-road vehicles to provide mobile tracking over large areas. For work in inaccessible or difficult terrain, portable, hand-held antennae are used.

Radio-tracking is used to monitor patterns of migration and distribution, especially when species are being reintroduced to an area after an absence, e.g. the gray wolf (above). Radio-tracking of pest species can determine dispersal rates, distribution, and habitat use in critical conservation areas, enabling more effective pest control.

Tracking Migrations

During 2002 and 2003, a number of great white sharks were radio-tagged in South African waters. The data recovered showed the first ever recorded intercontinental migration by a great white.

A female shark, known as P12, swam 11 000 km from South Africa to Australia in 99 days with a minimum speed just under 5 km h^{-1}. Within 9 months she had returned to South African waters, completing a round trip of more than 20 000 km.

1. Describe two applications of radio-tracking technology in endangered species management: ______________________________

2. Explain why radio-tracking might be used to monitor pest species: ______________________________

3. Explain how radio-tracking has increased our knowledge of the movement of marine animals: ______________________________

ISBN: 978-1-877462-96-2

Related activities: *Sampling Populations*
Weblinks: *Transoceanic migration of white sharks*

Quadrat Sampling

Quadrat sampling is a method by which organisms in a certain proportion (sample) of the habitat are counted directly. As with all sampling methods, it is used to estimate population parameters when the organisms present are too numerous to count in total. It can be used to estimate population **abundance** (number), **density, frequency of occurrence**, and **distribution**. Quadrats may be used without a transect when studying a relatively uniform habitat. In this case, the quadrat positions are chosen randomly using a random number table.

The general procedure is to count all the individuals (or estimate their percentage cover) in a number of quadrats of known size and to use this information to work out the abundance or percentage cover value for the whole area. The number of quadrats used and their size should be appropriate to the type of organism involved (e.g. grass vs tree).

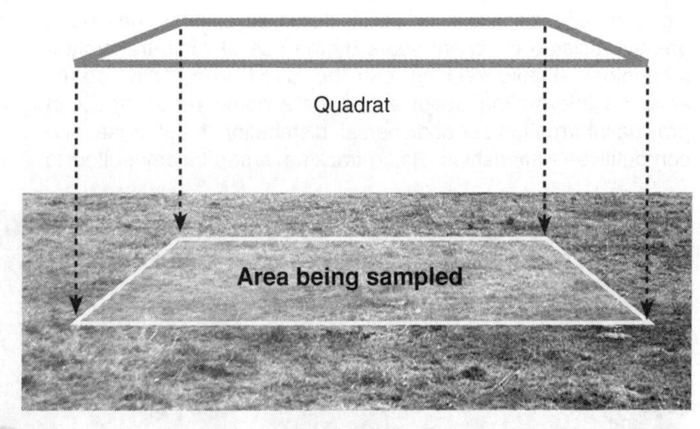

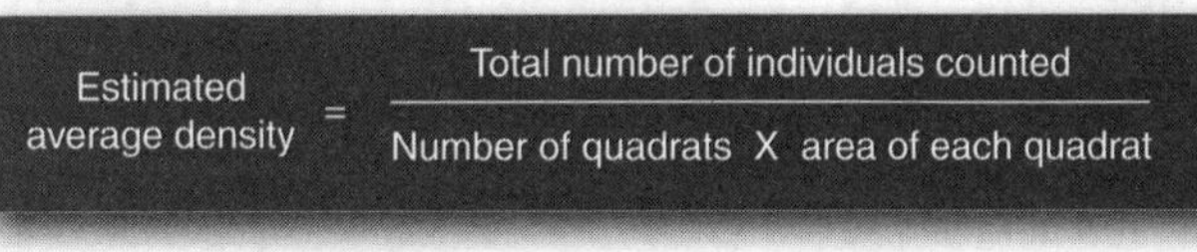

$$\text{Estimated average density} = \frac{\text{Total number of individuals counted}}{\text{Number of quadrats X area of each quadrat}}$$

Guidelines for Quadrat Use:

1. The **area of each quadrat** must be known exactly and ideally quadrats should be the same shape. The quadrat does not have to be square (it may be rectangular, hexagonal etc.).
2. **Enough quadrat samples** must be taken to provide results that are representative of the total population.
3. The **population of each quadrat** must be known exactly. Species must be distinguishable from each other, even if they have to be identified at a later date. It has to be decided beforehand what the count procedure will be and how organisms over the quadrat boundary will be counted.
4. The size of the quadrat should be appropriate to the organisms and habitat, e.g. a large size quadrat for trees.
5. The quadrats must be **representative of the whole area**. This is usually achieved by **random sampling** (right).

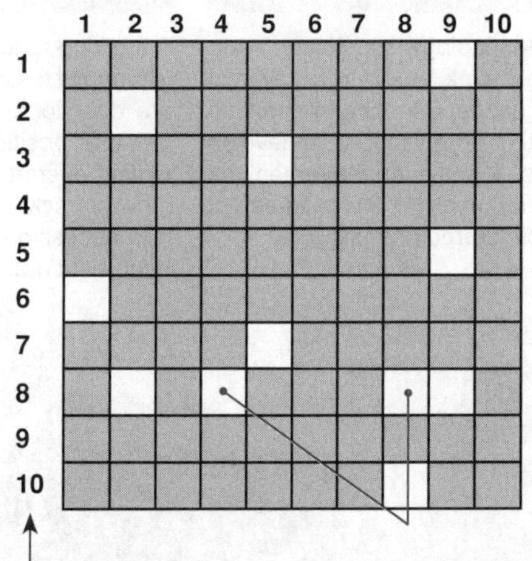

The area to be sampled is divided up into a grid pattern with indexed coordinates

Quadrats are applied to the predetermined grid on a random basis. This can be achieved by using a random number table.

Sampling a centipede population

A researcher by the name of Lloyd (1967) sampled centipedes in Wytham Woods, near Oxford in England. A total of 37 hexagon–shaped quadrats were used, each with a diameter of 30 cm (see diagram on right). These were arranged in a pattern so that they were all touching each other. Use the data in the diagram to answer the following questions.

1. Determine the average number of centipedes captured per quadrat:

____

2. Calculate the estimated average density of centipedes per square metre (remember that each quadrat is 0.08 square metres in area):

____

3. Looking at the data for individual quadrats, describe in general terms the distribution of the centipedes in the sample area:

____

____

4 Describe one factor that might account for the distribution pattern:

____

____

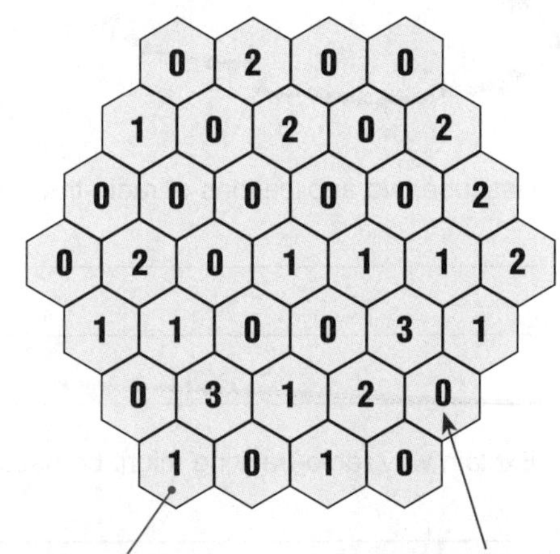

Each quadrat was a hexagon with a diameter of 30 cm and an area of 0.08 square meters.

The number in each hexagon indicates how many centipedes were caught in that quadrat.

ISBN: 978-1-877462-96-2

Related activities: *Quadrat-Based Estimates, Sampling a Leaf Litter Population*
Weblinks: *Investigating Marine Life, Using Quadrats to Sample*

Quadrat-Based Estimates

The simplest description of a plant community in a habitat is a list of the species that are present. This qualitative assessment of the community has the limitation of not providing any information about the **relative abundance** of the species present. Quick estimates can be made using **abundance scales**, such as the ACFOR scale described below. Estimates of percentage cover provide similar information. These methods require the use of **quadrats**. Quadrats are used extensively in plant ecology. This activity outlines some of the common considerations when using quadrats to sample plant communities.

What Size Quadrat?

Quadrats are usually square, and cover 0.25 m2 (0.5 m x 0.5 m) or 1 m2, but they can be of any size or shape, even a single point. The quadrats used to sample plant communities are often 0.25 m2. This size is ideal for low-growing vegetation, but quadrat size needs to be adjusted to habitat type. The quadrat must be large enough to be representative of the community, but not so large as to take a very long time to use.

A quadrat covering an area of 0.25 m^2 is suitable for most low growing plant communities, such as this alpine meadow, fields, and grasslands.

Larger quadrats (e.g. 1 m^2) are needed for communities with shrubs and trees. Quadrats as large as 4 m x 4 m may be needed in woodlands.

Small quadrats (0.01 m^2 or 100 mm x 100 mm) are appropriate for lichens and mosses on rock faces and tree trunks.

How Many Quadrats?

As well as deciding on a suitable quadrat size, the other consideration is how many quadrats to take (the sample size). In species-poor or very homogeneous habitats, a small number of quadrats will be sufficient. In species-rich or heterogeneous habitats, more quadrats will be needed to ensure that all species are represented adequately.

Determining the number of quadrats needed

- Plot the cumulative number of species recorded (on the y axis) against the number of quadrats already taken (on the x axis).
- The point at which the curve levels off indicates the suitable number of quadrats required.

Fewer quadrats are needed in species-poor or very uniform habitats, such as this bluebell woodland.

Describing Vegetation

Density (number of individuals per unit area) is a useful measure of abundance for animal populations, but can be problematic in plant communities where it can be difficult to determine where one plant ends and another begins. For this reason, plant abundance is often assessed using **percentage cover**. Here, the percentage of each quadrat covered by each species is recorded, either as a numerical value or using an abundance scale such as the ACFOR scale.

The ACFOR Abundance Scale

A = Abundant (30% +)
C = Common (20-29%)
F = Frequent (10-19%)
O = Occasional (5-9%)
R = Rare (1-4%)

The ACFOR scale could be used to assess the abundance of species in this wildflower meadow. Abundance scales are subjective, but it is not difficult to determine which abundance category each species falls into.

Field Studies

1. Describe one difference between the methods used to assess species abundance in plant and in animal communities:

___

2. Identify the main consideration when determining appropriate quadrat size: ___

3. Identify the main consideration when determining number of quadrats: ___

4. Explain two main disadvantages of using the ACFOR abundance scale to record information about a plant community:

(a) ___

(b) ___

ISBN: 978-1-877462-96-2

Periodicals: *Fieldwork: sampling plants*

Related activities: *Sampling Populations, Quadrat Sampling*
Weblinks: *Ecological Sampling Methods*

Sampling a Rocky Shore Community

The diagram opposite represents an area of seashore with its resident organisms. The distribution of coralline algae and four animal species are shown. This exercise is designed to prepare you for planning and carrying out a similar procedure in your practical investigation of a natural community. It is desirable, but not essential, that students work in groups of 2–4.

1. **Decide on the sampling method**
For the purpose of this exercise, it has been decided that the populations to be investigated are too large to be counted directly and a quadrat sampling method is to be used to estimate the average density of the four animal species as well as that of the algae.

2. **Mark out a grid pattern**
Use a ruler to mark out 3 cm intervals along each side of the sampling area (area of quadrat = 0.03 x 0.03 m). **Draw lines** between these marks to create a 6 x 6 grid pattern (total area = 0.18 x 0.18 m). This will provide a total of 36 quadrats that can be investigated.

3. **Number the axes of the grid**
Only a small proportion of the possible quadrat positions are going to be sampled. It is necessary to select the quadrats in a random manner. It is not sufficient to simply guess or choose your own on a 'gut feeling'. The best way to choose the quadrats randomly is to create a numbering system for the grid pattern and then select the quadrats from a random number table. Starting at the *top left hand corner*, **number the columns** and **rows** from 1 to 6 on each axis.

4. **Choose quadrats randomly**
To select the required number of quadrats randomly, use random numbers from a random number table. The random numbers are used as an index to the grid coordinates. Choose 6 quadrats from the total of 36 using table of random numbers provided for you at the bottom of the next page. Make a note of which column of random numbers you choose. Each member of your group should choose a different set of random numbers (i.e. different column: A–D) so that you can compare the effectiveness of the sampling method.

   Column of random numbers chosen: ______

   NOTE: Highlight the boundary of each selected quadrat with coloured pen/highlighter.

5. **Decide on the counting criteria**
Before the counting of the individuals for each species is carried out, the criteria for counting need to be established.

   There may be some problems here. You must decide before sampling begins as to what to do about individuals that are only partly inside the quadrat. Possible answers include:

   (a) Only counting individuals that are completely inside the quadrat.
   (b) Only counting individuals with a clearly defined part of their body inside the quadrat (such as the head).
   (c) Allowing for 'half individuals' (e.g. 3.5 barnacles).
   (d) Counting an individual that is inside the quadrat by half or more as one complete individual.

   Discuss the merits and problems of the suggestions above with other members of the class (or group). You may even have counting criteria of your own. Think about other factors that could cause problems with your counting.

6. **Carry out the sampling**
Carefully examine each selected quadrat and **count the number of individuals** of each species present. Record your data in the spaces provided on the next page.

7. **Calculate the population density**
Use the combined data TOTALS for the sampled quadrats to estimate the average density for each species by using the formula:

$$\textbf{Density} = \frac{\textbf{Total number in all quadrats sampled}}{\textbf{Number of quadrats sampled X area of a quadrat}}$$

   Remember that a total of 6 quadrats are sampled and each has an area of 0.0009 m^2. The density should be expressed as the number of individuals *per square metre (no.* m^{-2}*)*.

   Plicate barnacle: ______ Snakeskin chiton: ______

   Oyster borer: ______ Coralline algae: ______

   Limpet: ______

8. (a) In this example the animals are not moving. Describe the problems associated with sampling moving organisms. Explain how you would cope with sampling these same animals if they were really alive and very active:

____

____

____

(b) Carry out a direct count of all 4 animal species and the algae for the whole sample area (all 36 quadrats). Apply the data from your direct count to the equation given in (7) above to calculate the actual population density (remember that the number of quadrats in this case = 36):

Barnacle: ______ Oyster borer: ______ Chiton: ______ Limpet: ______ Algae: ______

Compare your estimated population density to the actual population density for each species:

____

____

____

ISBN: 978-1-877462-96-2

Related activities: *Quadrat Sampling, Quadrat-Based Estimates*

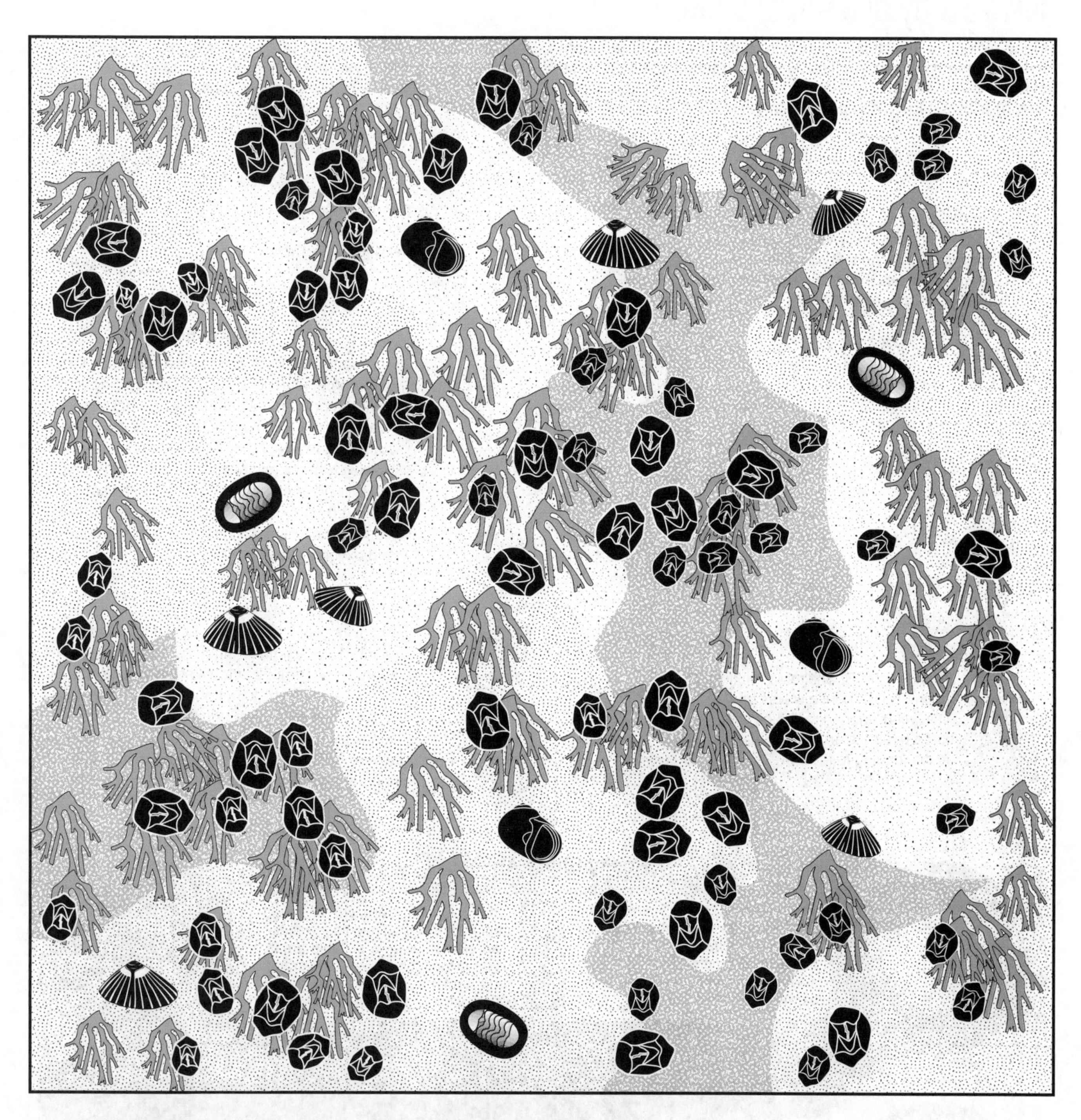

Coordinates for each quadrat	Plicate barnacle	Oyster borer	Snakeskin chiton	Limpet	Coralline algae
1:					
2:					
3:					
4:					
5:					
6:					
TOTAL					

Table of random numbers

A	B	C	D
2 2	3 1	6 2	2 2
3 2	1 5	6 3	4 3
3 1	5 6	3 6	6 4
4 6	3 6	1 3	4 5
4 3	4 2	4 5	3 5
5 6	1 4	3 1	1 4

The table above has been adapted from a table of random numbers from a statistics book. Use this table to select quadrats randomly from the grid above. Choose one of the columns (A to D) and use the numbers in that column as an index to the grid. The first digit refers to the row number and the second digit refers to the column number. To locate each of the 6 quadrats, find where the row and column intersect, as shown below:

Example: 5 2 refers to the 5th row and the 2nd column

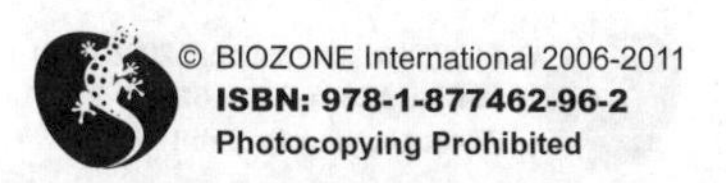

ISBN: 978-1-877462-96-2

Field Study of a Rocky Shore

Many biological investigations require data to be gathered from natural communities in the field. Recording the physical aspects of the site from which the data are collected (e.g. sheltered sandy beach) allows it to be compared with other sites. Collected data may include the total number of plants or animals at a site, the number per square metre of sample area, or some other aspect of a plant or animal's niche. The investigation below compares the animals found on an exposed and a sheltered rocky shore.

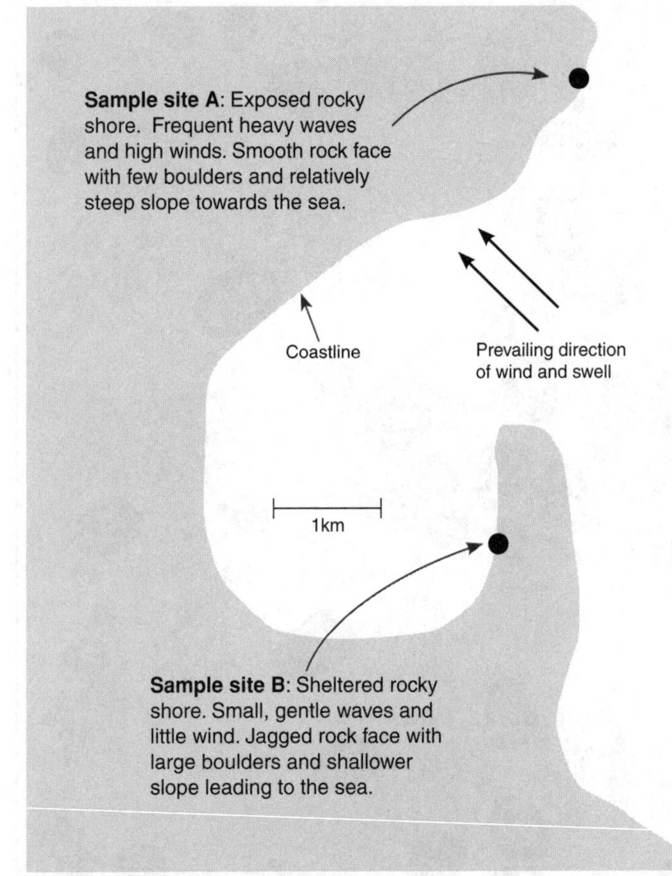

The Aim

To investigate the differences in the abundance of intertidal animals on an exposed rocky shore and a sheltered rocky shore.

Background

The composition of rocky shore communities is strongly influenced by the shore's physical environment. Animals that cling to rocks must keep their hold on the substrate while being subjected to intense wave action and currents. However, the constant wave action brings high levels of nutrients and oxygen. Communities on sheltered rocky shores, although encountering less physical stress, may face lower nutrient and oxygen levels.

To investigate differences in the abundance of intertidal animals, students laid out 1 m^2 quadrats at regular intervals along one tidal zone at two separate but nearby sites: a rocky shore exposed to wind and heavy wave action and a rocky shore with very little heavy wave action. The animals were counted and their numbers in each quadrat recorded.

All photos: C. Pilditch except where indicated

Related activities: *Investigating Plant Growth*

Periodicals: *Drawing Graphs, Descriptive statistics*

ISBN: 978-1-877462-96-2

1. Underline an appropriate hypothesis for this field study from the possible hypotheses below:

   (a) Wave action causes differences in communities on rocky shores.

   (b) The topography of the coastline affects rocky shore communities.

   (c) The communities of intertidal animals differ between exposed rocky shores and sheltered rocky shores.

   (d) Water temperature affects rocky shore communities.

2. During the field study, students counted the number of animals in each quadrat and recorded them in a note book. In the space below, tabulate the data to show the total number of each species and the mean number of animals per quadrat:

Field data notebook

Count per quadrat. Quadrats 1 m^2

Site A	1	2	3	4	5	6	7	8
Brown barnacle	39	38	37	21	40	56	36	41
Oyster borer	6	7	4	3	7	8	9	2
Columnar barnacle	6	8	14	10	9	12	8	11
Plicate barnacle	50	52	46	45	56	15	68	54
Ornate limpet	9	7	8	10	6	7	6	10
Radiate limpet	5	6	4	8	6	7	5	6
Black nerite	7	7	6	8	4	6	8	9
Site B								
Brown barnacle	7	6	7	5	8	5	7	7
Oyster borer	2	3	1	3	2	2	1	1
Columnar barnacle	56	57	58	55	60	47	58	36
Plicate barnacle	11	11	13	10	14	9	9	8
Rock oyster	7	8	8	6	2	4	8	6
Ornate limpet	7	8	5	6	5	7	9	3
Radiate limpet	13	14	11	10	14	12	9	13
Black nerite	6	5	3	1	4	5	2	3

ISBN: 978-1-877462-96-2

3. Use the grid below to draw a column graph of the mean number of species per 1 m^2 at each sample site. Remember to include a title, correctly labelled axes, and a key.

4. (a) Explain why more brown barnacles and plicate barnacles were found at site A:

(b) Explain why more oyster borers were found at site A:

5. Which species was entirely absent from site A?

6. A student wrote the following discussion of the field study. If you read it carefully, you can see that it restates the results of the study, but falls short of discussing them. Revise it to include explanatory detail that might account for the results:

We investigated the difference in communities between an exposed rocky shore and a sheltered rocky shore. The sample site A was more exposed than the second sample site with bigger waves and stronger winds. The animals we sampled were those that attach themselves to the rock surface. Quadrats were used to count the numbers of animals present. It was found that the brown barnacle and the plicate barnacles were the most common animal on the exposed rocky shore. Their numbers were reduced on the sheltered shore, but the columnar barnacle was more prevalent. Rock oysters were found only at site B. The abundance of the other animals varied only slightly except the oyster borer which was more abundant at site A.

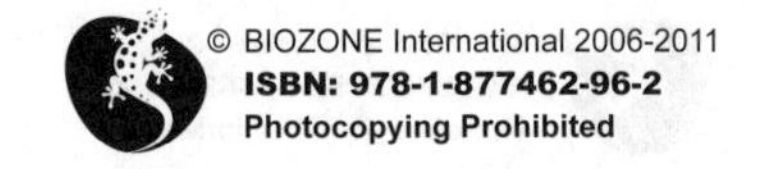

ISBN: 978-1-877462-96-2

KEY TERMS: Flash Card Game

The cards below have a keyword or term printed on one side and its definition printed on the opposite side. The aim is to win as many cards as possible from the table. To play the game.....

1) Cut out the cards and lay them definition side down on the desk. You will need one set of cards between two students.
2) Taking turns, choose a card and, BEFORE you pick it up, state your own best definition of the keyword to your opponent.
3) Check the definition on the opposite side of the card. If both you and your opponent agree that your stated definition matches, then keep the card. If your definition does not match then return the card to the desk.
4) Once your turn is over, your opponent may choose a card.

Abiotic factor	Population	Abundance
Quadrat	Distribution	Indirect sampling
Mark and recapture	Percentage cover	Sampling effort
Radio-tracking	Belt transect	*n*
Random sampling	Species richness	Sampling accuracy
Line transect	Species evenness	Sample size

Field Studies

ISBN: 978-1-877462-96-2

When you've finished the game keep these cutouts and use them as flash cards!

The relative representation of a species within an ecosystem.	The total number of individuals of a species within a set habitat or area.	One of the non-living, chemical or physical components of an ecosystem.
A sampling method for aspects of animal population biology (e.g. abundance) that is independent of sighting the animals themselves (e.g. by using the signs such as scat, calls, tracks).	The arrangement or spread of individuals in a population in an area.	A measured and marked region used to isolate a sample area for study.
A measure of the intensity the sampling programme, usually relative and quantified by measures such as number of samples or sampling time.	The percentage of area covered by a particular organism (normally a plant but sometimes sessile animals) within a sample area.	A method of estimating population size, used to gather information from highly mobile animal species.
A number denoting the sample size, e.g. n=4	A form of continuous quadrat sampling along a line.	A method of tracking individuals of a species using transmitters.
How close the results from the sample are to the actual population parameters.	The number of different species in a given area.	A sample taken using a technique to ensure that every possible sample of a given size has the same chance of selection.
The number of observations or units per sample or proportion of total population sampled.	The relative abundance of a species in a community compared with others.	A line across a habitat along which organisms are sampled at set intervals to determine changes in community composition.

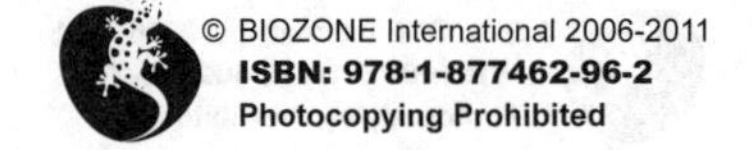

ISBN: 978-1-877462-96-2

Classification of Organisms

Key concepts

- Classification enables us to recognize and quantify the biological diversity on Earth.
- Organisms are put in taxonomic categories based on shared derived characters.
- Organisms are identified using binomial nomenclature: genus and species.
- Dichotomous classification keys can be used to identify unknown organisms.

Key terms

Animalia
Archaebacteria (Archaea)
binomial nomenclature
class
classification key
common name
dichotomous key
distinguishing feature
Eubacteria (Bacteria)
Eukarya
Eukaryotae
family
Fungi
genus
kingdom
morphology
order
phylogeny
phylum
Plantae
Prokaryotae
Protista
shared derived characters
species
taxon (*pl. taxa*)
taxonomic category

Objectives

☐ 1. Use the **KEY TERMS** to help you understand and complete these objectives.

Classification of Life

pages 102-126

☐ 2. Describe the principles and importance of biological **classification**. Recognize **taxonomy** as the study of the theory and practice of classification.

☐ 3. Describe the **distinguishing features** of each kingdom in the five kingdom classification system.

☐ 4. Know that there are other classification systems based on phylogenetic relationships determined in more recent times:

- The six kingdom system, which recognizes **Archaebacteria** and **Eubacteria** in addition to eukaryotic kingdoms.
- The three domain system, which recognizes Archaea (=Archaebacteria), Bacteria (=Eubacteria), and Eukarya.

☐ 5. Explain how organisms are assigned to different taxonomic categories on the basis of their **shared derived characters**.

☐ 6. Recognise at least seven major taxonomic categories: **kingdom**, **phylum**, **class**, **order**, **family**, **genus**, and **species**. Distinguish taxonomic categories from taxa, which are groups of organisms, e.g. 'genus' is a taxonomic category, whereas the genus *Drosophila* is a taxon.

☐ 7. Explain how **binomial nomenclature** is used to classify organisms. Identify the problems associated with using common names to describe organisms.

☐ 8. Explain the relationship between classification and **phylogeny**. Appreciate that newer classification schemes attempt to better reflect phylogeny.

☐ 9. Recognise and describe examples of morphological differences within the same species, e.g. in juvenile and adult life stages, male and female.

☐ 10. Explain the principles by which **dichotomous classification keys** are used to identify organisms. Use simple dichotomous keys to recognize and classify some common organisms.

Periodicals:
Listings for this chapter are on page 153

Weblinks:
www.thebiozone.com/weblink/Skills-2962.html

The New Tree of Life

With the advent of more efficient genetic (DNA) sequencing technology, the genomes of many bacteria began to be sequenced. In 1996, the results of a scientific collaboration examining DNA evidence confirmed the proposal that life comprises three major evolutionary lineages (domains) and not two as was the convention. The recognized lineages were the **Eubacteria**, the **Eukarya** and the **Archaea** (formerly the Archaebacteria). The new classification reflects the fact that there are very large differences between the archaea and the eubacteria. All three domains probably had a distant common ancestor.

A Five (or Six) Kingdom World (right)

The diagram (right) represents the **five kingdom system** of classification commonly represented in many biology texts. It recognizes two basic cell types: prokaryote and eukaryote. Superkingdom Prokaryotae includes all bacteria and cyanobacteria (the Kingdom Monera). Superkingdom Eukaryotae includes protists, fungi, plants, and animals. More recently, based on 16S ribosomal RNA sequence comparisons, Carl Woese divided the prokaryotes into two kingdoms, the Eubacteria and Archaebacteria. Such **six-kingdom systems** are also commonly recognized in texts.

A New View of the World (below)

In 1996, scientists deciphered the full DNA sequence of an unusual bacterium called *Methanococcus jannaschii*. An **extremophile**, this methane-producing archaebacterium lives at 85°C; a temperature lethal for most bacteria as well as eukaryotes. The DNA sequence confirmed that life consists of three major evolutionary lineages, not the two that have been routinely described. Only 44% of this archaebacterium's genes resemble those in bacteria or eukaryotes, or both.

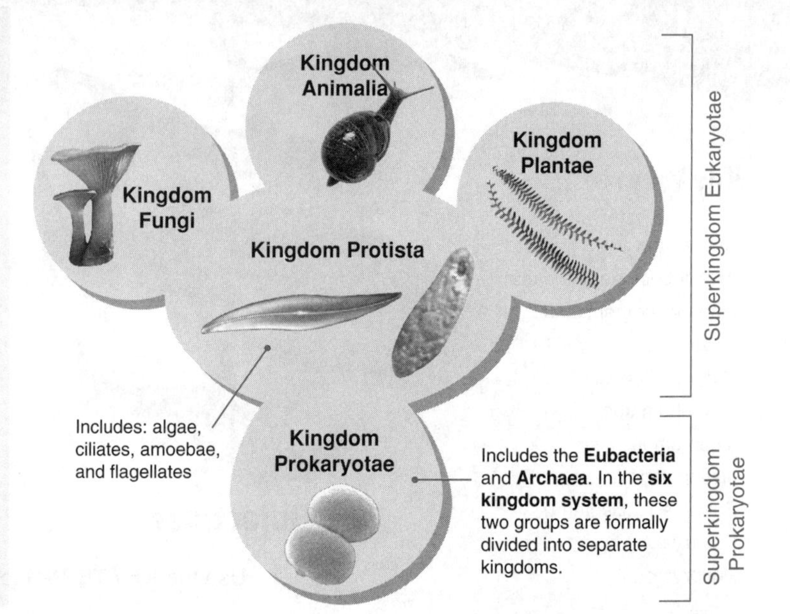

Domain Bacteria

Lack a distinct nucleus and cell organelles. Generally prefer less extreme environments than Archaea. Includes well-known pathogens, many harmless and beneficial species, and the cyanobacteria (photosynthetic bacteria containing the pigments chlorophyll a and phycocyanin).

Domain Archaea

Closely resemble eubacteria in many ways but cell wall composition and aspects of metabolism are very different. Live in extreme environments similar to those on primeval Earth. They may utilise sulfur, methane, or halogens (chlorine, fluorine), and many tolerate extremes of temperature, salinity, or pH.

Domain Eukarya

Complex cell structure with organelles and nucleus. This group contains four of the kingdoms classified under the more traditional system. Note that Kingdom Protista is separated into distinct groups: e.g. amoebae, ciliates, flagellates.

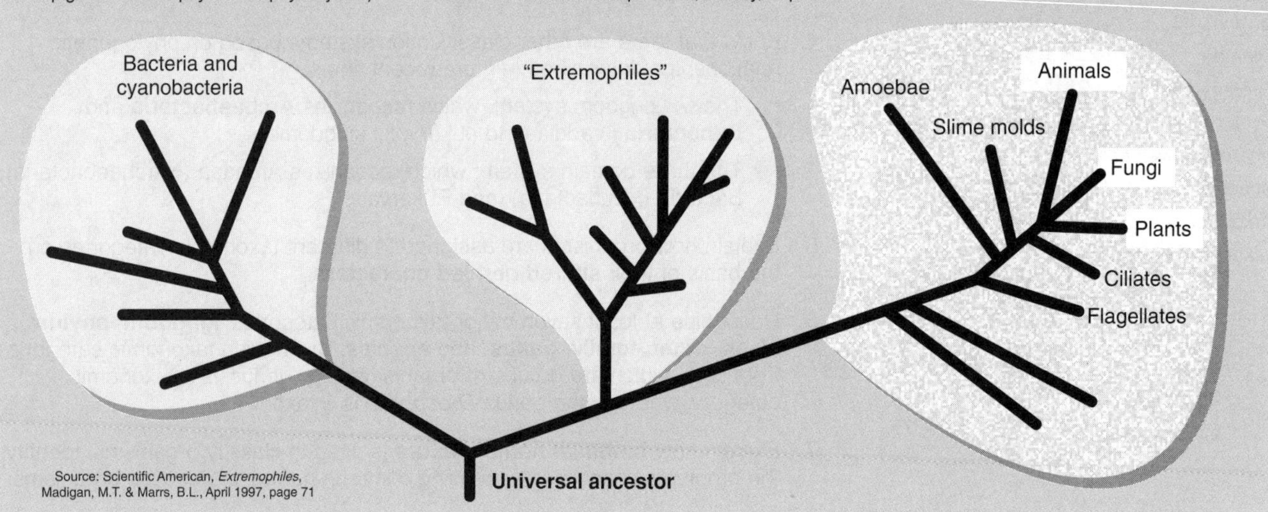

Source: Scientific American, *Extremophiles*, Madigan, M.T. & Marrs, B.L., April 1997, page 71

1. Describe one feature of the three domain system that is very different from the five kingdom classification:

2. How are the three domain system and the six kingdom classification alike?

3. Explain the rationale for revising traditional classification schemes and recognising a three domain scheme:

ISBN: 978-1-877462-96-2

Phylogeny and Classification

The aim of classification is to organise species in a way that most accurately reflects their evolutionary history (**phylogeny**). Each successive group in the taxonomic hierarchy should represent finer and finer branching from a common ancestor. Traditional classification systems emphasise morphological similarities in order to group species into genera and other higher level taxa. In contrast, **cladistic analysis** relies on **shared derived characters** (**synapomorphies**), and emphasises features that are the result of shared ancestry (homologies), rather than convergent evolution. Technology has assisted taxonomy by providing biochemical evidence for the relatedness of species. Traditional and cladistic schemes do not necessarily conflict, but there have been reclassifications of some taxa (notably the primates, but also the reptiles, dinosaurs, and birds). Popular classifications will probably continue to reflect similarities and differences in appearance, rather than a strict evolutionary history. In this respect, they are a compromise between phylogeny and the need for a convenient filing system for species diversity.

Constructing a Simple Cladogram

A table listing the features for comparison allows us to identify where we should make branches in the **cladogram**. An outgroup (one which is known to have no or little relationship to the other organisms) is used as a basis for comparison.

Comparative features	Jawless fish (outgroup)	Bony fish	Amphibians	Lizards	Birds	Mammals
Vertebral column	✔	✔	✔	✔	✔	✔
Jaws	✘	✔	✔	✔	✔	✔
Four supporting limbs	✘	✘	✔	✔	✔	✔
Amniotic egg	✘	✘	✘	✔	✔	✔
Diapsid skull	✘	✘	✘	✔	✔	✘
Feathers	✘	✘	✘	✘	✔	✘
Hair	✘	✘	✘	✘	✘	✔

The table above lists features shared by selected taxa. The outgroup (jawless fish) shares just one feature (vertebral column), so it gives a reference for comparison and the first branch of the cladogram (tree).

As the number of taxa in the table increases, the number of possible trees that could be drawn increases exponentially. To determine the most likely relationships, the rule of **parsimony** is used. This assumes that the tree with the least number of evolutionary events is most likely to show the correct evolutionary relationship.

Three possible cladograms are shown on the right. The top cladogram requires six events while the other two require seven events. Applying the rule of parsimony, the top cladogram must be taken as correct.

Parsimony can lead to some confusion. Some evolutionary events have occurred multiple times. An example is the evolution of a four chambered heart, which occurred separately in birds and mammals. The use of fossil evidence and DNA analysis can help to solve problems like this.

Possible Cladograms

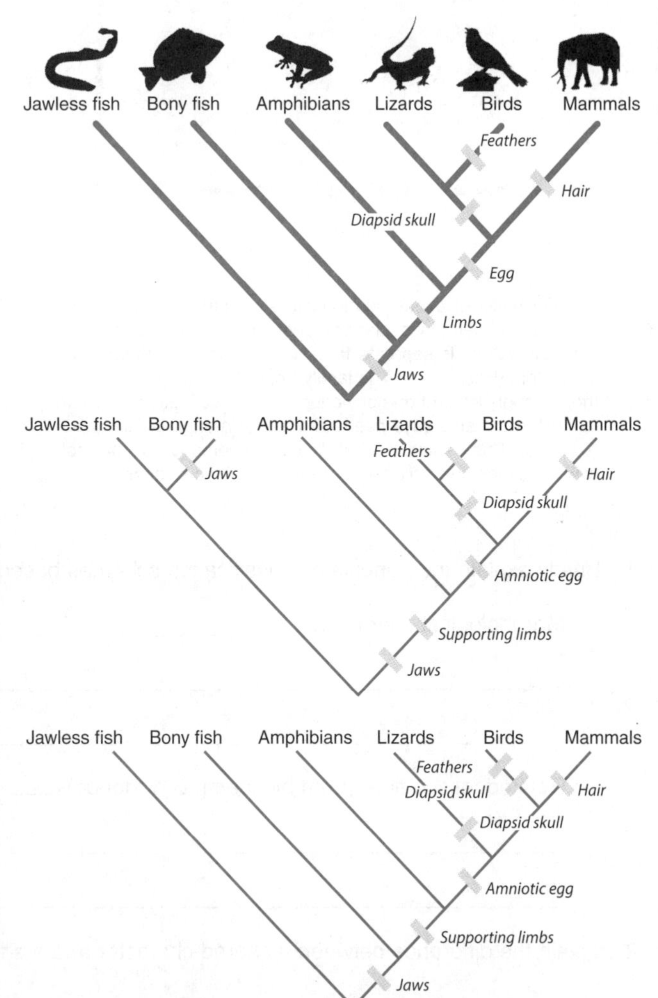

Using DNA Data

DNA analysis has allowed scientists to confirm many phylogenies and refute or redraw others. In a similar way to morphological differences, DNA sequences can be tabulated and analyzed. The ancestry of whales has been in debate since Darwin. The radically different morphologies of whales and other mammals makes it difficult work out the correct phylogenetic tree. However recently discovered fossil ankle bones, as well as DNA studies, show whales are more closely related to hippopotami than to any other mammal. Coupled with molecular clocks, DNA data can also give the time between each split in the lineage.

The DNA sequences on the right show part of a the nucleotide subset 141-200 and some of the matching nucleotides used to draw the cladogram. Although whales were once thought most closely related to pigs, based on the DNA analysis the most parsimonious tree disputes this.

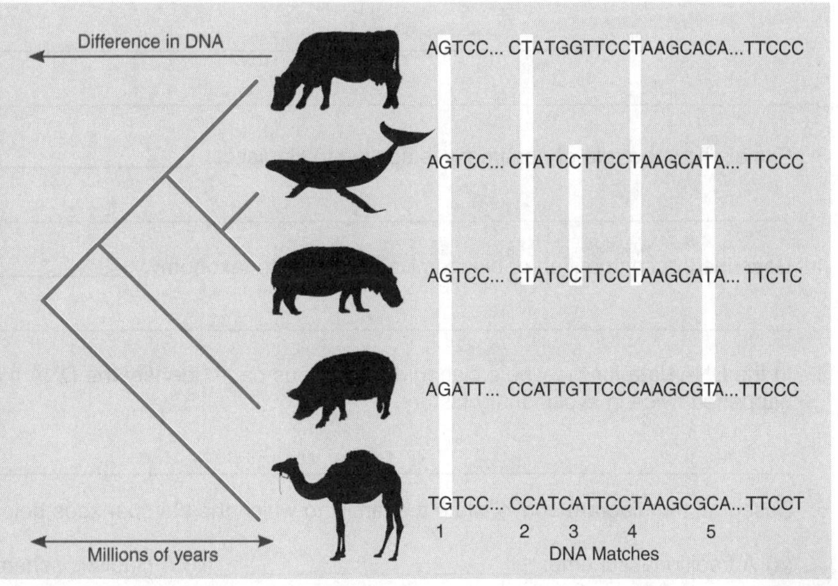

A Classical Taxonomic View

Hominidae

Pongidae

The 'great apes'

Humans Chimpanzees Gorillas Orangutans

On the basis of overall anatomical similarity (e.g. bones and limb length, teeth, musculature), apes are grouped into a family (Pongidae) that is separate from humans and their immediate ancestors (Hominidae). The family Pongidae (the great apes) is not monophyletic (of one phylogeny), because it stems from an ancestor that also gave rise to a species in another family (i.e. humans). This traditional classification scheme is now at odds with schemes derived after considering genetic evidence.

A Cladistic View

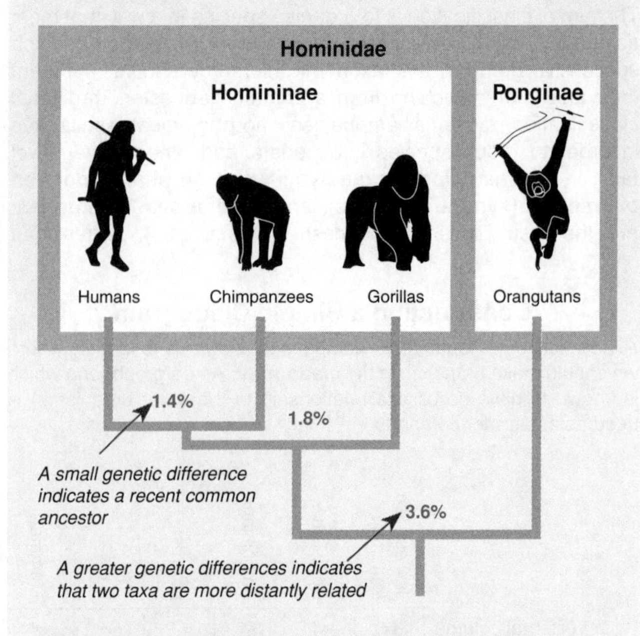

Based on the evidence of genetic differences (% values above), chimpanzees and gorillas are more closely related to humans than to orangutans, and chimpanzees are more closely related to humans than they are to gorillas. Under this scheme there is no true family of great apes. The family Hominidae includes two subfamilies: Ponginae and Homininae (humans, chimpanzees, and gorillas). This classification is monophyletic: the Hominidae includes all the species that arise from a common ancestor.

1. Briefly explain the benefits of classification schemes based on:

   (a) Morphological characters: ____________________

   (b) Relatedness in time (from biochemical evidence): ____________________

2. Explain the difference between a shared character and a shared derived character: ____________________

3. Explain how the rule of parsimony is applied to cladistics: ____________________

4. Describe the contribution of biochemical evidence to taxonomy: ____________________

5. In the DNA data for the whale cladogram (previous page) identify the DNA match that shows a mutation event must have happened twice in evolutionary history.

   ____

6. Based on the diagram above, state the family to which the chimpanzees belong under:

   (a) A traditional scheme: ____________ (b) A cladistic scheme: ____________

ISBN: 978-1-877462-96-2

The Phylogenetic Species Concept

Although the biological species concept is useful, there are many situations in which it is difficult to apply, e.g. for asexual populations, (including bacteria) or extinct organisms. In such situations, the phylogenetic species concept (PSC) can be more useful. It not reliant on the criterion of successful interbreeding and can be applied to asexually or sexually reproducing organisms, and to extinct organisms. Phylogenetic species are defined on the basis of their shared evolutionary ancestry, which is determined on the basis of **shared derived characteristics**, which may be morphological, especially for higher taxonomic ranks, or biochemical (e.g. DNA differences). The PSC defines a species as the smallest group that all share a derived character state. It is widely applicable in palaeontology because biologists can compare both living and extinct organisms. While the phylogenetic species concept solves some difficulties, it creates others. It does not apply well to morphologically different species that are connected by gene flow. Similarly, the ability to distinguish genetically distinct but morphologically identical cryptic species on the basis of DNA analyses can lead to a proliferation of living species that is not helpful in establishing a phylogeny.

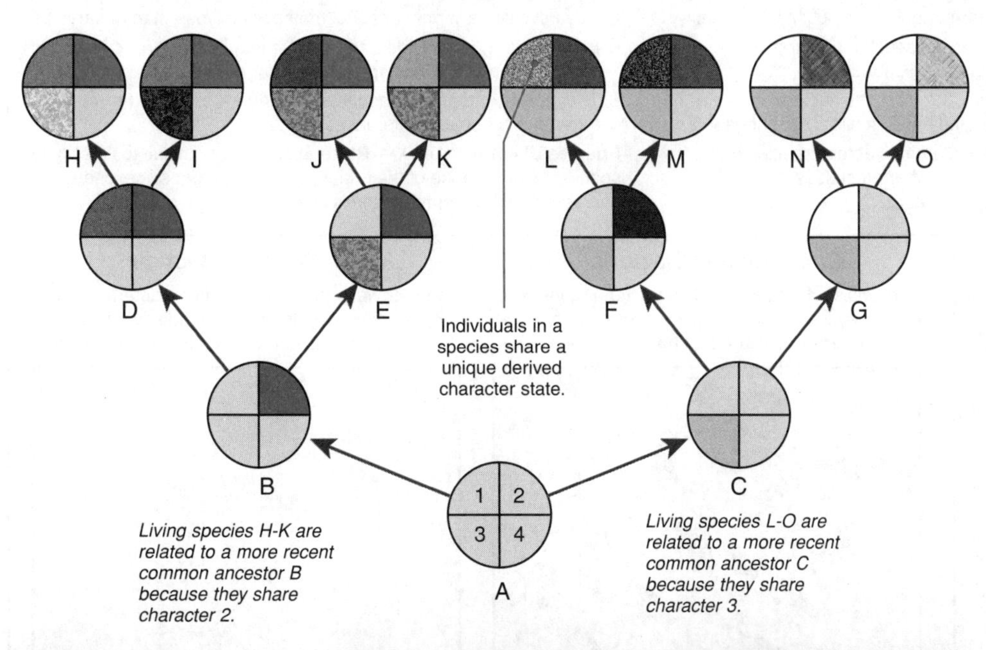

This simplified phylogenetic tree traces four characters among 15 species (8 present and 7 ancestral). The 8 modern species (species H-O) share a character (4) derived from a distant common ancestor (A). Although the primitive character unites all 8 species, the branching of the tree is based on characters derived from the ancestral ones. Classification on the basis of shared derived characters defines the species as the smallest group diagnosable by a unique combination of characters. If large numbers of characters are included in the analysis, it is easy to see how this method results in a proliferation of species that may or may not be meaningful. Under the PSC model, there are no subspecies; either a population is a phylogenetic species or it is not taxonomically distinguishable.

Tree sparrows (*P. montanus*) are ~10% smaller than the similar house sparrow but the two species hybridize freely.

House sparrows (*P. domesticus*) are widespread with many intermediate "subspecies" of unknown status.

Mallards are infamous for their ability to hybridise freely with a large number of other duck "species".

True sparrows all belong to the genus *Passer*. There are a large number of species distinguished on the basis of song, plumage, and size. A vestigial dorsal outer primary feather and an extra bone in the tongue are ancestral characters. Many populations are not good biological species in that they hybridise freely to produce fertile offspring. A similar situation exists within the genus *Anas* of dabbling ducks (which includes the mallards). Many birds are best described using the PSC rather than the BSC.

1. (a) Explain the basis by which species are assigned under the PSC: ______________________

   ____

   ____

   (b) Describe one problem with the use of the PSC: ______________________

   ____

   (c) Describe situations where the use of the PSC might be more appropriate than the BSC: ______________________

   ____

   ____

2. Suggest how genetic techniques could be used to elucidate the phylogeny of a cluster of related phylogenetic species:

   ____

   ____

ISBN: 978-1-877462-96-2

Features of Taxonomic Groups

In order to distinguish organisms, it is desirable to classify and name them (a science known as **taxonomy**). An effective classification system requires features that are distinctive to a particular group of organisms. Revised classification systems, recognizing three domains (rather than five or six kingdoms) are now recognized as better representations of the true diversity of life. However, for the purposes of describing the groups with which we are most familiar, the five kingdom system (used here) is still appropriate. The distinguishing features of some major **taxa** are provided in the following pages by means of diagrams and brief summaries. Note that most animals show **bilateral symmetry** (body divisible into two halves that are mirror images). **Radial symmetry** (body divisible into equal halves through various planes) is a characteristic of cnidarians and ctenophores.

SUPERKINGDOM: PROKARYOTAE (Bacteria)

- Also known as prokaryotes. The term moneran is no longer in use.
- Two major bacterial lineages are recognised: the primitive **Archaebacteria** and the more advanced **Eubacteria**.
- All have a prokaryotic cell structure: they lack the nuclei and chromosomes of eukaryotic cells, and have smaller (70S) ribosomes.
- Have a tendency to spread genetic elements across species barriers by conjugation, viral transduction, and other processes.
- Asexual. Can reproduce rapidly by binary fission.
- Have evolved a wider variety of metabolism types than eukaryotes.
- Bacteria grow and divide or aggregate into filaments or colonies of various shapes. Colony type is often diagnostic.
- They are taxonomically identified by their appearance (form) and through biochemical differences.

Species diversity: 10 000+ Bacteria are rather difficult to classify to species level because of their relatively rampant genetic exchange, and because their reproduction is asexual.

Eubacteria

- Also known as 'true bacteria', they probably evolved from the more ancient Archaebacteria.
- Distinguished from Archaebacteria by differences in cell wall composition, nucleotide structure, and ribosome shape.
- Diverse group includes most bacteria.
- The **gram stain** is the basis for distinguishing two broad groups of bacteria. It relies on the presence of peptidoglycan in the cell wall. The stain is easily washed from the thin peptidoglycan layer of gram negative walls but is retained by the thick peptidoglycan layer of gram positive cells, staining them a dark violet color.

Gram-Positive Bacteria

The walls of gram positive bacteria consist of many layers of peptidoglycan forming a thick, single-layered structure that holds the gram stain.

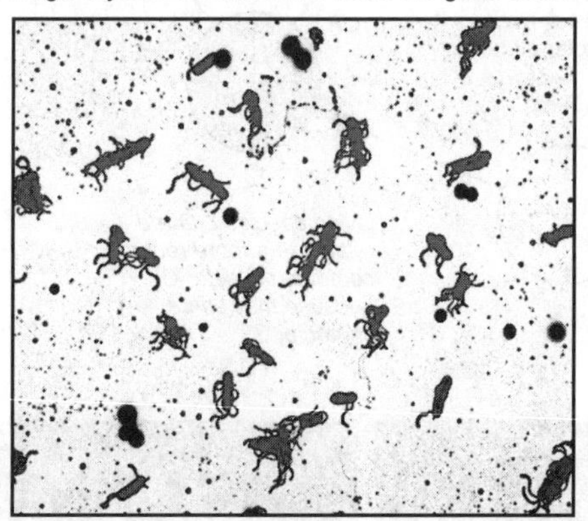

Photos: CDC

Bacillus alvei: a gram positive, flagellated bacterium. Note how the cells appear dark.

Gram-Negative Bacteria

The cell walls of gram negative bacteria contain only a small proportion of peptidoglycan, so the dark violet stain is not retained by the organisms.

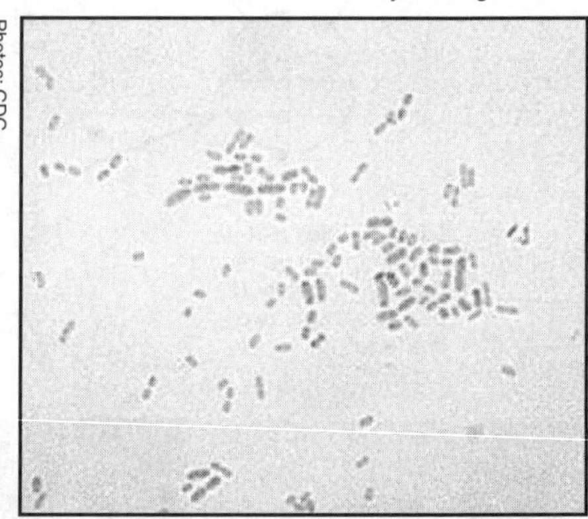

Alcaligenes odorans: a gram negative bacterium. Note how the cells appear pale.

SUPERKINGDOM EUKARYOTAE

Kingdom: FUNGI

- Heterotrophic.
- Rigid cell wall made of chitin.
- Vary from single celled to large multicellular organisms.
- Mostly saprotrophic (ie. feeding on dead or decaying material).
- Terrestrial and immobile.

Examples:
Mushrooms/toadstools, yeasts, truffles, morels, molds, and lichens.

Species diversity: 80 000 +

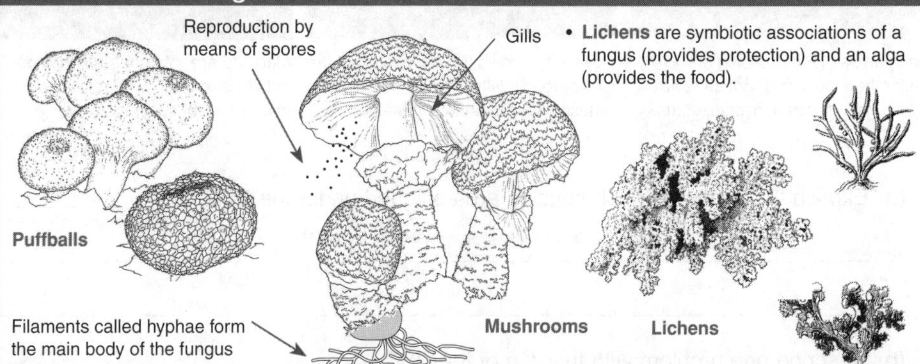

- **Lichens** are symbiotic associations of a fungus (provides protection) and an alga (provides the food).

Kingdom: PROTISTA

- A diverse group of organisms which do not fit easily into other taxonomic groups.
- Unicellular or simple multicellular.
- Widespread in moist or aquatic environments.

Examples of algae: green, red, and brown algae, dinoflagellates, diatoms.

Examples of protozoa: amoebas, foraminiferans, radiolarians, ciliates.

Species diversity: 55 000 +

Algae 'plant-like' protists

- Autotrophic (photosynthesis)
- Characterised by the type of chlorophyll present

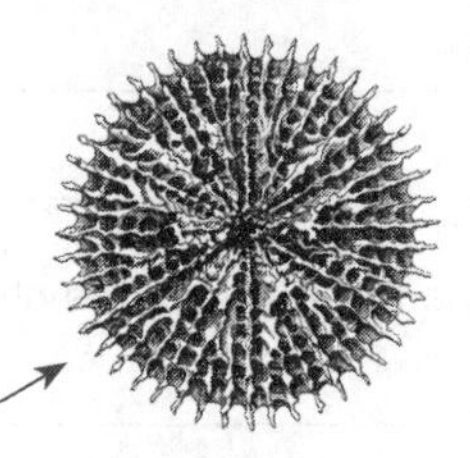

Protozoa 'animal-like' protists

- Heterotrophic nutrition and feed via ingestion
- Most are microscopic (5 µm - 250 µm)

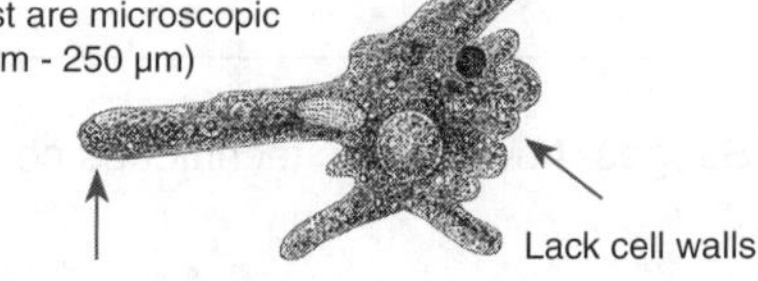

ISBN: 978-1-877462-96-2

Kingdom: PLANTAE

- Multicellular organisms (the majority are photosynthetic and contain chlorophyll).
- Cell walls made of cellulose; Food is stored as starch.
- Subdivided into two major divisions based on tissue structure: ***Bryophytes*** (non-vascular) and ***Tracheophytes*** (vascular) plants.

Non-Vascular Plants:

- Non vascular, lacking transport tissues (no xylem or phloem).
- They are small and restricted to moist, terrestrial environments.
- Do not possess 'true' roots, stems or leaves.

Phylum Bryophyta: Mosses, liverworts, and hornworts.

Species diversity: 18 600 +

Phylum: Bryophyta

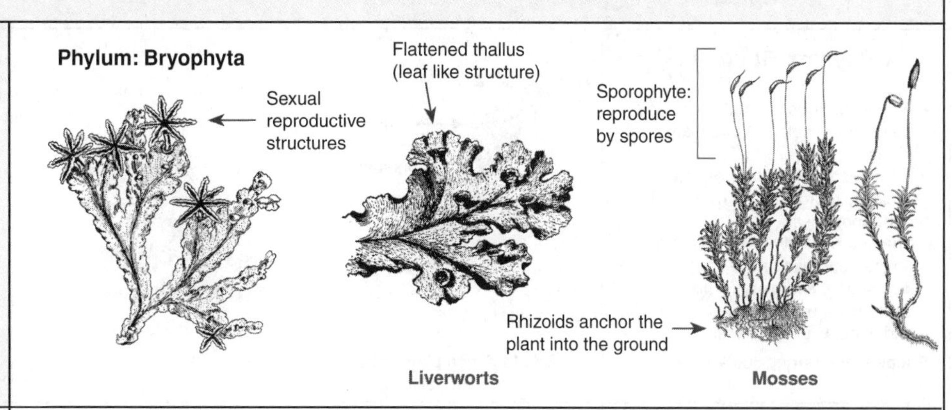

Vascular Plants:

- Vascular: possess transport tissues.
- Possess true roots, stems, and leaves, as well as stomata.
- Reproduce via spores, not seeds.
- Clearly defined alternation of sporophyte and gametophyte generations.

Seedless Plants:

Spore producing plants, includes:

Phylum Filicinophyta: Ferns

Phylum Sphenophyta: Horsetails

Phylum Lycophyta: Club mosses

Species diversity: 13 000 +

Phylum: Lycophyta

Leaves

Club moss

Phylum: Sphenophyta

Leaves

Horsetail

Phylum: Filicinophyta

Large dividing leaves called fronds

Reproduce via spores on the underside of leaf

Rhizome

Adventitious roots

Fern

Seed Plants:

Also called Spermatophyta. Produce seeds housing an embryo. Includes:

Gymnosperms

- Lack enclosed chambers in which seeds develop.
- Produce seeds in cones which are exposed to the environment.

Phylum Cycadophyta: Cycads

Phylum Ginkgophyta: Ginkgoes

Phylum Coniferophyta: Conifers

Species diversity: 730 +

Phylum: Cycadophyta

Cycad

Phylum: Ginkophyta

Ginkgo

Phylum: Coniferophyta

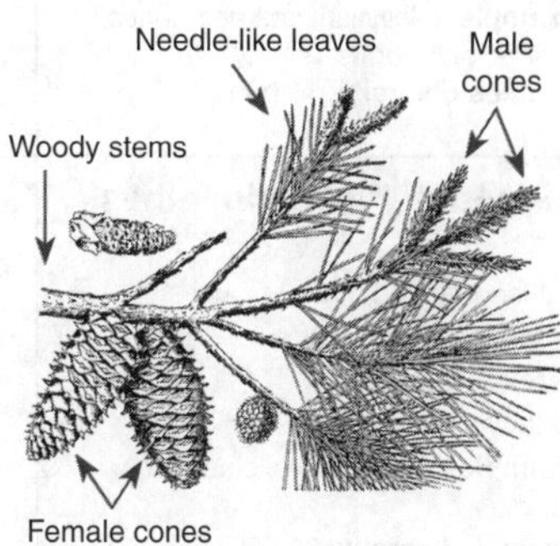

Conifer

Angiosperms

Phylum: Angiospermophyta

- Seeds in specialized reproductive structures called flowers.
- Female reproductive ovary develops into a fruit.
- Pollination usually via wind or animals.

Species diversity: 260 000 +

The phylum Angiospermophyta may be subdivided into two classes:

Class Monocotyledoneae (Monocots)

Class Dicotyledoneae (Dicots)

Angiosperms: **Monocotyledons**

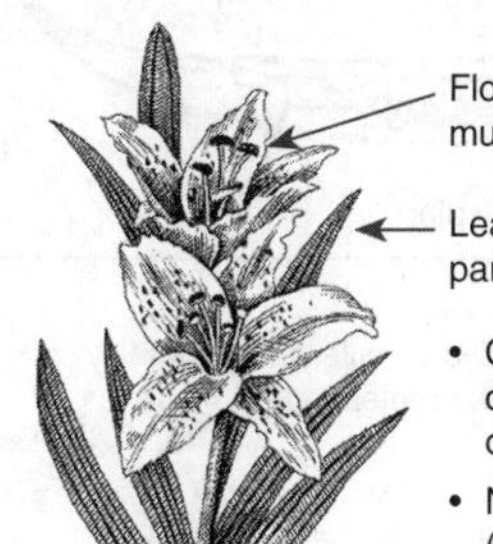

- Only have one cotyledon (food storage organ)
- Normally herbaceous (non-woody) with no secondary growth

Lily

Examples: cereals, lilies, daffodils, palms, grasses.

Angiosperms: **Dicotyledons**

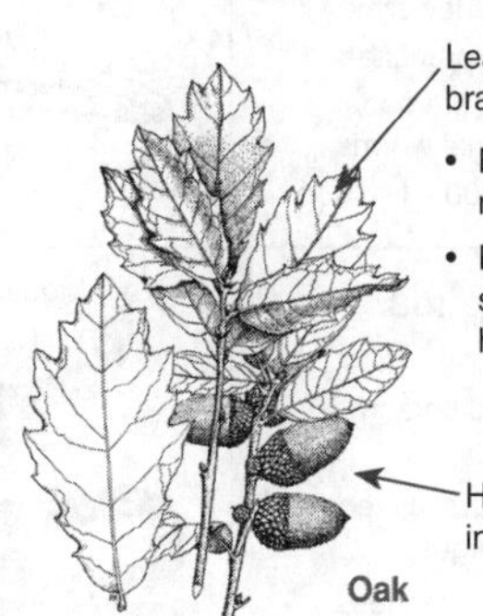

- Flower parts occur in multiples of 4 or 5
- Possible to have secondary growth (either herbaceous or woody)

Oak

Examples: many annual plants, trees and shrubs.

ISBN: 978-1-877462-96-2

Kingdom: ANIMALIA

- Over 800 000 species described in 33 existing phyla.
- Multicellular, heterotrophic organisms.
- Animal cells lack cell walls.
- Further subdivided into various major phyla on the basis of body symmetry, type of body cavity, and external and internal structures.

Phylum: Rotifera

- A diverse group of small organisms with sessile, colonial, and planktonic forms.
- Most freshwater, a few marine.
- Typically reproduce via cyclic parthenogenesis.
- Characterised by a wheel of cilia on the head used for feeding and locomotion, a large muscular pharynx (mastax) with jaw like trophi, and a foot with sticky toes.

Species diversity: 1500 +

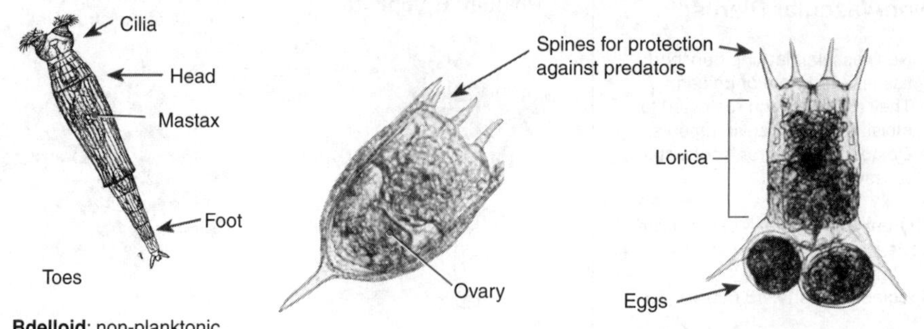

Bdelloid: non-planktonic, creeping rotifer

Planktonic forms swim using their crown of cilia

Phylum: Porifera

- Lack organs.
- All are aquatic (mostly marine).
- Asexual reproduction by budding.
- Lack a nervous system.

Examples: sponges.

Species diversity: 8000 +

Body wall perforated by pores through which water enters

- Capable of regeneration (the replacement of lost parts)
- Possess spicules (needle-like internal structures) for support and protection

Water leaves by a larger opening - the osculum

Tube sponge

Phylum: Cnidaria

- Two basic body forms:
  Medusa: umbrella shaped and free swimming by pulsating bell.
  Polyp: cylindrical, some are sedentary, others can glide, or somersault or use tentacles as legs.
- Some species have a life cycle that alternates between a polyp stage and a medusa stage.
- All are aquatic (most are marine).

Examples: Jellyfish, sea anemones, hydras, and corals.

Species diversity: 11 000 +

Some have air-filled floats

Nematocysts (stinging cells)

Jellyfish (Portuguese man-o-war)

Single opening acts as mouth and anus

Polyps stick to seabed

Sea anemone

Polyps may aggregate in colonies

Brain coral

Colonial polyps

Contraction of the bell propels the free swimming medusa

Phylum: Platyhelminthes

- Unsegmented body.
- Flattened body shape.
- Mouth, but no anus.
- Many are parasitic.

Examples: Tapeworms, planarians, flukes.

Species diversity: 20 000 +

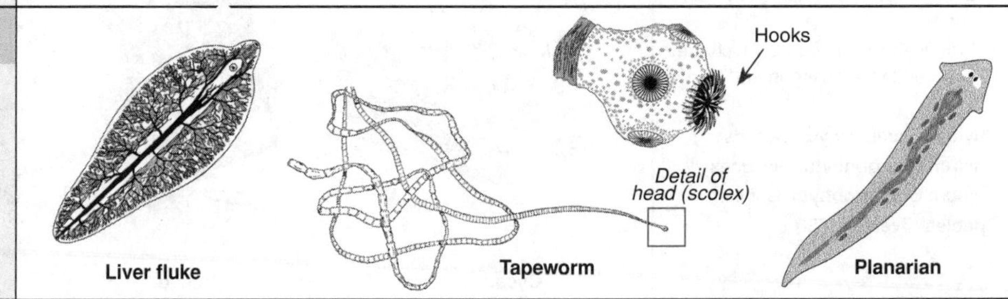

Liver fluke **Tapeworm** **Planarian**

Phylum: Nematoda

- Tiny, unsegmented roundworms.
- Many are plant/animal parasites

Examples: Hookworms, stomach worms, lung worms, filarial worms

Species diversity: 80 000 - 1 million

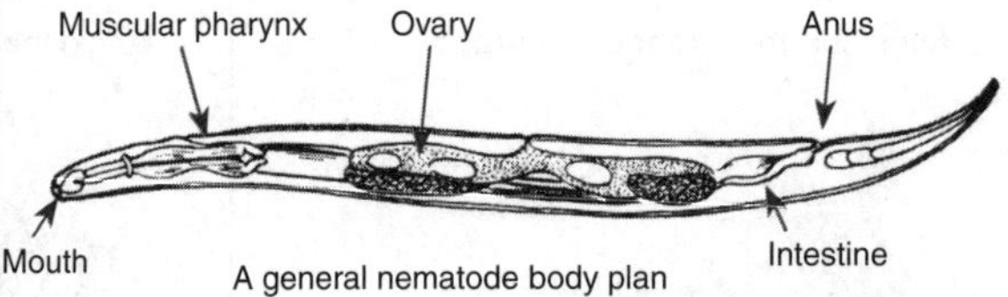

A general nematode body plan

A roundworm parasite

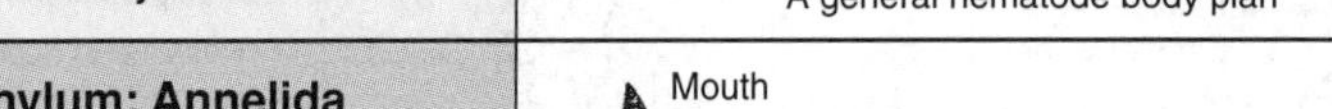

Phylum: Annelida

- Cylindrical, segmented body with chaetae (bristles).
- Move using hydrostatic skeleton and/or parapodia (appendages).

Examples: Earthworms, leeches, polychaetes (including tubeworms).

Species diversity: 15 000 +

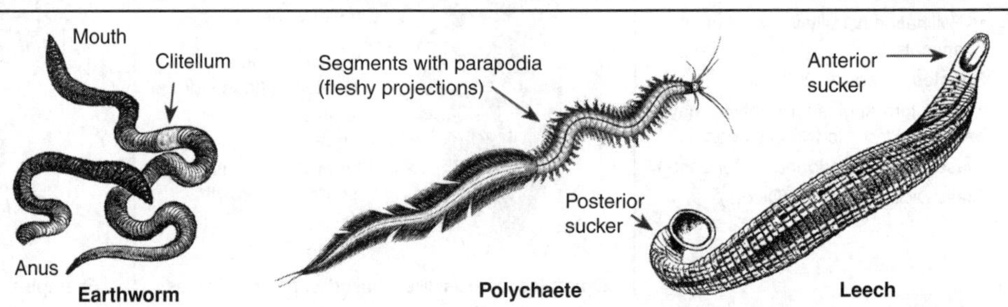

Earthworm **Polychaete** **Leech**

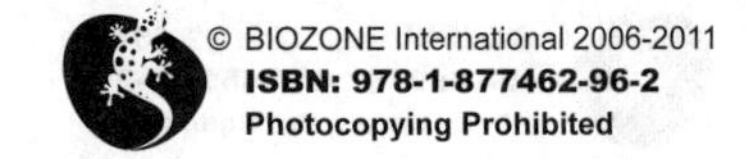

ISBN: 978-1-877462-96-2

Kingdom: ANIMALIA (continued)

Phylum: Mollusca

- Soft bodied and unsegmented.
- Body comprises head, muscular foot, and visceral mass (organs).
- Most have radula (rasping tongue).
- Aquatic and terrestrial species.
- Aquatic species possess gills.

Examples: Snails, mussels, squid.
Species diversity: 110 000 +

Class: Bivalvia

Radula lost in bivalves
Mantle secretes shell
Two shells hinged together
Scallop

Class: Gastropoda

Mantle secretes shell
Tentacles with eyes
Head
Muscular foot for locomotion
Land snail

Class: Cephalopoda

Well developed eyes
Squid
Foot divided into tentacles

Phylum: Arthropoda

- Exoskeleton made of chitin.
- Grow in stages after moulting.
- Jointed appendages.
- Segmented bodies.
- Heart found on dorsal side of body.
- Open circulation system.
- Most have compound eyes.

Species diversity: 1 million +
Make up 75% of all living animals.

Arthropods are subdivided into the following classes:

Class: Crustacea (crustaceans)
- Mainly marine.
- Exoskeleton impregnated with mineral salts.
- Gills often present.
- Includes: Lobsters, crabs, barnacles, prawns, shrimps, isopods, amphipods
- **Species diversity**: 35 000 +

Class: Arachnida (chelicerates)
- Almost all are terrestrial.
- 2 body parts: cephalothorax and abdomen (except horseshoe crabs).
- Includes: spiders, scorpions, ticks, mites, horseshoe crabs.
- **Species diversity**: 57 000 +

Class: Insecta (insects)
- Mostly terrestrial.
- Most are capable of flight.
- 3 body parts: head, thorax, abdomen.
- Include: Locusts, dragonflies, cockroaches, butterflies, bees, ants, beetles, bugs, flies, and more
- **Species diversity**: 800 000 +

Myriapods (=many legs)
Class Diplopoda (millipedes)
- Terrestrial.
- Have a rounded body.
- Eat dead or living plants.
- **Species diversity**: 2000 +

Class Chilopoda (centipedes)
- Terrestrial.
- Have a flattened body.
- Poison claws for catching prey.
- Feed on insects, worms, and snails.
- **Species diversity**: 7000 +

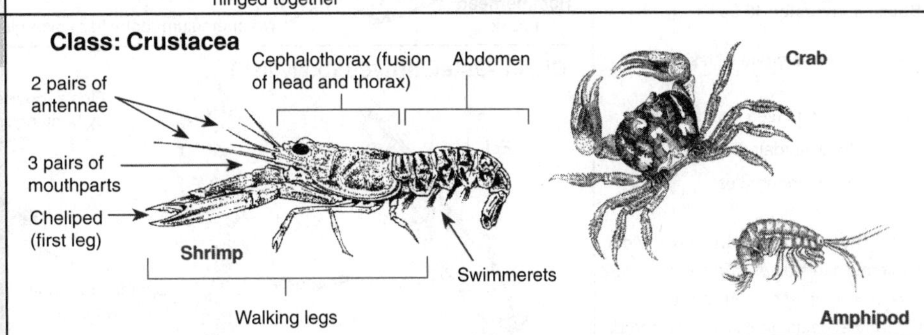

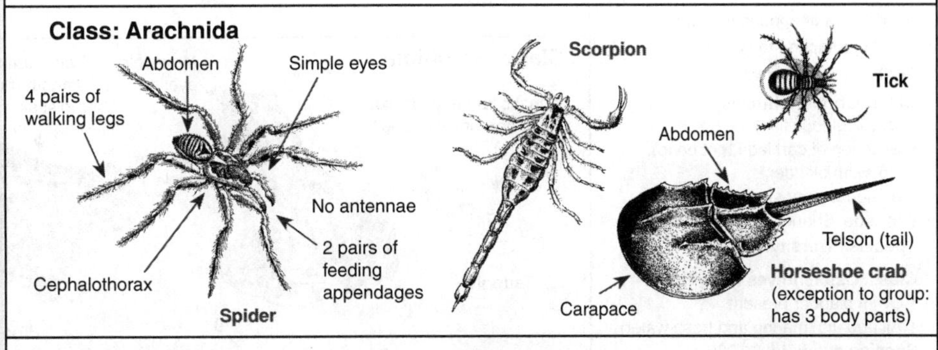

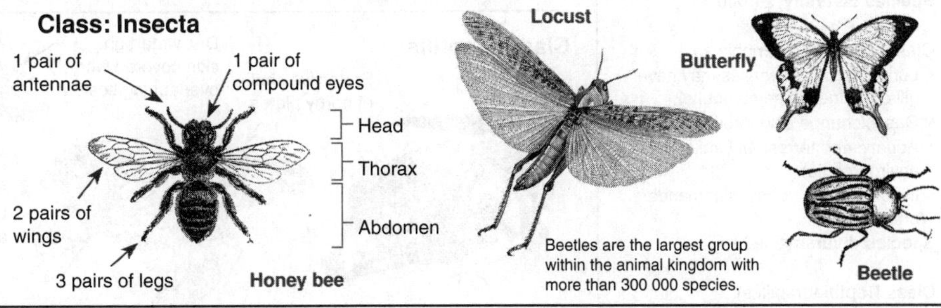

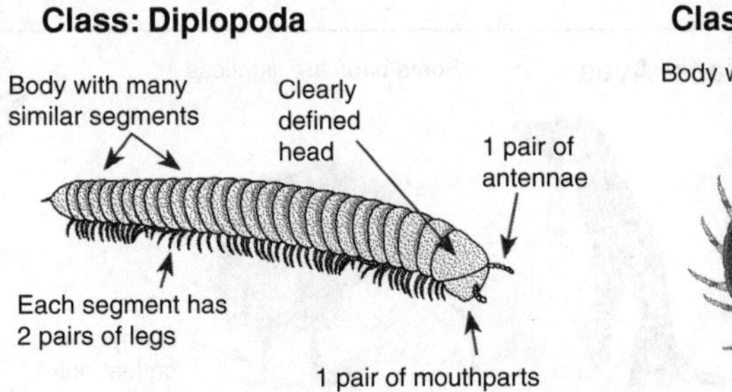

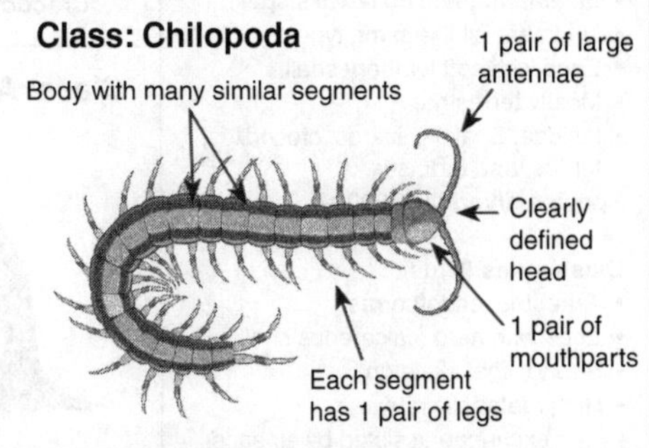

Phylum: Echinodermata

- Rigid body wall, internal skeleton made of calcareous plates.
- Many possess spines.
- Ventral mouth, dorsal anus.
- External fertilization.
- Unsegmented, marine organisms.
- Tube feet for locomotion.
- Water vascular system.

Examples: Starfish, brittlestars, feather stars, sea urchins, sea lilies.
Species diversity: 6000 +

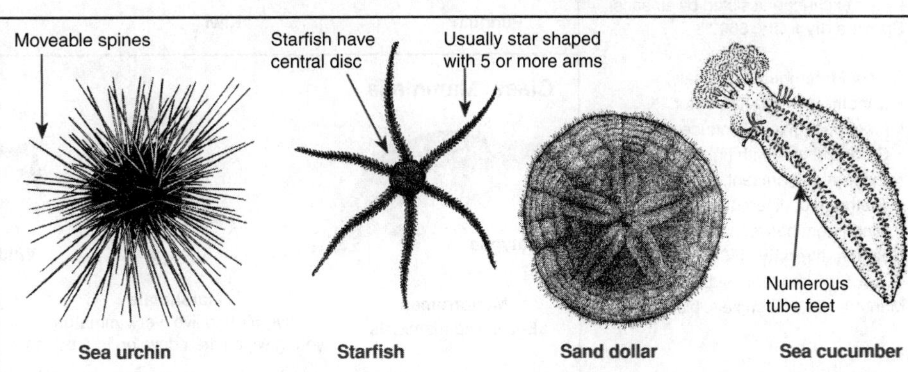

ISBN: 978-1-877462-96-2

Kingdom: ANIMALIA (continued)

Phylum: Chordata

- Dorsal notochord (flexible, supporting rod) present at some stage in the life history.
- Post-anal tail present at some stage in their development.
- Dorsal, tubular nerve cord.
- Pharyngeal slits present.
- Circulation system closed in most.
- Heart positioned on ventral side.

Species diversity: 48 000 +

- A very diverse group with several sub-phyla:
  - Urochordata (sea squirts, salps)
  - Cephalochordata (lancelet)
  - Craniata (vertebrates)

Sub-Phylum Craniata (vertebrates)
- Internal skeleton of cartilage or bone.
- Well developed nervous system.
- Vertebral column replaces notochord.
- Two pairs of appendages (fins or limbs) attached to girdles.

Further subdivided into:

Class: Chondrichthyes (cartilaginous fish)
- Skeleton of cartilage (not bone).
- No swim bladder.
- All aquatic (mostly marine).
- Include: Sharks, rays, and skates.

Species diversity: 850 +

Class: Osteichthyes (bony fish)
- Swim bladder present.
- All aquatic (marine and fresh water).

Species diversity: 21 000 +

Class: Amphibia (amphibians)
- Lungs in adult, juveniles may have gills (retained in some adults).
- Gas exchange also through skin.
- Aquatic and terrestrial (limited to damp environments).
- Include: Frogs, toads, salamanders, and newts.

Species diversity: 3900 +

Class Reptilia (reptiles)
- Ectotherms with no larval stages.
- Teeth are all the same type.
- Eggs with soft leathery shell.
- Mostly terrestrial.
- Include: Snakes, lizards, crocodiles, turtles, and tortoises.

Species diversity: 7000 +

Class: Aves (birds)
- Terrestrial endotherms.
- Eggs with hard, calcareous shell.
- Strong, light skeleton.
- High metabolic rate.
- Gas exchange assisted by air sacs.

Species diversity: 8600 +

Class: Mammalia (mammals)
- Endotherms with hair or fur.
- Mammary glands produce milk.
- Glandular skin with hair or fur.
- External ear present.
- Teeth are of different types.
- Diaphragm between thorax/abdomen.

Species diversity: 4500 +

Subdivided into three subclasses: Monotremes, marsupials, placentals.

Class: Chondrichthyes (cartilaginous fish)

Lateral line sense organ

Asymmetrical tail fin provides lift

Skin with toothlike scales

Ectotherms with endoskeleton made of cartilage

Pelvic fin

Pectoral fin

Hammerhead shark

No operculum (bony flap) over gills

Stingray

Class: Osteichthyes (bony fish)

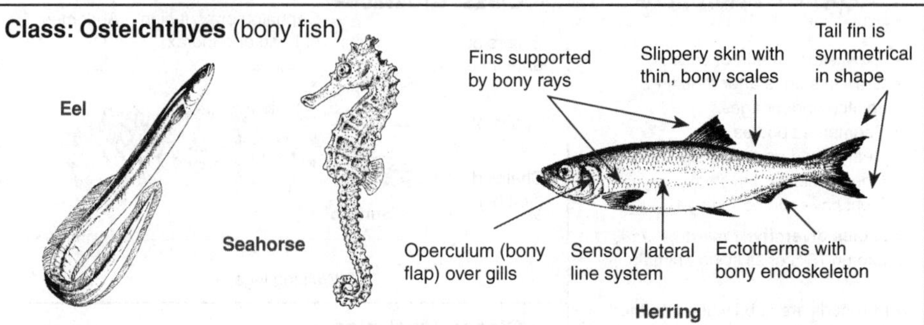

Class: Amphibia

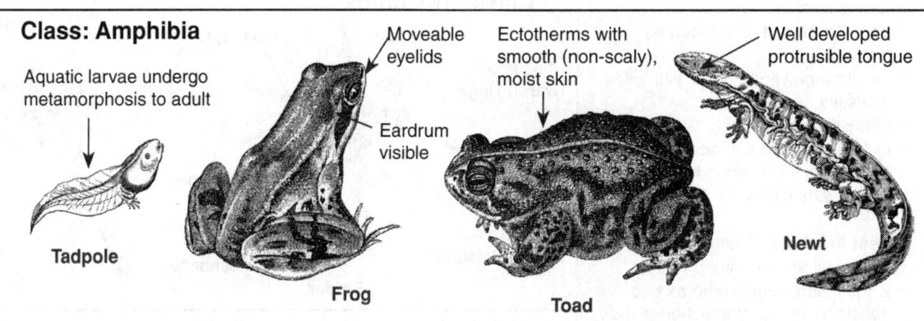

Class: Reptilia

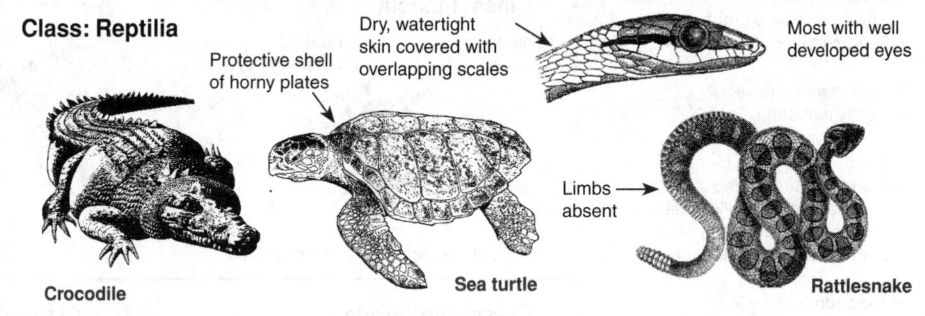

Class: Aves

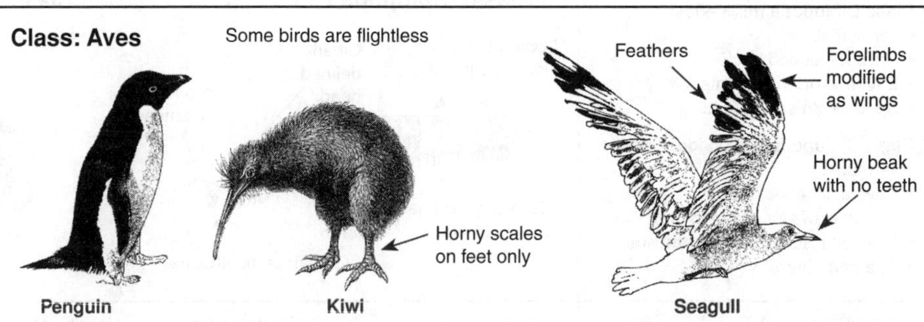

Class: Mammalia

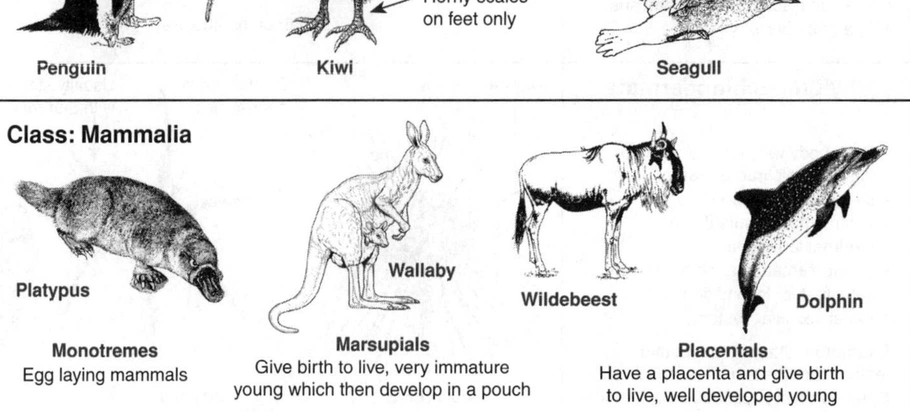

Monotremes
Egg laying mammals

Marsupials
Give birth to live, very immature young which then develop in a pouch

Placentals
Have a placenta and give birth to live, well developed young

ISBN: 978-1-877462-96-2

Classification System

The classification of organisms is designed to reflect how they are related to each other. The fundamental unit of classification of living things is the **species**. Its members are so alike genetically that they can interbreed. This genetic similarity also means that they are almost identical in their physical and other characteristics. Species are classified further into larger, more comprehensive categories (higher taxa). It must be emphasized that all such higher classifications are human inventions to suit a particular purpose.

1. The table below shows part of the classification for humans using the seven major levels of classification. For this question, use the example of the classification of the red kangaroo, on the next page, as a guide.

   (a) Complete the list of the taxonomic groupings on the left hand side of the table below:

	Taxonomic Group	Human Classification
1.		
2.		
3.		
4.		
5.	Family	Hominidae
6.		
7.		

   (b) Complete the classification for humans (*Homo sapiens*) on the table above.

2. Construct your own acronym or mnemonic to help you remember the principal taxonomic groupings in biology:

3. Describe the two-part scientific naming system (**binomial nomenclature**) which is used to name organisms:

4. Give two reasons why the classification of organisms is important:

   (a)

   (b)

5. Classification has traditionally been based on similarities in morphology but new biochemical methods are now widely used to determine species relatedness. Explain how these are being used to clarify the relationships between species:

6. As an example of physical features being used to classify organisms, mammals have been divided into three major sub-classes: monotremes, marsupials, and placentals. Describe the main physical feature distinguishing each of these taxa:

   (a) Monotreme:

   (b) Marsupial:

   (c) Placental:

ISBN: 978-1-877462-96-2

Periodicals: *A passion for order*

Related activities: *Features of Taxonomic Groups, Classification Keys*
Weblinks: *The Principles of Classification*

Classification of the Ethiopian Hedgehog

Below is the classification for the **Ethiopian hedgehog**. Only one of each group is subdivided in this chart showing the levels that can be used in classifying an organism. Not all possible subdivisions have been shown here. For example, it is possible to indicate such categories as **super-class** and **sub-family**. The only natural category is the **species**, often separated into geographical **races**, or **sub-species**, which generally differ in appearance.

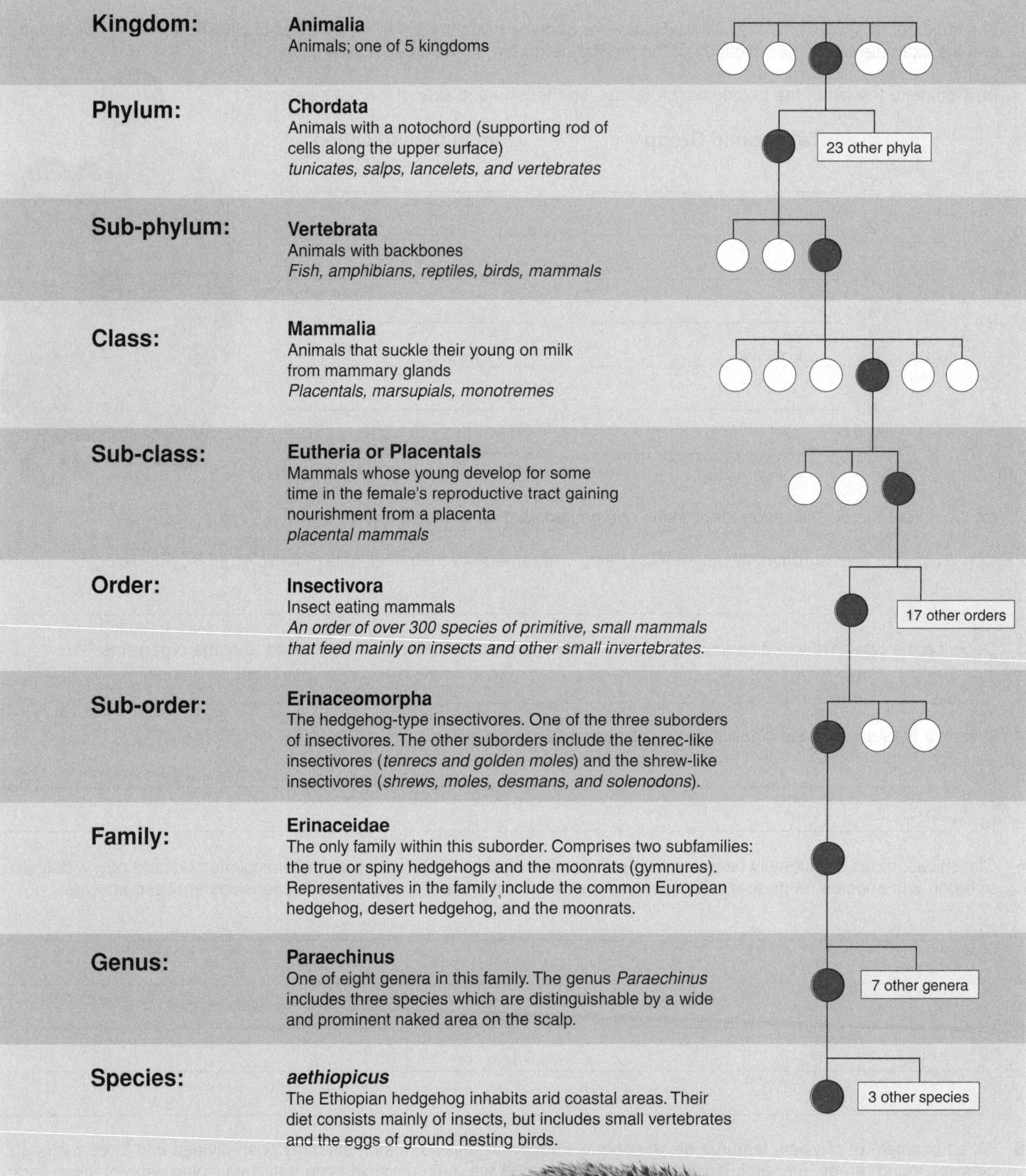

Kingdom: **Animalia**
Animals; one of 5 kingdoms

Phylum: **Chordata**
Animals with a notochord (supporting rod of cells along the upper surface)
tunicates, salps, lancelets, and vertebrates

Sub-phylum: **Vertebrata**
Animals with backbones
Fish, amphibians, reptiles, birds, mammals

Class: **Mammalia**
Animals that suckle their young on milk from mammary glands
Placentals, marsupials, monotremes

Sub-class: **Eutheria or Placentals**
Mammals whose young develop for some time in the female's reproductive tract gaining nourishment from a placenta
placental mammals

Order: **Insectivora**
Insect eating mammals
An order of over 300 species of primitive, small mammals that feed mainly on insects and other small invertebrates.

Sub-order: **Erinaceomorpha**
The hedgehog-type insectivores. One of the three suborders of insectivores. The other suborders include the tenrec-like insectivores (*tenrecs and golden moles*) and the shrew-like insectivores (*shrews, moles, desmans, and solenodons*).

Family: **Erinaceidae**
The only family within this suborder. Comprises two subfamilies: the true or spiny hedgehogs and the moonrats (gymnures). Representatives in the family include the common European hedgehog, desert hedgehog, and the moonrats.

Genus: **Paraechinus**
One of eight genera in this family. The genus *Paraechinus* includes three species which are distinguishable by a wide and prominent naked area on the scalp.

Species: ***aethiopicus***
The Ethiopian hedgehog inhabits arid coastal areas. Their diet consists mainly of insects, but includes small vertebrates and the eggs of ground nesting birds.

The order *Insectivora* was first introduced to group together shrews, moles, and hedgehogs. It was later extended to include tenrecs, golden moles, desmans, tree shrews, and elephant shrews and the taxonomy of the group became very confused. Recent reclassification of the elephant shrews and tree shrews into their own separate orders has made the *Insectivora* a more cohesive group taxonomically.

Ethiopian hedgehog
Paraechinus aethiopicus

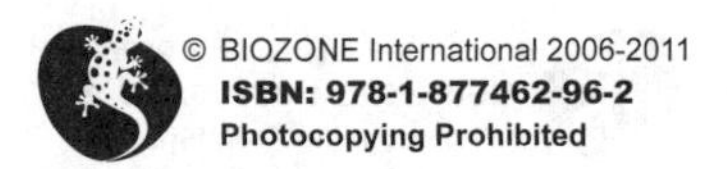

ISBN: 978-1-877462-96-2

Classification Keys

Classification systems provide biologists with a way in which to identify species. They also indicate how closely related, in an evolutionary sense, each species is to others. An organism's classification should include a clear, unambiguous **description**, an accurate **diagram**, and its unique name, denoted by the **genus** and **species**. Classification keys are used to identify an organism and assign it to the correct species (assuming that the organism has already been formally classified and is included in the key). Typically, keys are **dichotomous** and involve a series of linked steps. At each step, a choice is made between two features; each alternative leads to another question until an identification is made. If the organism cannot be identified, it may be a new species or the key may need revision. Two examples of **dichotomous keys** are provided here. The first (below) describes features for identifying the larvae of various genera within the order Trichoptera (caddisflies). From this key you should be able to assign a generic name to each of the caddisfly larvae pictured. The key on the next page identifies aquatic insect orders.

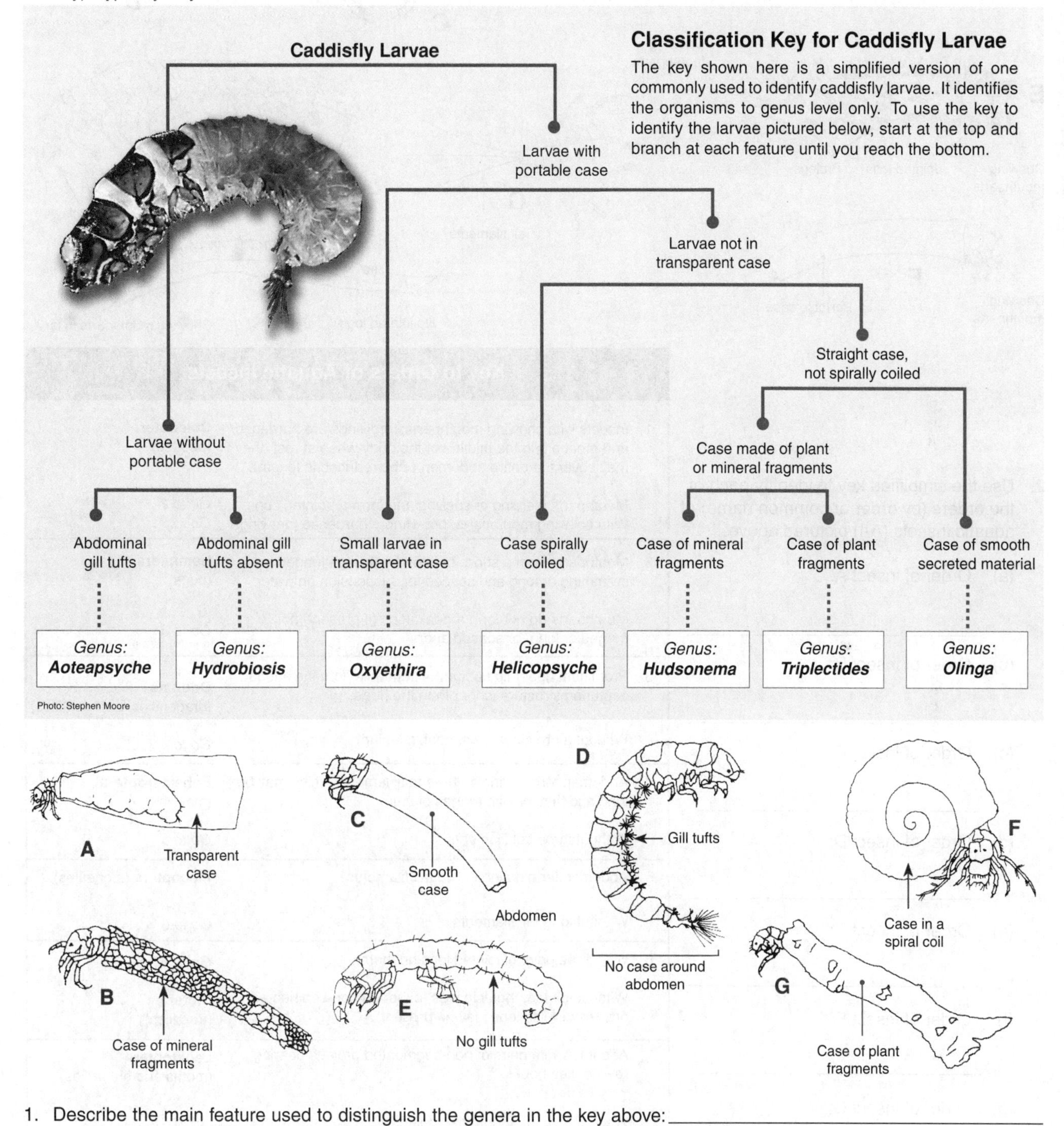

Classification Key for Caddisfly Larvae

The key shown here is a simplified version of one commonly used to identify caddisfly larvae. It identifies the organisms to genus level only. To use the key to identify the larvae pictured below, start at the top and branch at each feature until you reach the bottom.

1. Describe the main feature used to distinguish the genera in the key above: ______________________

____

2. Use the key above to assign each of the caddisfly larvae (**A-G**) to its correct genus:

A: ____________ D: ____________ G: ____________

B: ____________ E: ____________

C: ____________ F: ____________

ISBN: 978-1-877462-96-2

***Related activities:** Keying Out Plant Species*
***Weblinks:** What is the Key to Classification?*

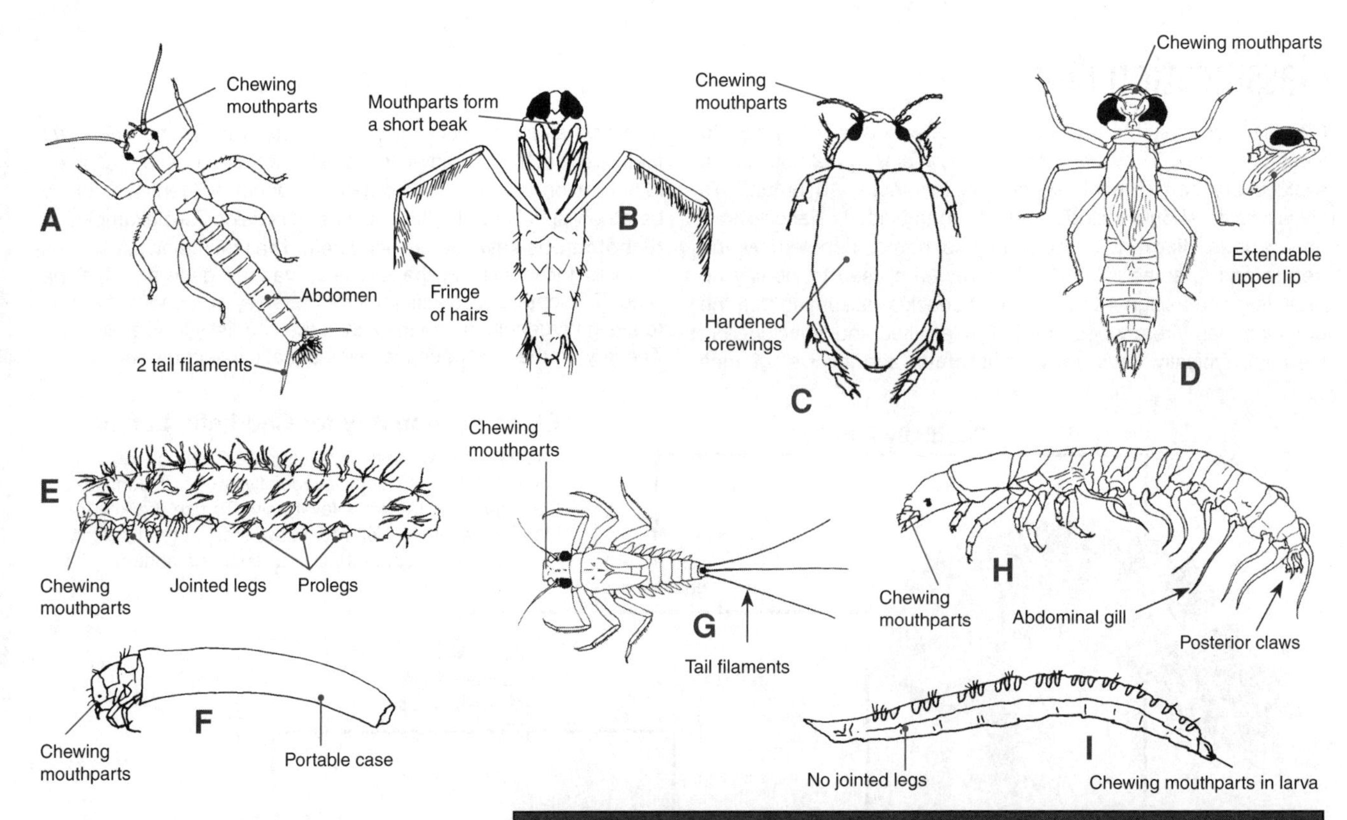

2. Use the simplified key to identify each of the orders (by order or common name) of aquatic insects (A-I) pictured above:

(a) Order of insect A: ______________________

(b) Order of insect B: ______________________

(c) Order of insect C: ______________________

(d) Order of insect D: ______________________

(e) Order of insect E: ______________________

(f) Order of insect F: ______________________

(g) Order of insect G: ______________________

(h) Order of insect H: ______________________

(i) Order of insect I: ______________________

Key to Orders of Aquatic Insects

1	Insects with chewing mouthparts; forewings are hardened and meet along the midline of the body when at rest (they may cover the entire abdomen or be reduced in length).	**Coleoptera** (beetles)
	Mouthparts piercing or sucking and form a pointed cone With chewing mouthparts, but without hardened forewings	*Go to 2* *Go to 3*
2	Mouthparts form a short, pointed beak; legs fringed for swimming or long and spaced for suspension on water.	**Hemiptera** (bugs)
	Mouthparts do not form a beak; legs (if present) not fringed or long, or spaced apart.	*Go to 3*
3	Prominent upper lip (labium) extendable, forming a food capturing structure longer than the head.	**Odonata** (dragonflies & damselflies)
	Without a prominent, extendable labium	*Go to 4*
4	Abdomen terminating in three tail filaments which may be long and thin, or with fringes of hairs.	**Ephemeroptera** (mayflies)
	Without three tail filaments	*Go to 5*
5	Abdomen terminating in two tail filaments	**Plecoptera** (stoneflies)
	Without long tail filaments	*Go to 6*
6	With three pairs of jointed legs on thorax	*Go to 7*
	Without jointed, thoracic legs (although non-segmented prolegs or false legs may be present).	**Diptera** (true flies)
7	Abdomen with pairs of non-segmented prolegs bearing rows of fine hooks.	**Lepidoptera** (moths and butterflies)
	Without pairs of abdominal prolegs	*Go to 8*
8	With eight pairs of finger-like abdominal gills; abdomen with two pairs of posterior claws.	**Megaloptera** (dobsonflies)
	Either, without paired, abdominal gills, or, if such gills are present, without posterior claws.	*Go to 9*
9	Abdomen with a pair of posterior prolegs bearing claws with subsidiary hooks; sometimes a portable case.	**Trichoptera** (caddisflies)

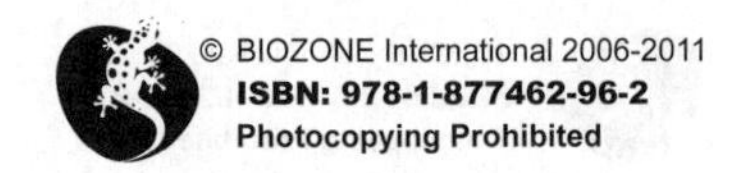

ISBN: 978-1-877462-96-2

Keying Out Plant Species

Dichotomous keys are a useful tool in biology and can enable identification to the species level provided the characteristics chosen are appropriate for separating species. Keys are extensively used by botanists as they are quick and easy to use in the field, although they sometimes rely on the presence of particular plant parts such as fruits or flowers. Some also require some specialist knowledge of plant biology. The following simple activity requires you to identify five species of the genus *Acer* from illustrations of the leaves. It provides valuable practice in using characteristic features to identify plants to species level.

A Dichotomous Key to Some Common Maple Species

1a Adult leaves with five lobes 2

1b Adult leaves with three lobes 4

2a Leaves 7.5-13 cm wide, with smooth edges, lacking serrations along the margin. U shaped sinuses between lobes.

Sugar maple, *Acer saccharum*

2b Leaves with serrations (fine teeth) along the margin 3

3a Leaves 5-13 cm wide and deeply lobed.

Japansese maple, *Acer palmatum*

3b Leaves 13-18 cm wide and deeply lobed.

Silver maple, *Acer saccharinum*

4a Leaves 5-15 cm wide with small sharp serrations on the margins. Distinctive V shaped sinuses between the lobes.

Red maple, *Acer rubrum*

4b Leaves 7.5-13 cm wide without serrations on the margins. Shallow sinuses between the lobes.

Black maple, *Acer nigrum*

A

B

Sinus

Lobe

C

D

E

0 1 2 3 4
cm

1. Use the dichotomous key to the common species of *Acer* to identify the species illustrated by the leaves (drawn to scale). Begin at the top of the key and make a choice as to which of the illustrations best fits the description:

(a) Species A: ____________________

(b) Species B: ____________________

(c) Species C: ____________________

(d) Species D: ____________________

(e) Species E: ____________________

2. Identify a feature that could be used to identify maple species when leaves are absent: ____________________

3. Suggest why it is usually necessary to consider a number of different features in order to classify plants to species level:

____

____

4. When identifying a plant, suggest what you should be sure of before using a key to classify it to species level:

____

____

ISBN: 978-1-877462-96-2

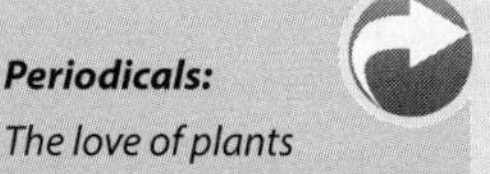

The Classification of Life

For this activity, cut away the two pages of diagrams that follow from your book. The five kingdoms that all living things are grouped into, are listed on this page and the following page.

1. Cut out all of the images of different living organisms (cut around each shape closely, taking care to include their names).
2. Sort them into their classification groups by placing them into the spaces provided on this and the following page.
3. To fix the images in place, first use a temporary method (e.g. a gluestick or sellotape folded into a loop), so that you can easily reposition them if you need to. Make a permanent fixture when you are completely satisfied with your placements on the page.

Bacteria

Protists

Fungi

Plants

Bryophytes

Seedless plants

Angiosperms: Monocotyledon

Angiosperms: Dicotyledon

Gymnosperms: Cycads

Gymnosperms: Conifers

Related activities: *Features of Taxonomic Groups*

ISBN: 978-1-877462-96-2

Cut out the organisms on this page and paste them into the spaces provided at the start of this activity. Organisms are not to scale.

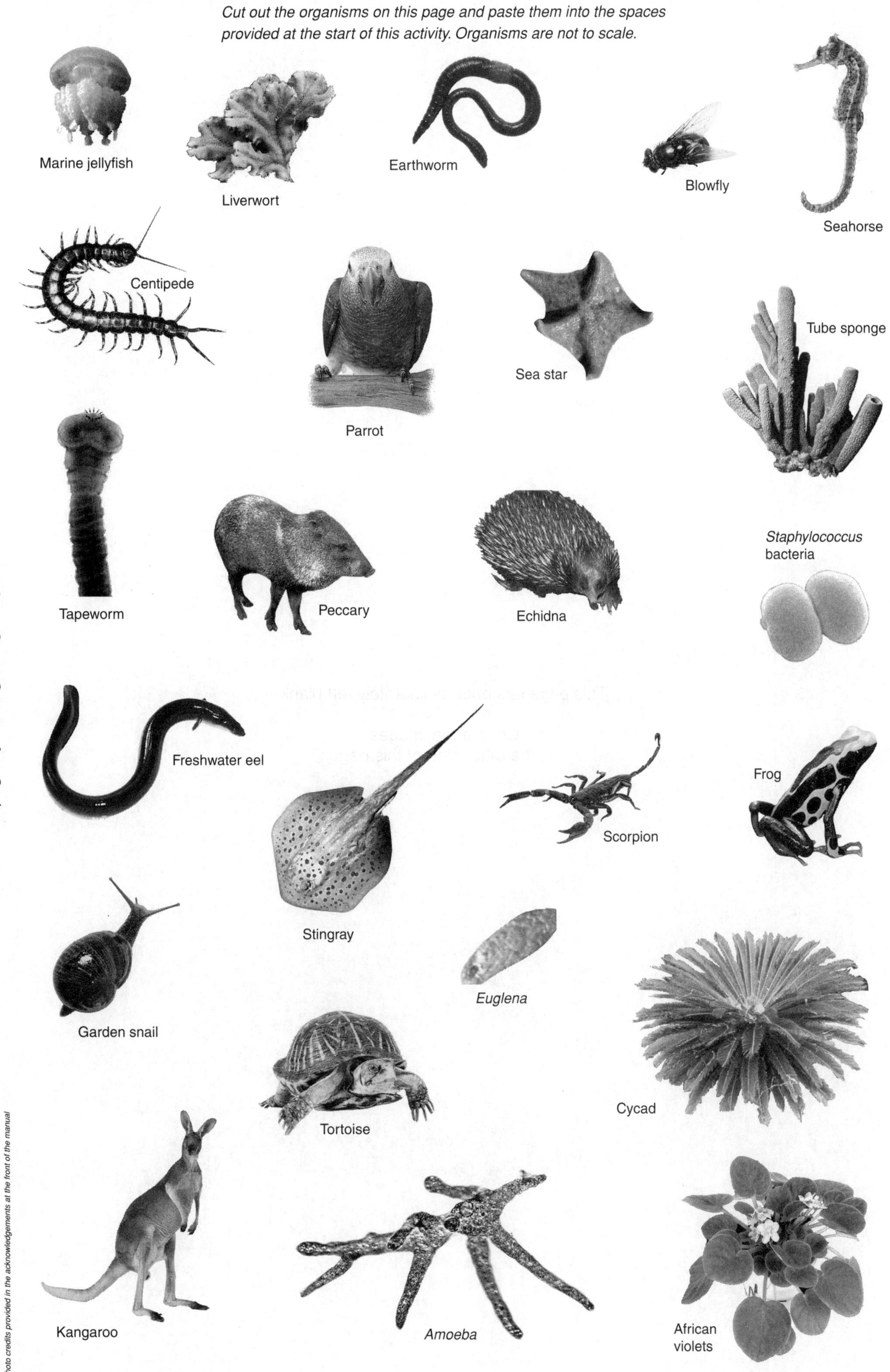

Remove this page by tearing along the perforation

Photo credits provided in the acknowledgements at the front of the manual

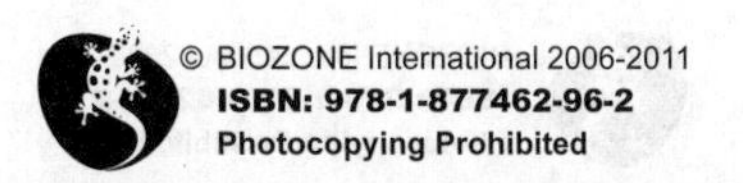

ISBN: 978-1-877462-96-2

This page has been deliberately left blank

Cut out the images
on the other side of this page

ISBN: 978-1-877462-96-2

Cut out the organisms on this page and paste them into the spaces provided at the start of this activity. Organisms are not to scale.

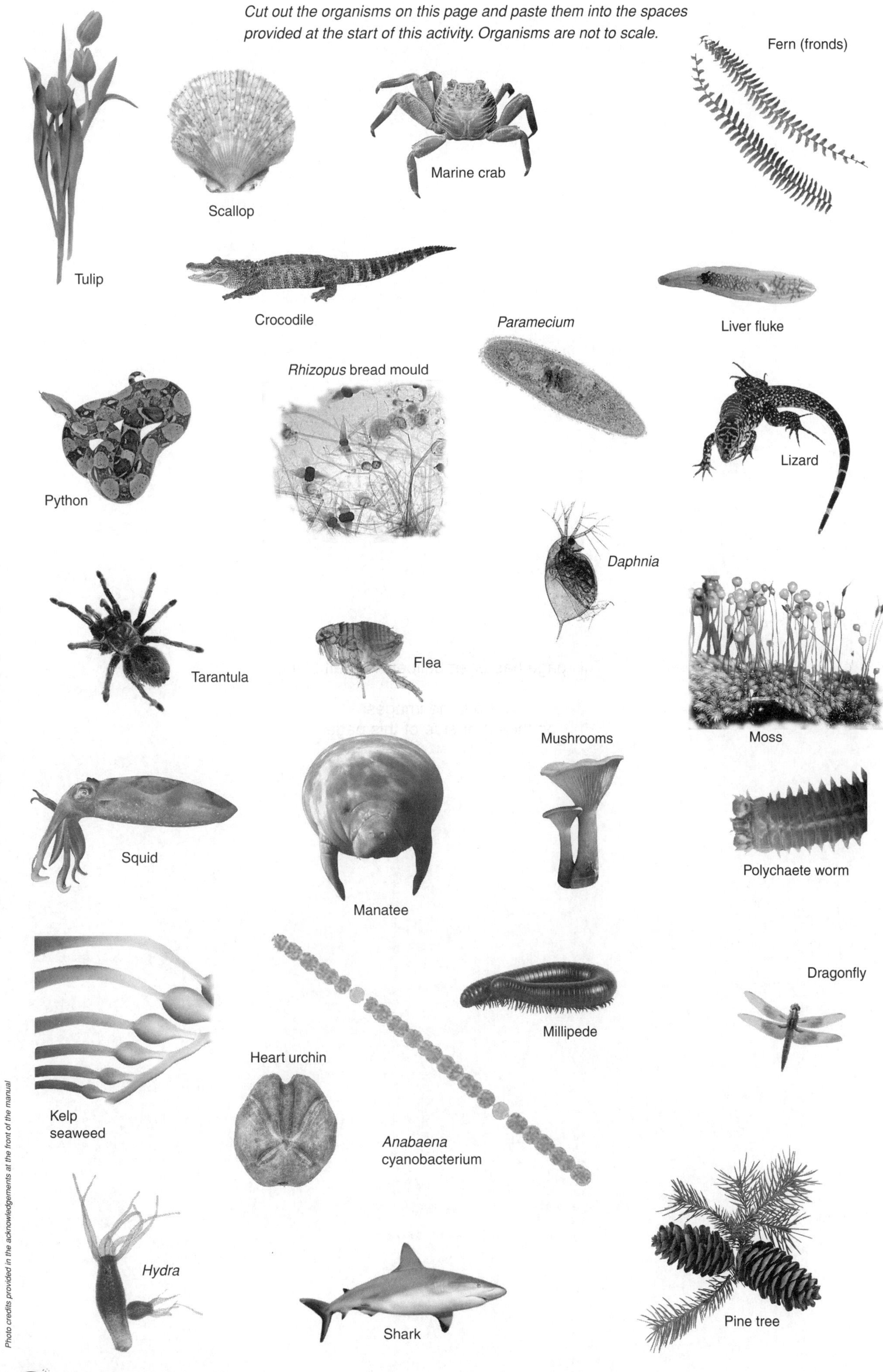

Remove this page by tearing along the perforation

Photo credits provided in the acknowledgements at the front of the manual

ISBN: 978-1-877462-96-2

This page has been deliberately left blank

Cut out the images
on the other side of this page

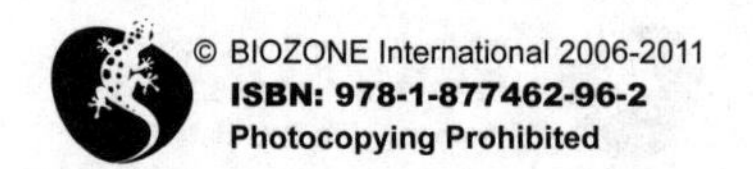

ISBN: 978-1-877462-96-2

Animals			
Sponges	**Cnidarians**	**Flatworms**	**Annelids**

Mollusks: Gastropods	Bivalves	Cephalopods	**Echinoderms**

Arthropods: Crustaceans	Myriapods	Arachnids	Insects

Cartilaginous fish	**Bony fish**	**Amphibians**

Reptiles	**Birds**

Mammals: Monotremes	Marsupials	Placentals

ISBN: 978-1-877462-96-2

Features of the Five Kingdoms

The classification of organisms into taxonomic groups is based on how biologists believe they are related in an evolutionary sense. Organisms in a taxonomic group share features which set them apart from other groups. By identifying these **distinguishing features**, it is possible to develop an understanding of the evolutionary history of the group. The focus of this activity is to summarize the distinguishing features of each of the five kingdoms in the five kingdom classification system.

1. Distinguishing features of Kingdom **Prokaryotae**:

2. Distinguishing features of Kingdom **Protista**:

3. Distinguishing features of Kingdom **Fungi**:

4. Distinguishing features of Kingdom **Plantae:**

5. Distinguishing features of Kingdom **Animalia**:

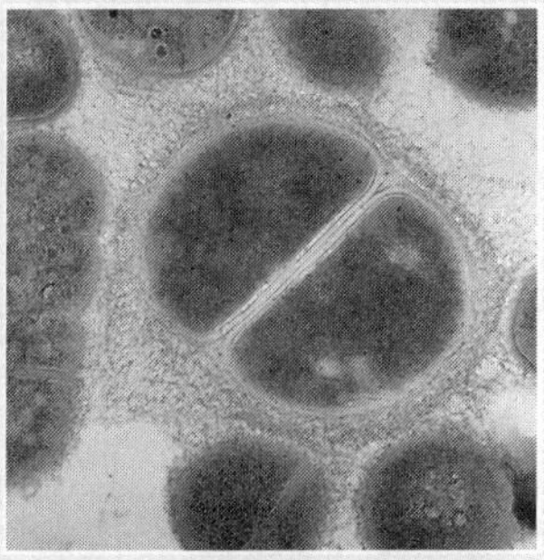

EII

***Staphylococcus* dividing**

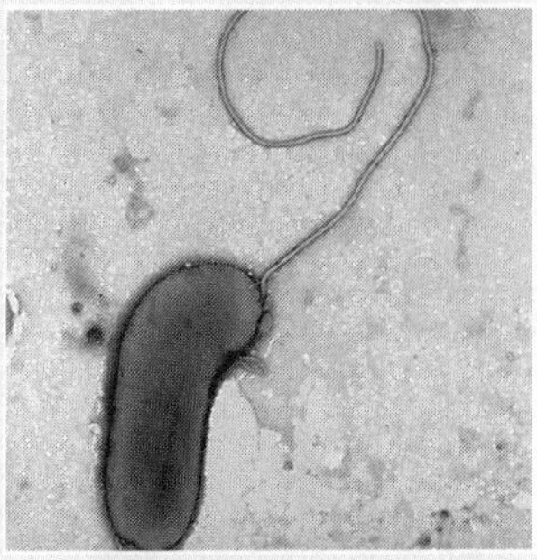

EII

Helicobacter pylori

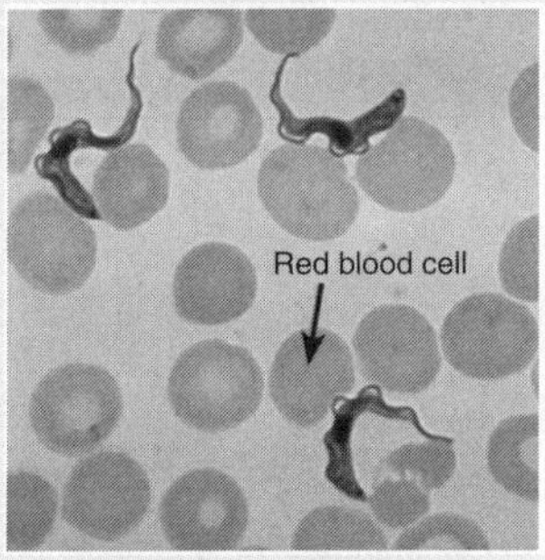

CDC

Red blood cell

Trypanosoma parasite

RCN

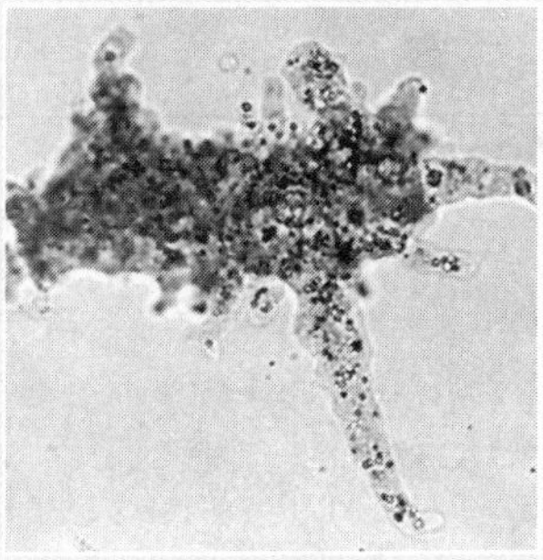

Amoeba

Mushrooms

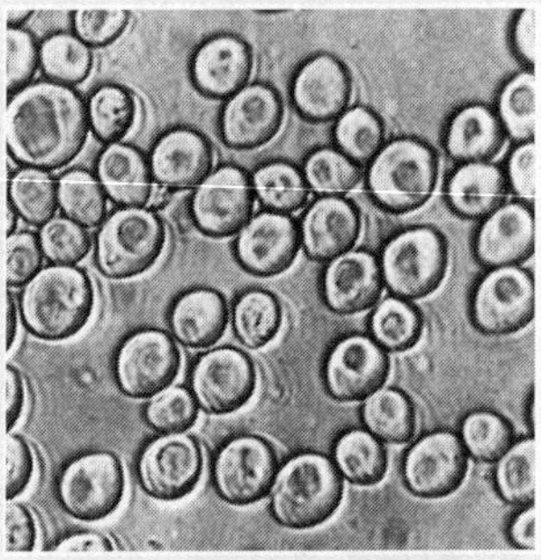

Yeast cells in solution

Moss

Pea plants

RA

Cicada moulting

Gibbon

ISBN: 978-1-877462-96-2

Related activities: *The New Tree of Life, Features of Taxonomic Groups*

Features of Microbial Groups

A microorganism (or microbe) is literally a microscopic organism. The term is usually reserved for the organisms studied in microbiology: bacteria, fungi, microscopic protistans, and viruses. The first three of these represent three of the five kingdoms for which you described distinguishing features in an earlier activity (viruses are non-cellular and therefore not included in the five-kingdom classification). Most microbial taxa, but particularly the fungi, also have macroscopic representatives. The distinction between a macrofungus and a microfungus is an artificial but convenient one. Unlike microfungi, which are made conspicuous by the diseases or decay they cause, macrofungi are most likely to be observed with the naked eye. The microfungi include yeasts and pathogenic species. Macrofungi, e.g. mushrooms, toadstools, and lichens, are illustrated in *Features of Macrofungi and Plants*.

1. Describe aspects of each of the following for the bacteria and cyanobacteria (Kingdom Prokaryotae):

   (a) Environmental range: ______________________________

   ____

   (b) Ecological role: ______________________________

   ____

2. Identify an example within the bacteria of the following:

   (a) Photosynthetic: ______________________________

   (b) Pathogen: ______________________________

   (c) Decomposer: ______________________________

   (d) Nitrogen fixer: ______________________________

3. Describe aspects of each of the following for the microscopic protistans (Kingdom Protista):

   (a) Environmental range: ______________________________

   ____

   (b) Ecological role: ______________________________

   ____

4. Identify an example within the protists of the following:

   (a) Photosynthetic: ______________________________

   (b) Pathogen: ______________________________

   (c) Biological indicator: ______________________________

5. Describe aspects of each of the following for the microfungi (Kingdom Fungi):

   (a) Environmental range: ______________________________

   ____

   (b) Ecological role: ______________________________

   ____

6. Identify examples within the microfungi of the following:

   (a) Animal pathogen: ______________________________

   ____

   (b) Plant pathogens: ______________________________

   ____

   ____

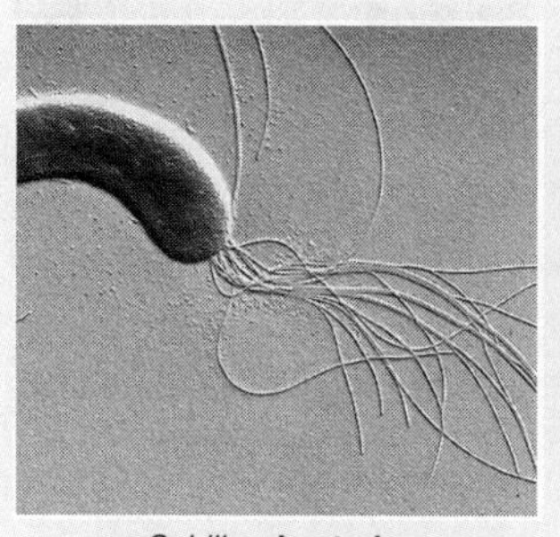

Spirillum **bacteria**

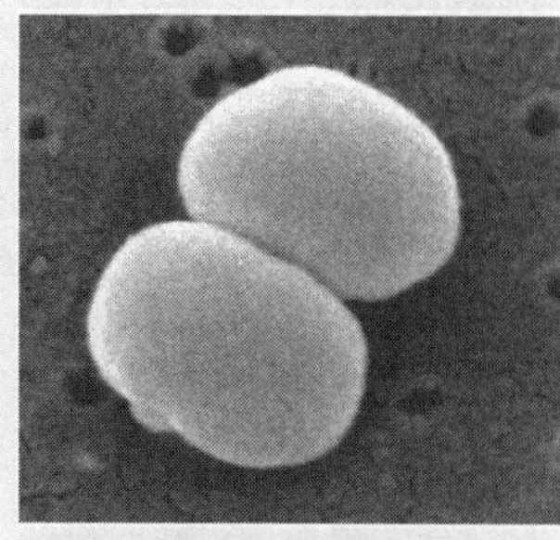

CDC

Staphylococcus

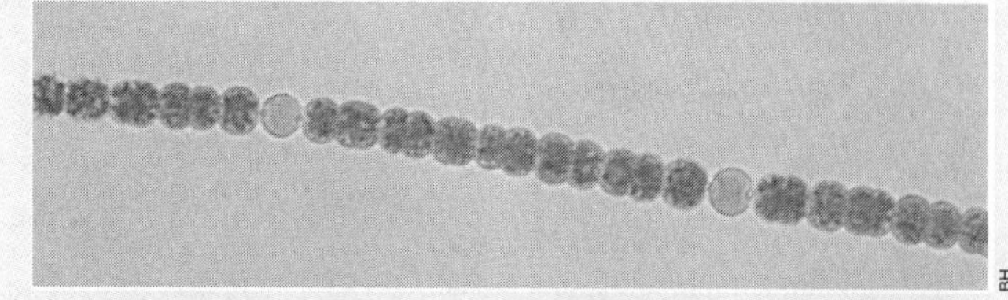

BH

Anabaena cyanobacterium

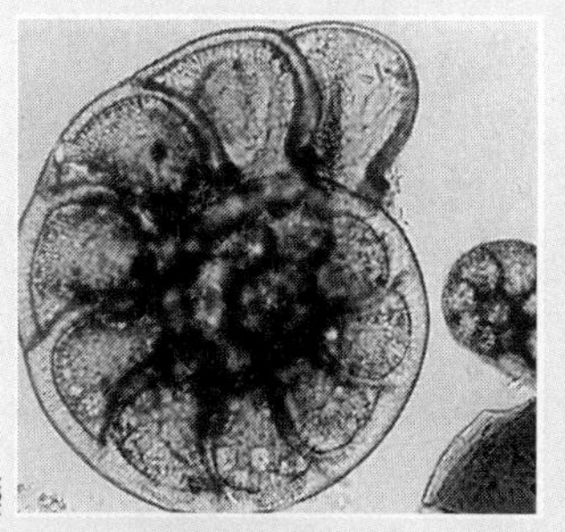

RCN

Foraminiferan

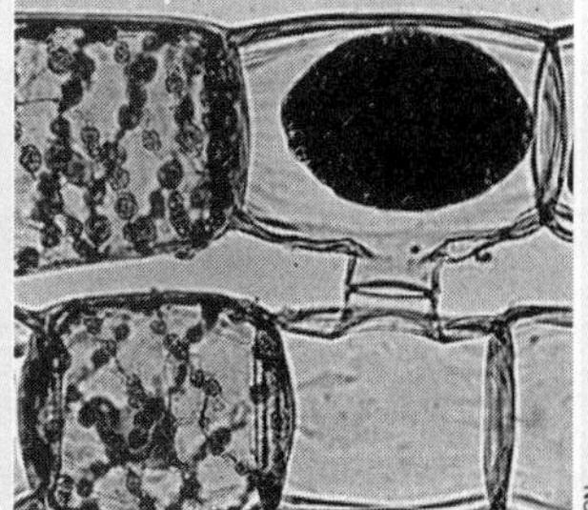

RCN

***Spirogyra* algae**

Diatoms: *Pleurosigma*

***Curvularia* sp. conidiophore**

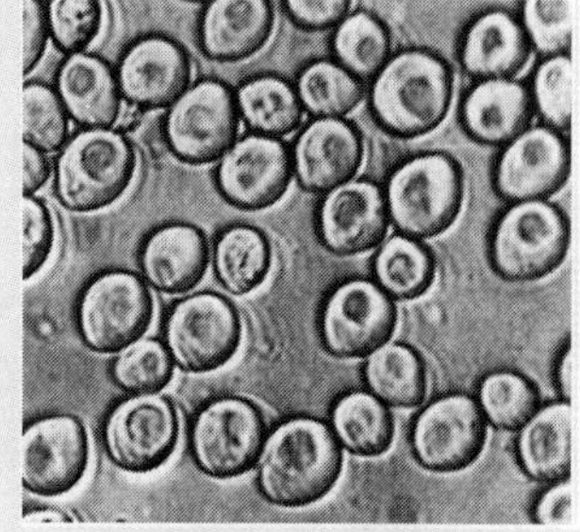

Yeast cells in solution

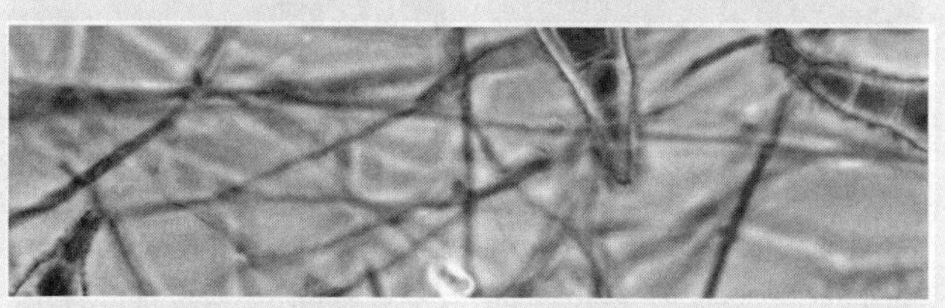

***Microsporum distortum* (a pathogenic fungus)**

ISBN: 978-1-877462-96-2

Related activities: *The New Tree of Life, Features of Taxonomic Group*
Weblinks: *Types of Microbes*

Features of Macrofungi and Plants

Although plants and fungi are some of the most familiar organisms in our environment, their classification has not always been straightforward. We know now that the plant kingdom is monophyletic, meaning that it is derived from a common ancestor. The variety we see in plant taxa today is a result of their enormous diversification from the first plants. Although the fungi were once grouped together with the plants, they are unique organisms that differ from other eukaryotes in their mode of nutrition, structural organization, growth, and reproduction. The focus of this activity is to summarize the features of the fungal kingdom, the major divisions of the plant kingdom, and the two classes of flowering plants (angiosperms).

Lichen

Bracket fungus

Liverwort

Moss

Fern frond

Ground fern

Pine tree cone

Cycad

Coconut palms

Wheat plants

Deciduous tree

Flowering plant

1. **Macrofungi** features: ______________________

2. **Moss** and **liverwort** features: ______________________

3. **Fern** features: ______________________

4. **Gymnosperm** features: ______________________

5. **Monocot angiosperm** features: ______________________

6. **Dicot angiosperm** features: ______________________

Related activities: *The New Tree of Life, Features of Taxonomic Groups*

Periodicals: *World flowers bloom after recount*

ISBN: 978-1-877462-96-2

Features of Animal Taxa

The animal kingdom is classified into about 35 major **phyla**. Representatives of the more familiar taxa are illustrated below: **cnidarians** (includes jellyfish, sea anemones, and corals), **annelids** (segmented worms), **arthropods** (insects, crustaceans, spiders, scorpions, centipedes and millipedes), **molluscs** (snails, bivalve shellfish, squid and octopus), **echinoderms** (starfish and sea urchins), **vertebrates** from the phylum **chordates** (fish, amphibians, reptiles, birds, and mammals). The **arthropods** and the **vertebrates** have been represented in more detail, giving the **classes** for each of these **phyla**. This activity asks you to describe the **distinguishing features** of each of the taxa represented below.

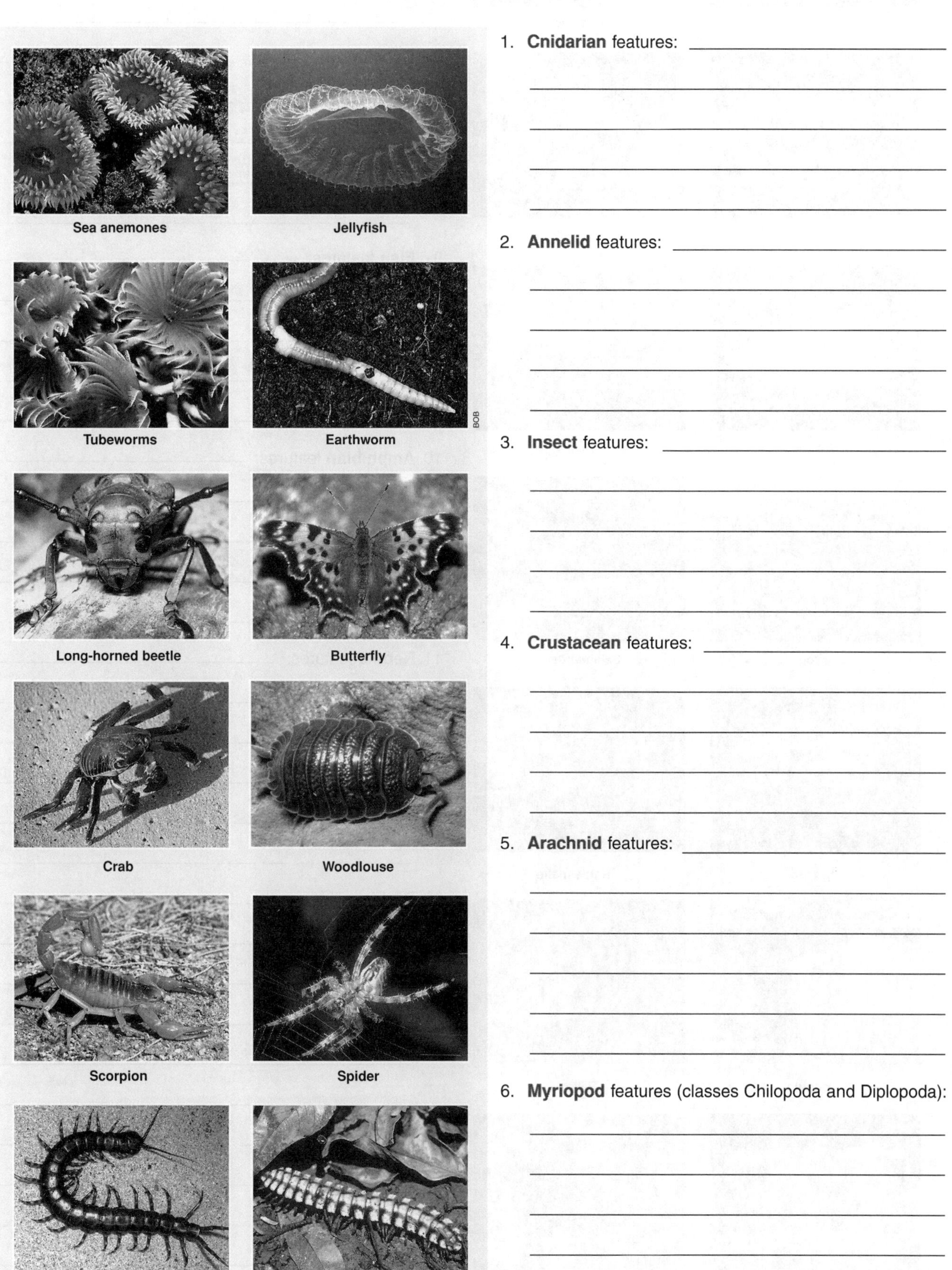

Sea anemones

Jellyfish

Tubeworms

Earthworm

Long-horned beetle

Butterfly

Crab

Woodlouse

Scorpion

Spider

Centipede

Millipede

1. **Cnidarian** features: ______________________

2. **Annelid** features: ______________________

3. **Insect** features: ______________________

4. **Crustacean** features: ______________________

5. **Arachnid** features: ______________________

6. **Myriopod** features (classes Chilopoda and Diplopoda): ______________________

ISBN: 978-1-877462-96-2

Periodicals:
The family line

Related activities: *The New Tree of Life, Features of Taxonomic Groups*

7. **Mollusk** features: ______________________________

8. **Echinoderm** features: ______________________________

9. **Fish** features: ______________________________

10. **Amphibian** features: ______________________________

11. **Reptile** features: ______________________________

12. **Bird** features: ______________________________

13. **Mammal** features: ______________________________

ISBN: 978-1-877462-96-2

KEY TERMS: Crossword

Complete the crossword below, which will test your understanding of key terms in this chapter and their meanings

Clues Across

3. The 'true' bacteria, which under the five kingdom classification system were included in the Kingdom Prokaryotae along with the Archaebacteria.
5. Kingdom of multicellular, heterotrophic organisms. Cells do not possess cell walls.
7. The study of form. How an organism physically appears.
9. Arthropods with eight legs. Includes spiders and scorpions.
10. A unit of classification. A group of related species.
12. The smallest, most precise unit of classification; a closely related group of organisms able to interbreed.
15. A unit of classification – a group of related genera.
16. Superkingdom of organisms with cells containing organelles. DNA is present as chromosomes.
19. Key that gives two options at each step of the identification process.
20. Phylum characterized by the presence of a fleshy, muscular foot and mantle. Most have shells, although this may be internal in some.
21. Diverse group of eukaryotes, either unicellular or multicellular but lacking specialized tissues.

Clues Down

1. Primitive group of animals with jelly-like bodies and a gastrovascular cavity.
2. Group of multicellular organisms that use chlorophyll to harness light energy to produce carbohydrates.
4. Phylum whose name literally means "jointed foot".
5. Ancient line of bacteria distinct from the Eubacteria. It includes a number of extremophiles.
6. Kingdom including organisms with cells that lack organelles and have a single circular chromosome.
8. Unit of classification used to group together related families.
11. Sub phylum of the kingdom Animalia. Possess backbones, normally made of bone, that protect a dorsal nerve cord.
13. The largest, least specific unit of classification within a kingdom.
14. A taxonomic category ranking below a phylum or division and above an order.
17. Historically, the highest rank in biological taxonomy.
18. A group of organisms that possess a chitinous cell wall, feed using hyphae, and reproduce by spores.

ISBN: 978-1-877462-96-2

Laboratory Techniques

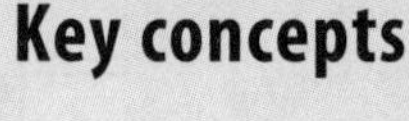

Key concepts

- Accurate biological drawings are an appropriate method for recording the details of biological specimens.
- Microscopy can be used to understand cellular structure and function.
- A variety of basic laboratory techniques are used to isolate and analyze biological material.
- Aseptic technique is a critical procedure in microbiology.

Key terms

aseptic
biological drawing
biological stain
chromatography
colorimetry
differential centrifugation
electron microscope
gel electrophoresis
light (optical) microscope
linear magnification
magnification
micropropagation (plant tissue culture)
microscopy
resolution
r_f value
scanning electron microscopy (SEM)
serial dilution
streak plating
temporary mount
transmission electron microscopy (TEM)

Objectives

☐ 1. Use the **KEY TERMS** to help you understand and complete these objectives.

Making Biological Drawings

pages 132-133, 135

☐ 2. Demonstrate an ability to make accurate **biological drawings**. Understand that a good biological drawing is a way to accurately record information.

Microscopy

pages 129-131, 134, 136-140

☐ 3. Compare and contrast the structure and basic principles of **light** (optical) **microscopes** and **electron microscopes**. Distinguish between **TEM** (transmission electron microscopy) and **SEM** (scanning electron microscopy).

☐ 4. Interpret photomicrographs of typical plant and animal cells as seen using light and electron microscopy.

☐ 5. Demonstrate an ability to prepare a **temporary mount** for viewing with a light microscope.

☐ 6. Explain the role of sample preparation (including **stains**) in microscopy. Demonstrate an ability use simple staining techniques to show features of cells.

☐ 7. Explain the difference between **magnification** and **resolution**. Calculate the **linear magnification** of images viewed with a microscope. Compare the magnification and resolution achieved using a light microscope, TEM and SEM.

Basic Laboratory Techniques

pages 141-148

☐ 8. Describe simple tests for reducing and non-reducing sugars, starch, proteins, and lipids. Describe the use of **colorimetry** to determine the concentration of a reducing sugar (e.g. glucose) in a solution.

☐ 9. Describe the principles of **differential centrifugation** (cell fractionation).

☐ 10. Explain the basis of **chromatography** as a technique for separating and identifying biological molecules. Describe the calculation and use of R_f **values**.

☐ 11. Explain how DNA fragments are separated by **gel electrophoresis**.

☐ 12. Describe plant cloning using **micropropagation** (plant **tissue culture**).

Microbial Techniques

pages 149-151

☐ 13. Use **aseptic** technique to prepare and inoculate microbial cultures. Explain how **streak plating** is used to isolate bacterial strains.

☐ 14. Discuss the role of **serial dilution** as a fundamental microbiology technique.

Periodicals:

Listings for this chapter are on page 153

Weblinks:

www.thebiozone.com/weblink/Skills-2962.html

Optical Microscopes

The light (optical) microscope is an important tool in biology and using it correctly is an essential skill. High power **compound light microscopes** (below) use a combination of lenses to magnify objects up to several hundred times. A specimen viewed with this type of microscope must be thin and mostly transparent so that light can pass through it. No detail will be seen in specimens that are thick or opaque. Modern microscopes are binocular (have two adjustable eyepieces). Dissecting microscopes are a special type of binocular microscope used for observations at low total magnification (X4 to X50), where a large working distance between the objectives and stage is required. A dissecting microscope has two separate lens systems, one for each eye. Such microscopes produce a 3-D view of the specimen and are sometimes called stereo microscopes for this reason.

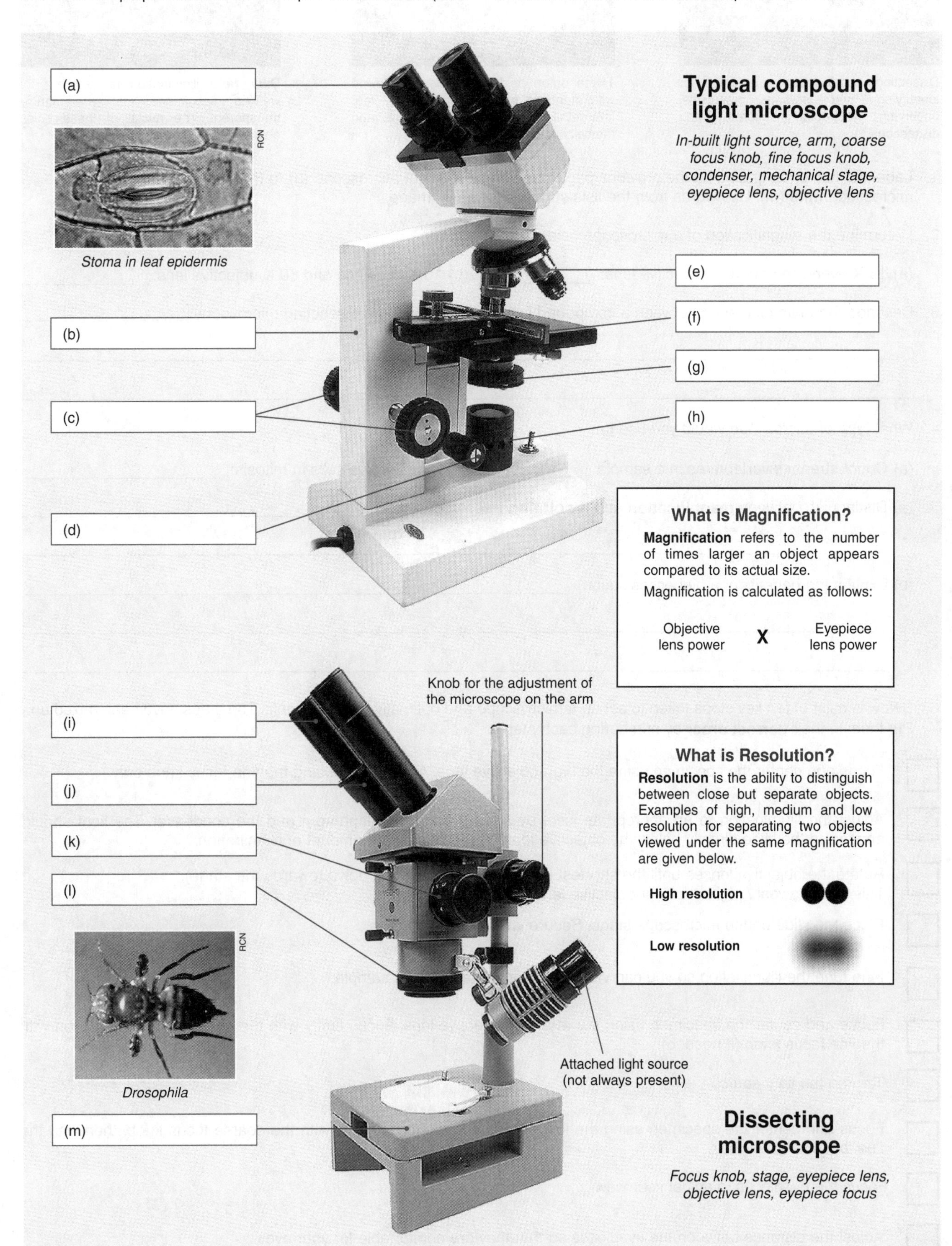

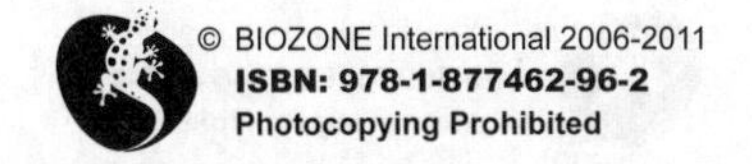

ISBN: 978-1-877462-96-2

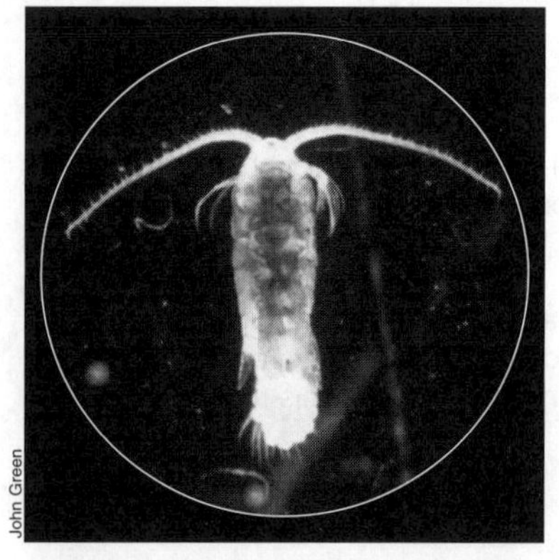

Dissecting microscopes are used for identifying and sorting organisms, observing microbial cultures, and dissections.

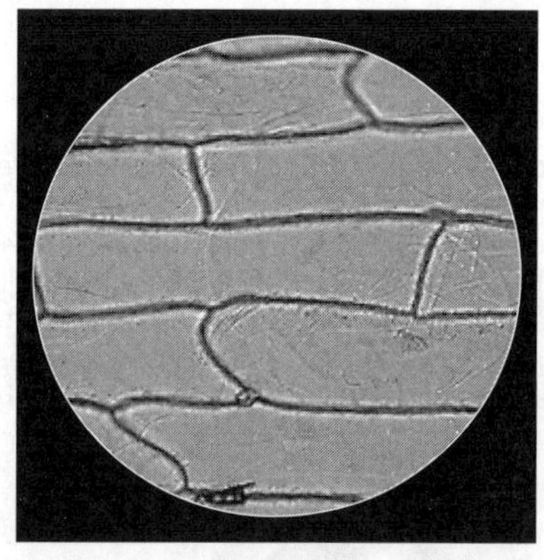

These onion epidermal cells are viewed with standard **bright field** lighting. Very little detail can be seen (only cell walls) and the cell nuclei are barely visible.

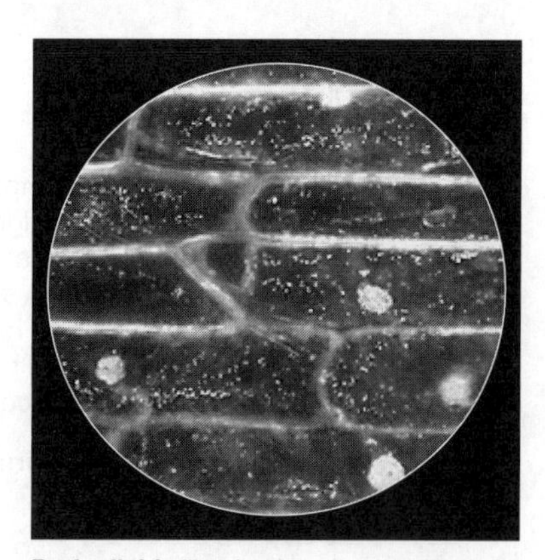

Dark field illumination is excellent for viewing specimens that are almost transparent. The nuclei of these onion epidermal cells are clearly visible.

1. Label the two photographs on the previous page, the compound light microscope (a) to (h) and the dissecting microscope (i) to (m). Use words from the lists supplied for each image.

2. Determine the magnification of a microscope using:

   (a) 15 X eyepiece and 40 X objective lens: ________ (b) 10 X eyepiece and 60 X objective lens: ________

3. Describe the main difference between a compound light microscope and a dissecting microscope: ________

4. What type of microscope would you use to:

   (a) Count stream invertebrates in a sample: ________ (b) Observe cells in mitosis: ________

5. (a) Distinguish between **magnification** and **resolution** (resolving power): ________

   (b) Explain the benefits of a higher resolution: ________

6. Below is a list of ten key steps taken to set up a microscope and optimally view a sample. The steps have been mixed up. Put them in their **correct order** by numbering each step:

- ☐ Focus and center the specimen using the high objective lens. Adjust focus using the fine focus knob only.
- ☐ Adjust the illumination to an appropriate level by adjusting the iris diaphragm and the condenser. The light should appear on the slide directly below the objective lens, and give an even amount of illumination.
- ☐ Rotate the objective lenses until the shortest lens is in place (pointing down towards the stage). This is the lowest / highest power objective lens (delete one).
- ☐ Place the slide on the microscope stage. Secure with the sample clips.
- ☐ Fine tune the illumination so you can view maximum detail on your sample.
- ☐ Focus and center the specimen using the medium objective lens. Focus firstly with the coarse focus knob, then with the fine focus knob (if needed).
- ☐ Turn on the light source.
- ☐ Focus and center the specimen using the low objective lens. Focus firstly with the coarse focus knob, then with the fine focus knob.
- ☐ Focus the eyepieces to adjust your view.
- ☐ Adjust the distance between the eyepieces so that they are comfortable for your eyes.

ISBN: 978-1-877462-96-2

Microscopy Techniques

Specimens are often prepared in some way before viewing in order to highlight features and reveal details. A **wet mount** is a temporary preparation in which a specimen and a drop of fluid are trapped under a thin coverslip. Wet mounts are used to view live microscopic organisms but can also be used to view suspensions such as blood. A wet mount improves a sample's appearance and enhances visible detail. **Stains** and dyes can also be used to highlight specific components or structures. Most stains are **non-viable**, and are used on dead specimens, but harmless **viable stains** can be applied to living material.

Making a Temporary Wet Mount

1. **Sectioning:** Very thin sections of fresh material are cut with a razorblade.
2. **Mounting:** The thin section(s) are placed in the center of a clean glass microscope slide and covered with a drop of mounting liquid (e.g. water, glycerol, or stain). A coverslip is placed on top to exclude air (below).
3. If too much liquid is added the coverslip will sit too high, and it will be difficult to focus on the sample. If not enough liquid is used, it may quickly evaporate and the sample may dry up before it can be fully examined.

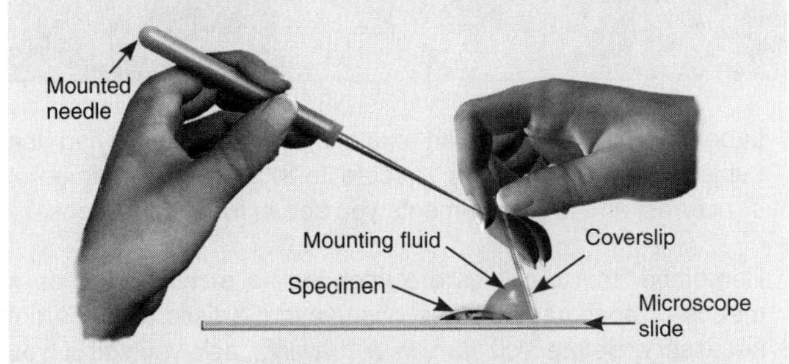

A mounted needle supports the coverslip and lower it gently over the specimen. This avoids including air in the mount.

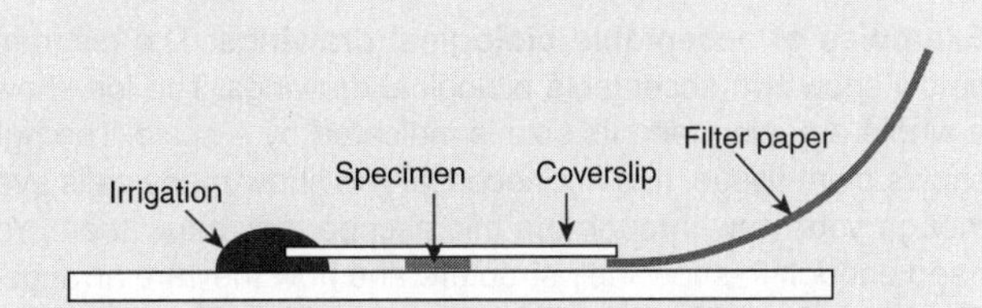

If a specimen is already mounted, a drop of stain can be placed at one end of the coverslip and drawn through using filter paper (above). Water can be drawn through in the same way to remove excess stain.

Staining Techniques

Some commonly used stains		
Stain	**Final color**	**Used for**
Iodine solution	blue-black	Starch
Crystal violet	purple	Gram staining
Aniline sulfate	yellow	lignin
Methylene blue	blue	Nuclei

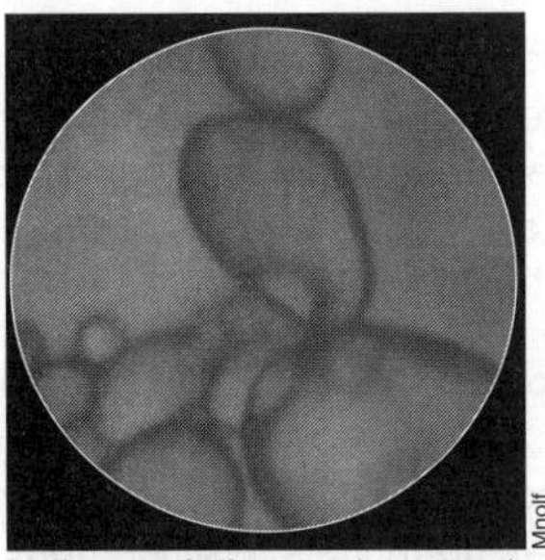

Iodine solution stains starch containing organelles, such as **potato amyloplasts**, blue-black.

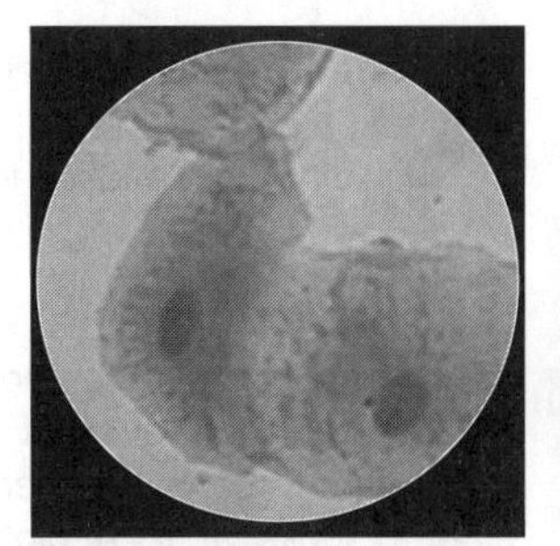

Methylene blue is a commonly used temporary stain for animal cells. It makes **nuclei** more visible

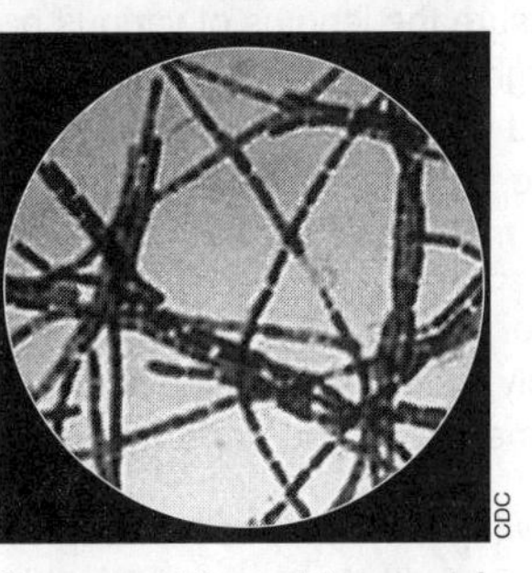

The gram stain contains **crystal violet**, which binds strongly to the peptidoglycan component in the cell walls of **gram positive bacteria** turning them purple.

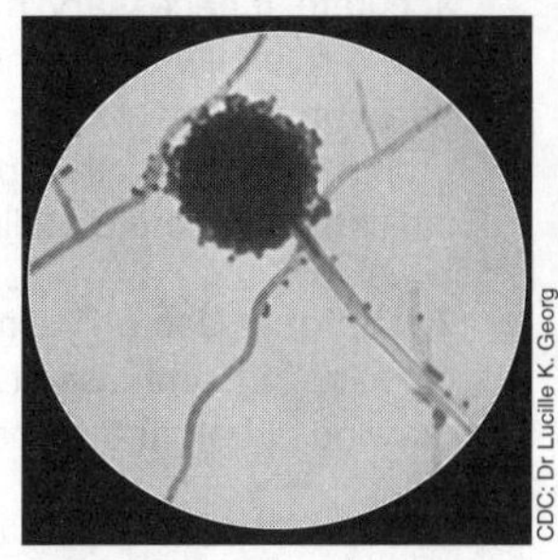

Viable (or vital) **stains** do not immediately harm living cells. **Trypan blue** distinguishes living and dead cells, and is used to study fungal hyphae (above).

1. Why are many microscope samples wet mounted prior to viewing under a microscope? ______________________

____

2. What is the main purpose of using a stain? ______________________

____

____

3. What is the difference between a **viable** and **non-viable** stain? ______________________

____

4. Identify a stain that would be appropriate for improving identification of the following:

(a) Fungal hyphae: ______________________ (d) Lignin in a plant root section: ______________________

(b) Starch in potato cells: ______________________ (e) Nuclei in cheek cells: ______________________

(c) Cell wall of bacteria: ______________________

ISBN: 978-1-877462-96-2

Biological Drawings

Many observational studies made using microscopes will require you to make accurate representations of what you see. Although some observations will be made using relatively low power (X40) microscopy, some histological preparations require higher magnifications to identify the finer structure of the tissue. Tissue sections will usually be provided as longitudinal (LS) or traverse sections (TS). When you have access to both TS and LS images from the same specimen it is also possible to visualize the three dimensional shape of the structure under view. Observational drawing from a microscope is a skill that must be developed. It requires **relaxed viewing** (right) in which the image is viewed with one eye, while the other eye attends to the drawing being made. Attention should be given to the symmetry and proportions of the structure, accurate labeling, statement of magnification and sectioning, and stain used, if this is appropriate. In this activity, you will practise the skills required to translate what is viewed into a good biological drawing.

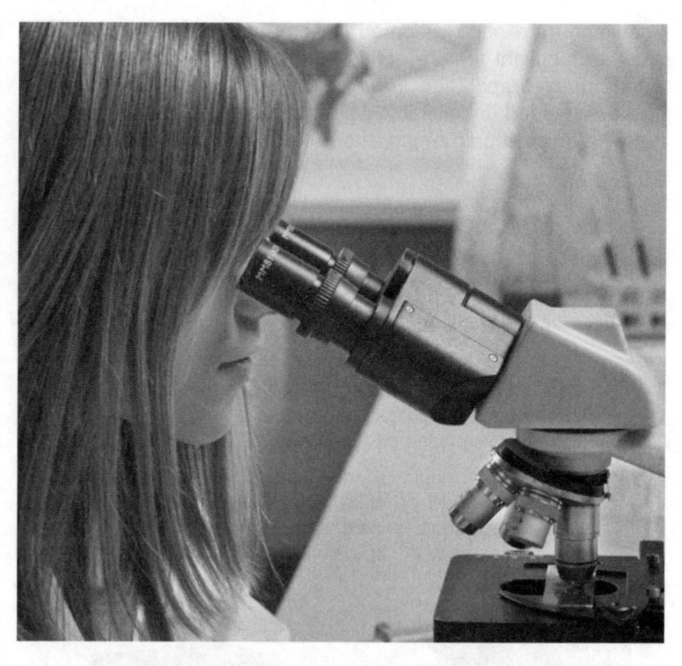

1. **Materials**: Use clear pencil lines on good quality paper. You will need a sharp HB pencil and a good quality eraser.
2. **Size and positioning**: Center your diagram on the page, not in a corner. This will leave room for labels. The drawing should be large enough to easily represent all the details you see without crowding. Show only as much as is necessary for an understanding of the structure.
3. **Accuracy**: Your drawing should be a complete, accurate representation of what you have observed, and should communicate your understanding of the material to anyone who looks at it. A biological drawing is distinct from a diagram, which is idealized and may contain more structure than can be seen in one section. Proportions should be accurate. If necessary, measure the lengths of various parts with a ruler. If viewing through a microscope, estimate them as a proportion of the field of view, then translate these proportions onto the page. When drawing shapes that indicate an discrete outline, make sure the line is complete.
4. **Technique**: Use only simple, narrow lines. Represent depth by stippling and use it only when it is essential to your drawing. Look at the specimen while you are drawing it.
6. **Labels**: All parts of your drawing must be labelled accurately. Labeling lines should be drawn with a ruler and should not cross. Where possible, keep label lines vertical or horizontal.

Label the drawing with an explanatory **title**, identifying the subject, **magnification** or a **scale** to indicate size, names of structures, and any movements you see in living specimens.

Remember that drawings are intended as a record and as a means of encouraging close observation; artistic ability is not necessary. Before you turn in a drawing, ask yourself if you know what every line represents. If you do not, look more closely at the material.

Draw what you see, not what you think you see!

Examples of acceptable biological drawings: The diagrams below show two acceptable biological drawings. The left shows a whole organism and its size is indicated by a scale. The right shows plant tissue. It is not necessary to show many cells even though your view through the microscope may show them. You need enough to show their structure and how they are arranged. Scale is indicated by stating how many times larger it has been drawn. Do not confuse this with what magnification it was viewed at under the microscope. **T.S.** indicates a *transverse section.*

Cyclopoid copepod

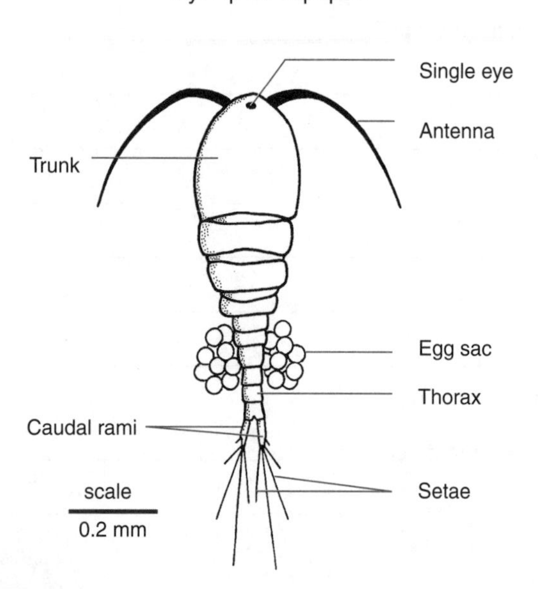

Collenchyma T.S. from <u>Helianthus</u> stem
Magnification x 450

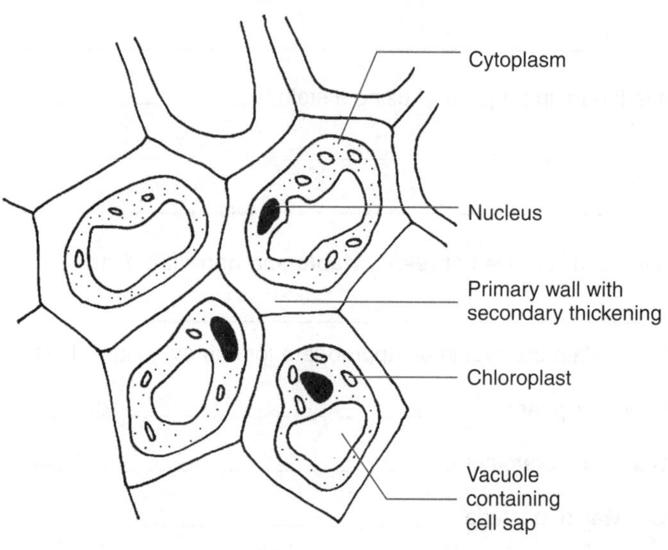

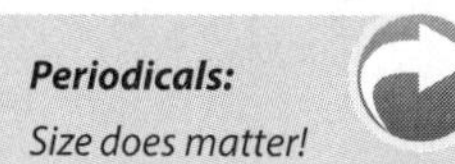

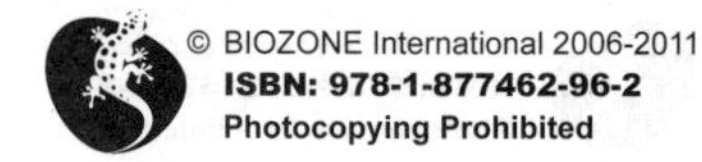

ISBN: 978-1-877462-96-2

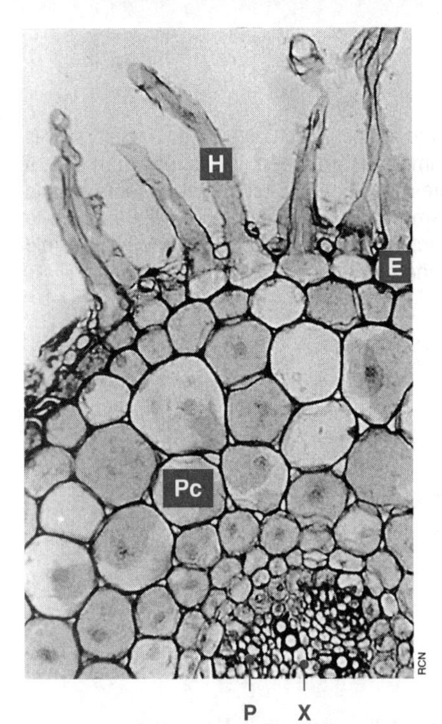

Specimen used for drawing

The photograph above is a light microscope view of a stained transverse section (cross section) of a root from a *Ranunculus* (buttercup) plant. It shows the arrangement of the different tissues in the root. The vascular bundle is at the center of the root, with the larger, central xylem vessels (**X**) and smaller phloem vessels (**P**) grouped around them. The root hair cells (**H**) are arranged on the external surface and form part of the epidermal layer (**E**). Parenchyma cells (**Pc**) make up the bulk of the root's mass. The distance from point **X** to point **E** on the photograph (above) is about 0.15 mm (150 µm).

An Unacceptable Biological Drawing

The diagram below is an example of how *not* to produce a biological drawing; it is based on the photograph to the left. There are many aspects of the drawing that are unacceptable. The exercise below asks you to identify the errors in this student's attempt.

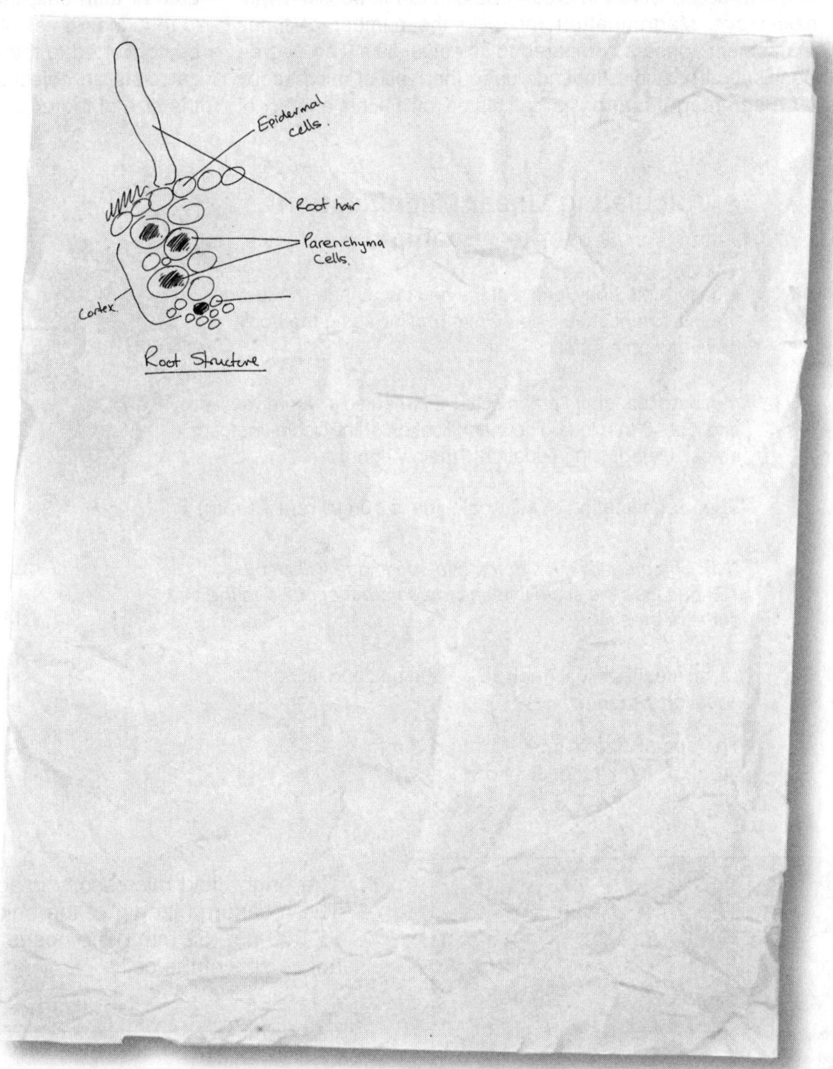

1. Identify and describe eight unacceptable features of the student's biological diagram above:

(a) ____________________

(b) ____________________

(c) ____________________

(d) ____________________

(e) ____________________

(f) ____________________

(g) ____________________

(h) ____________________

2. In the remaining space next to the 'poor example' (above) or on a blank piece of refill paper, attempt your own version of a biological drawing for the same material, based on the photograph above. Make a point of correcting all of the errors that you have identified in the sample student's attempt.

3. Explain why accurate biological drawings are more valuable to a scientific investigation than an 'artistic' approach:

____

____

____

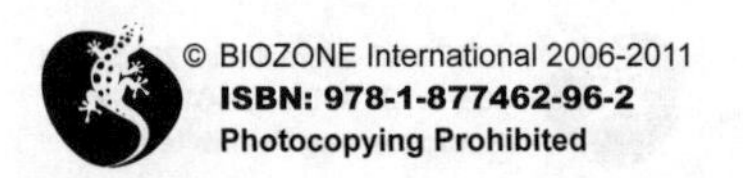

ISBN: 978-1-877462-96-2

Calculating Linear Magnification

Microscopes produce an enlarged (magnified) image of an object allowing it to be observed in greater detail than is possible with the naked eye. **Magnification** refers to the number of times larger an object appears compared to its actual size. The degree of magnification possible depends upon the type of microscopy used. **Linear magnification** is calculated by taking a ratio of the image height to the object's actual height. If this ratio is greater than one, the image is enlarged, if it is less than one, it is reduced. To calculate magnification, all measurements should be converted to the same units. Most often, you will be asked to calculate an object's actual size, in which case you will be told the size of the object and given the magnification.

Calculating Linear Magnification: A Worked Example

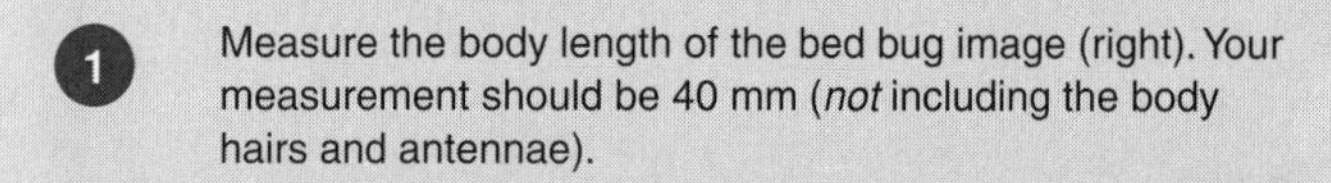

1. Measure the body length of the bed bug image (right). Your measurement should be 40 mm (*not* including the body hairs and antennae).

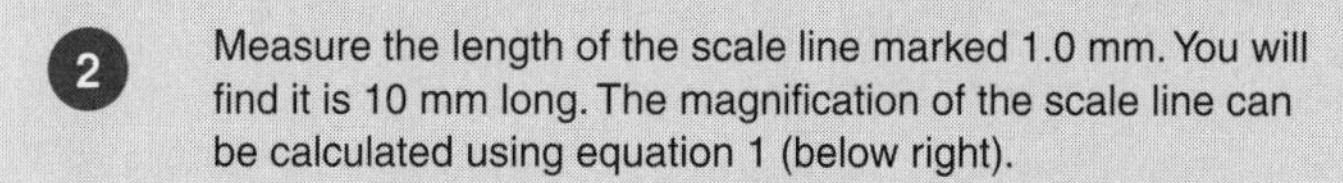

2. Measure the length of the scale line marked 1.0 mm. You will find it is 10 mm long. The magnification of the scale line can be calculated using equation 1 (below right).

   The magnification of the scale line is **10** (10 mm / 1 mm)

   **NB: The magnification of the bed bug image will also be 10x because the scale line and image are magnified to the same degree.*

3. Calculate the actual (real) size of the bed bug using equation 2 (right):

   The actual size of the bed bug is **4 mm**
   (40 mm / 10 x magnification)

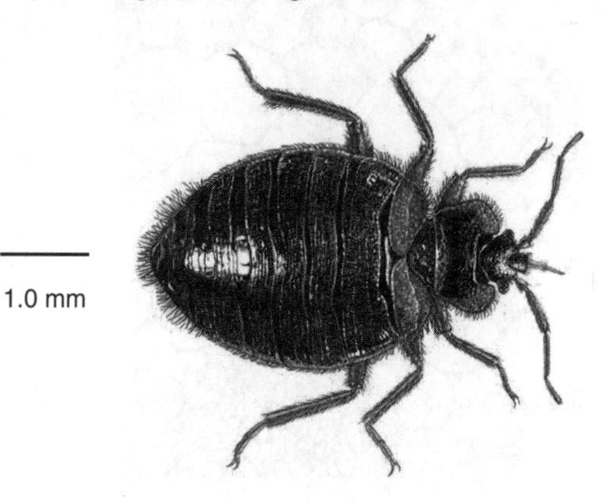

Microscopy Equations

1. $\text{Magnification} = \dfrac{\text{size of the image}}{\text{actual size of object}}$

2. $\text{Actual object size} = \dfrac{\text{size of the image}}{\text{magnification}}$

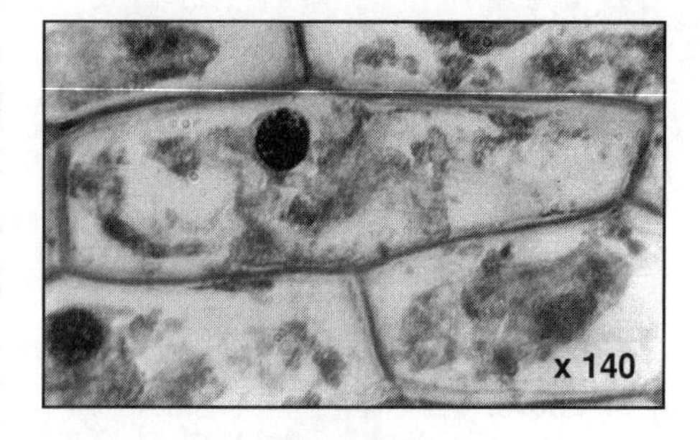

1. The bright field microscopy image on the left is of onion epidermal cells. The measured length of the onion cell in the center of the photograph is 52 000 µm (52 mm). The image has been magnified 140 x. Calculate the actual size of the cell:

____

____

____

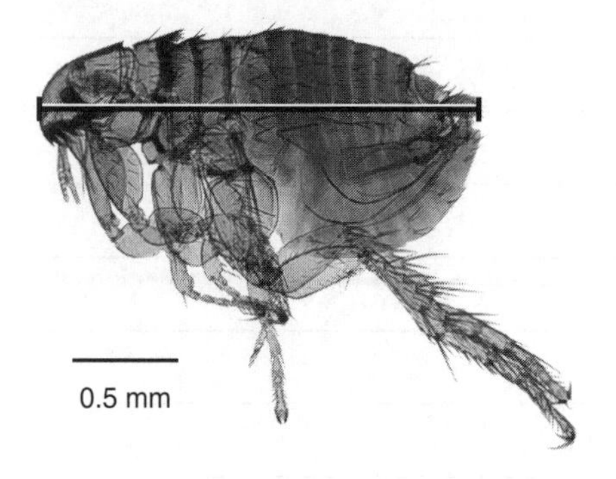

2. The image of the flea (left) has been captured using light microscopy.

   (a) Calculate the magnification using the scale line on the image:

   ____

   ____

   ____

   (b) The body length of the flea is indicated by a line. Measure along the line and calculate the actual length of the flea:

   ____

   ____

   ____

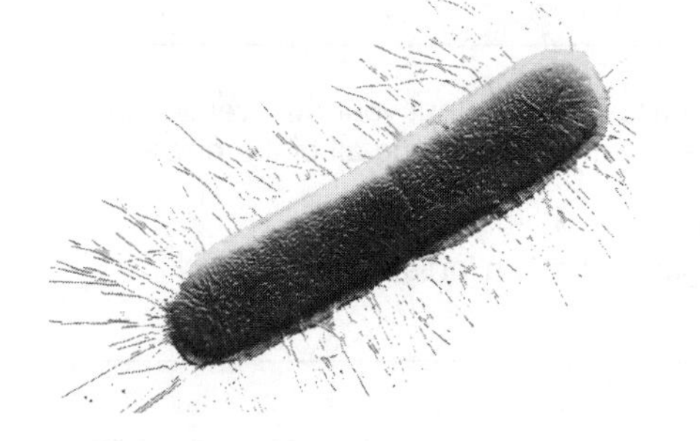

3. The image size of the *E.coli* cell (left) is 43 mm, and its actual size is 2 µm. Using this information, calculate the magnification of the image:

____

____

____

Related activities: *Biological Drawings*

Periodicals:
Size does matter!

ISBN: 978-1-877462-96-2

Qualitative Practical Work

Biological drawings should include as much detail as you need to distinguish different structures and types of tissue, but avoid unnecessary detail. Tissue preparations are rarely neat and tidy and there may be areas where you cannot see detail and where cells will appear to overlie one another. In these cases you will need to infer detail where possible from adjacent cells. Avoid shading as this can smudge and obscure detail. Labeling involves interpretation based on your knowledge and labels should be away from the drawing with label lines pointing to the structures identified. Add a title and any details of the image such as magnification. In this activity, you will practise the skills required to translate what is viewed into a good biological drawing.

__Above__: Use relaxed viewing when drawing at the microscope. Use one eye (the left for right handers) to view and the right eye to view and direct your drawing.

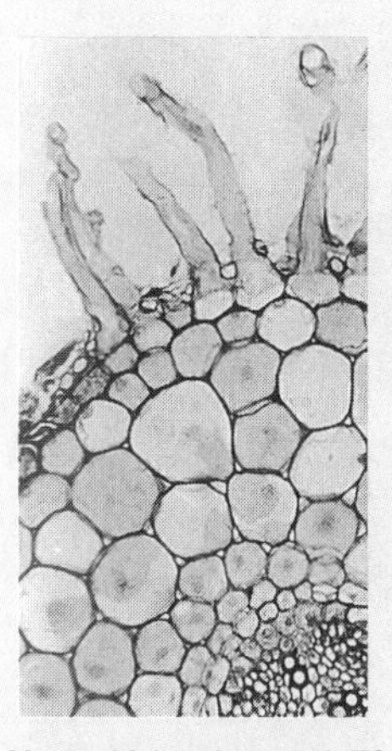

Above: Light micrograph TS through a *Ranunculus* root.
Left: Use one eye (the left for right handers) to view and the right eye to view and direct your drawing.

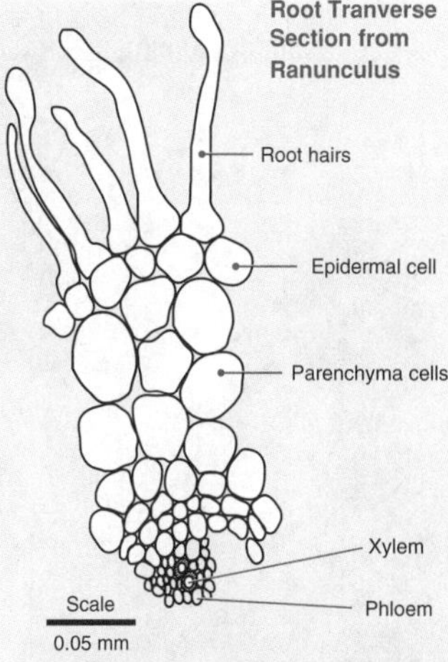

A biological drawing of the same section. A biological drawing is different from a diagram, which is idealised and may contain more structure than can be seen in one section.

TASK

Complete the biological drawing of a cross section through a dicot leaf (below). Use the example above of the *Ranunculus* root as a guide to the detail required in your drawing

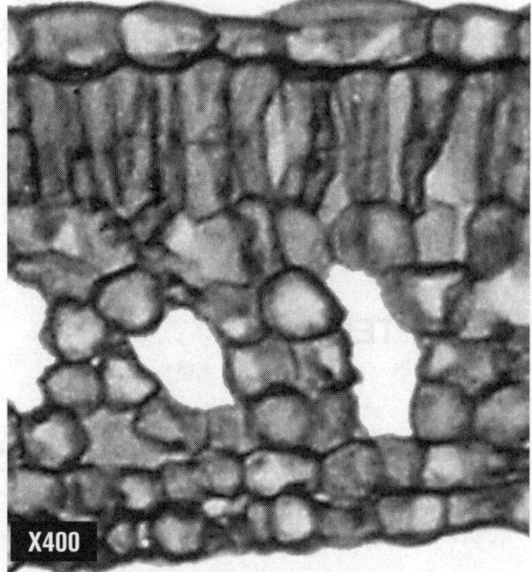

Light micrograph of a cross section through a leaf.

ISBN: 978-1-877462-96-2

Periodicals:
Size does matter!

Related activities: *Biological Drawings*
Weblinks: *Scientific Drawings for Biological Courses*

Electron Microscopes

Electron microscopes (EMs) use a beam of electrons, instead of light, to produce an image. The higher resolution of EMs is due to the shorter wavelengths of electrons. There are two basic types of electron microscope: **scanning electron microscopes** (SEM) and **transmission electron microscopes** (TEM). In SEMs, the electrons are bounced off the surface of an object to produce detailed images of the external appearance. TEMs produce very clear images of specially prepared thin sections.

Transmission Electron Microscope (TEM)

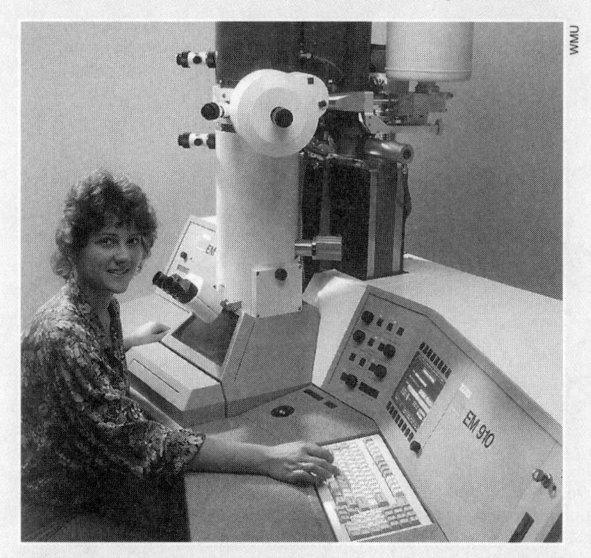

The transmission electron microscope is used to view extremely thin sections of material. Electrons pass through the specimen and are scattered. Magnetic lenses focus the image onto a fluorescent screen or photographic plate. The sections are so thin that they have to be prepared with a special machine, called an ultramicrotome, that can cut wafers to just 30 thousandths of a millimetre thick. It can magnify several hundred thousand times.

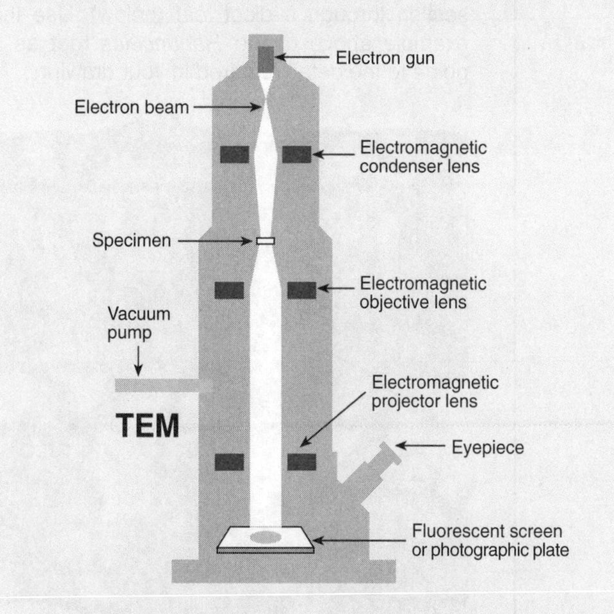

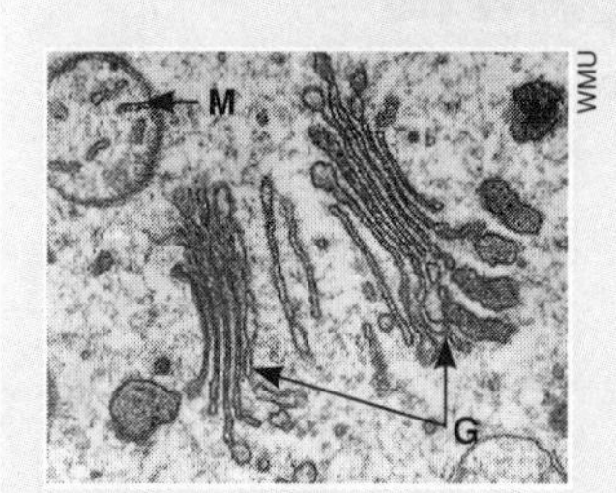

TEM photo showing the Golgi (**G**) and a mitochondrion (**M**).

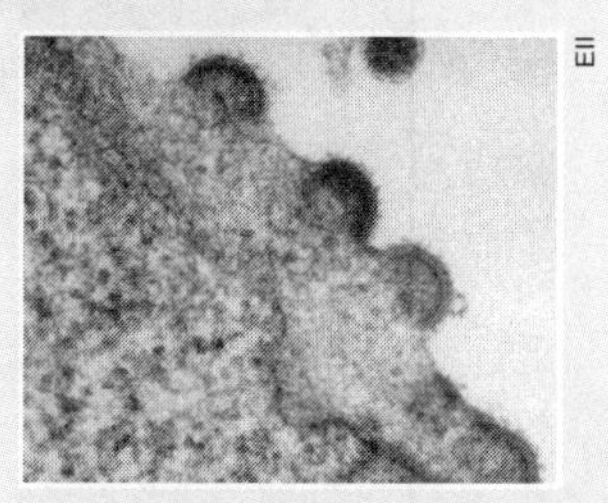

Three HIV viruses budding out of a human lymphocyte (TEM).

Scanning Electron Microscope (SEM)

The scanning electron microscope scans a sample with a beam of primary electrons that knock electrons from its surface. These secondary electrons are picked up by a collector, amplified, and transmitted onto a viewing screen or photographic plate, producing a superb 3-D image. A microscope of this power can easily obtain clear pictures of organisms as small as bacteria and viruses. The image produced is of the outside surface only.

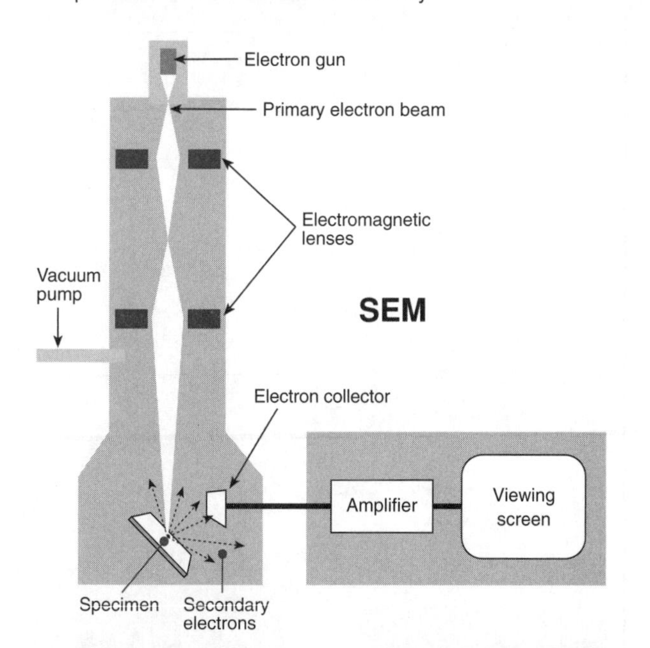

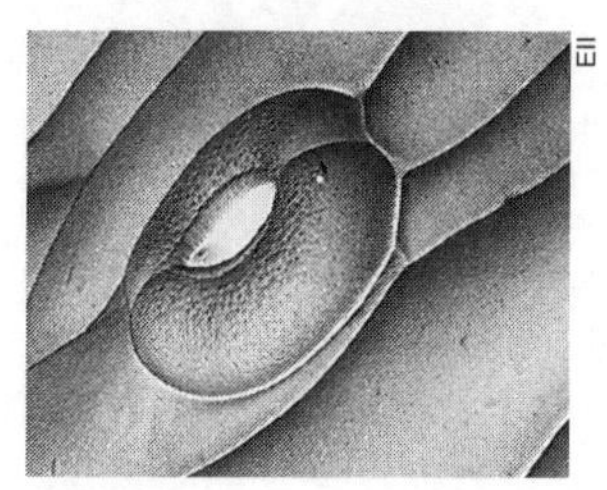

SEM photo of stoma and epidermal cells on the upper surface of a leaf.

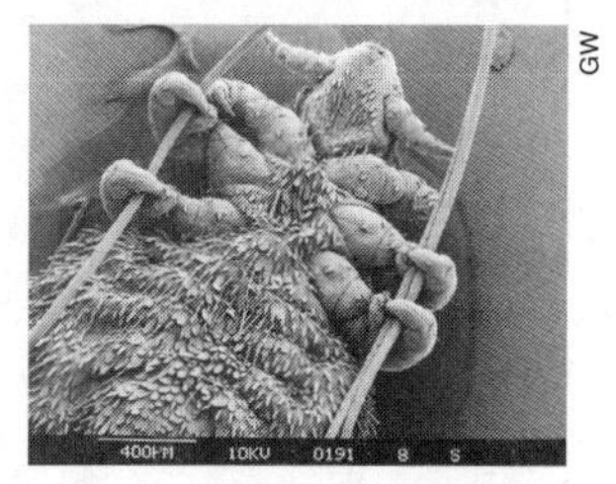

Image of hair louse clinging to two hairs on a Hooker's sealion (SEM).

ISBN: 978-1-877462-96-2

	Light Microscope	Transmission Electron Microscope (TEM)	Scanning Electron Microscope (SEM)
Radiation source:	light	electrons	electrons
Wavelength:	400-700 nm	0.005 nm	0.005 nm
Lenses:	glass	electromagnetic	electromagnetic
Specimen:	living or non-living supported on glass slide	non-living supported on a small copper grid in a vacuum	non-living supported on a metal disc in a vacuum
Maximum resolution:	200 nm	1 nm	10 nm
Maximum magnification:	1500 x	250 000 x	100 000 x
Stains:	colored dyes	impregnated with heavy metals	coated with carbon or gold
Type of image:	colored	monochrome (black & white)	monochrome (black & white)

1. Explain why electron microscopes are able to resolve much greater detail than a light microscope:

____

____

____

2. Describe two typical applications for each of the following types of microscope:

(a) Transmission electron microscope (TEM): _______________

____

(b) Scanning electron microscope (SEM): _______________

____

(c) Compound light microscope (thin section): _______________

____

(d) Dissecting microscope: _______________

____

3. Identify which type of electron microscope (SEM or TEM) or optical microscope (compound light microscope or dissecting) was used to produce each of the images in the photos below (A-H):

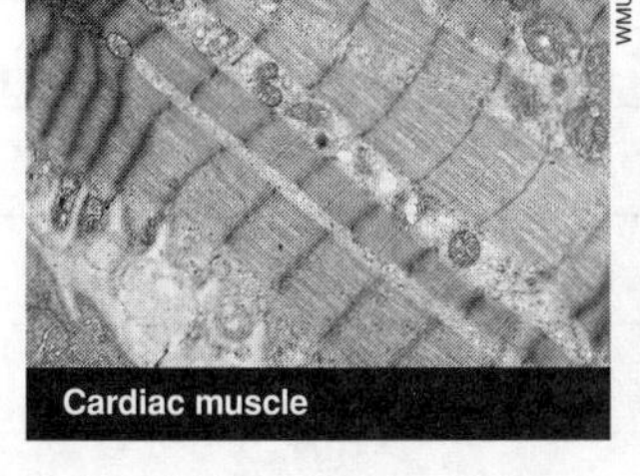

Cardiac muscle

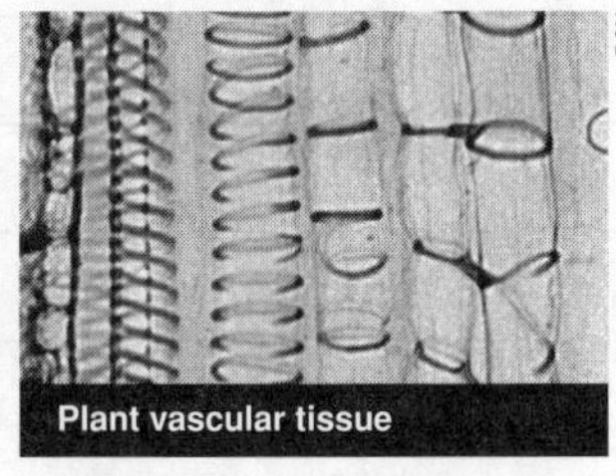

Plant vascular tissue

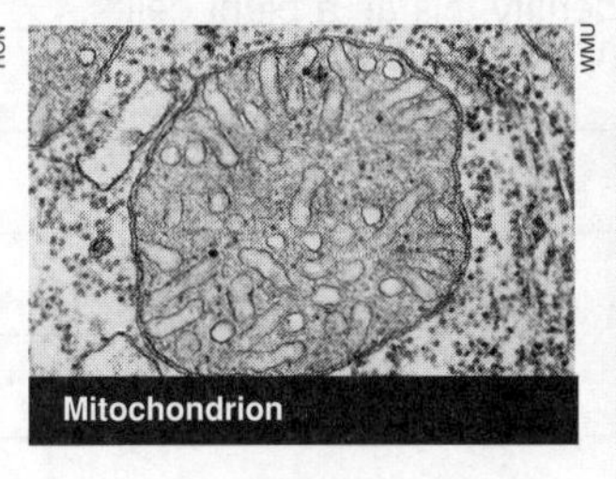

Mitochondrion

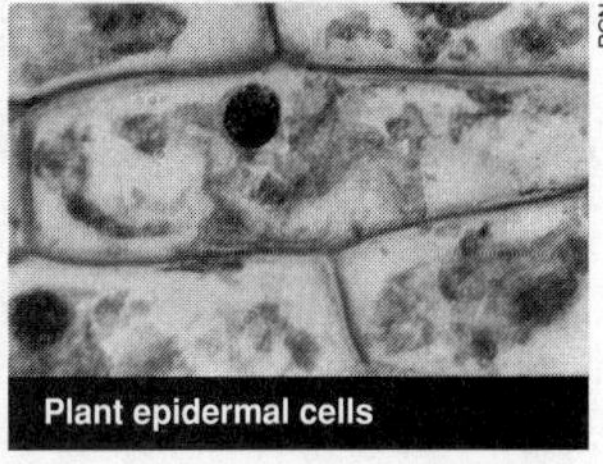

Plant epidermal cells

A _______________ B _______________ C _______________ D _______________

Head louse

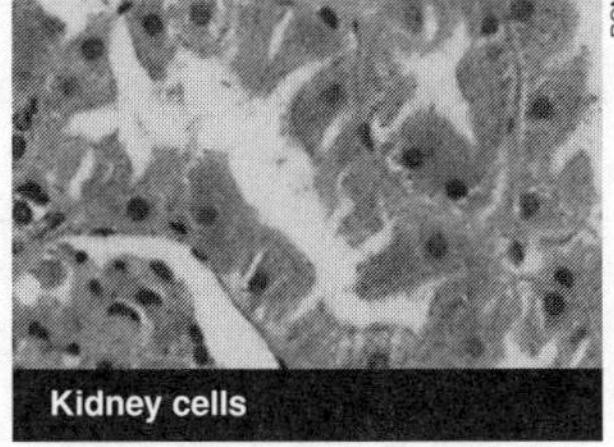

Kidney cells

Alderfly larva

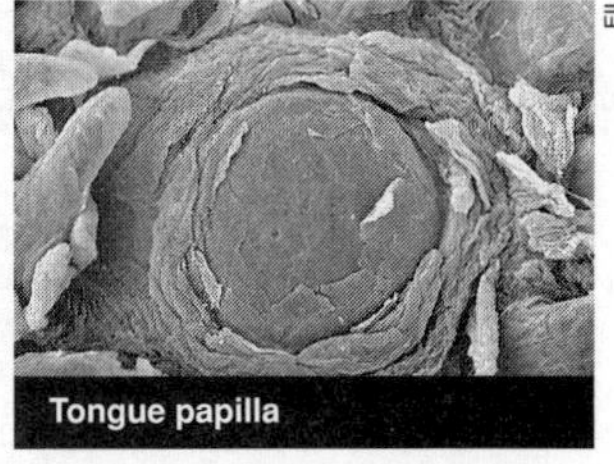

Tongue papilla

E _______________ F _______________ G _______________ H _______________

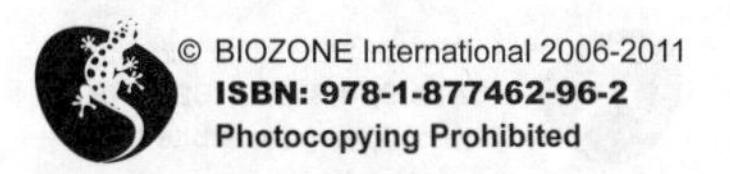

ISBN: 978-1-877462-96-2

Periodicals:
Scanning electron microscopy

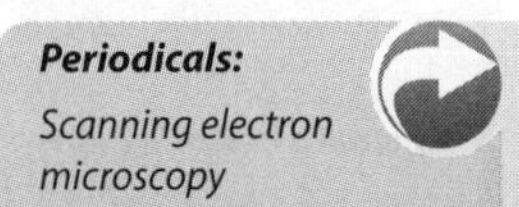

Identifying Structures in a Plant Cell

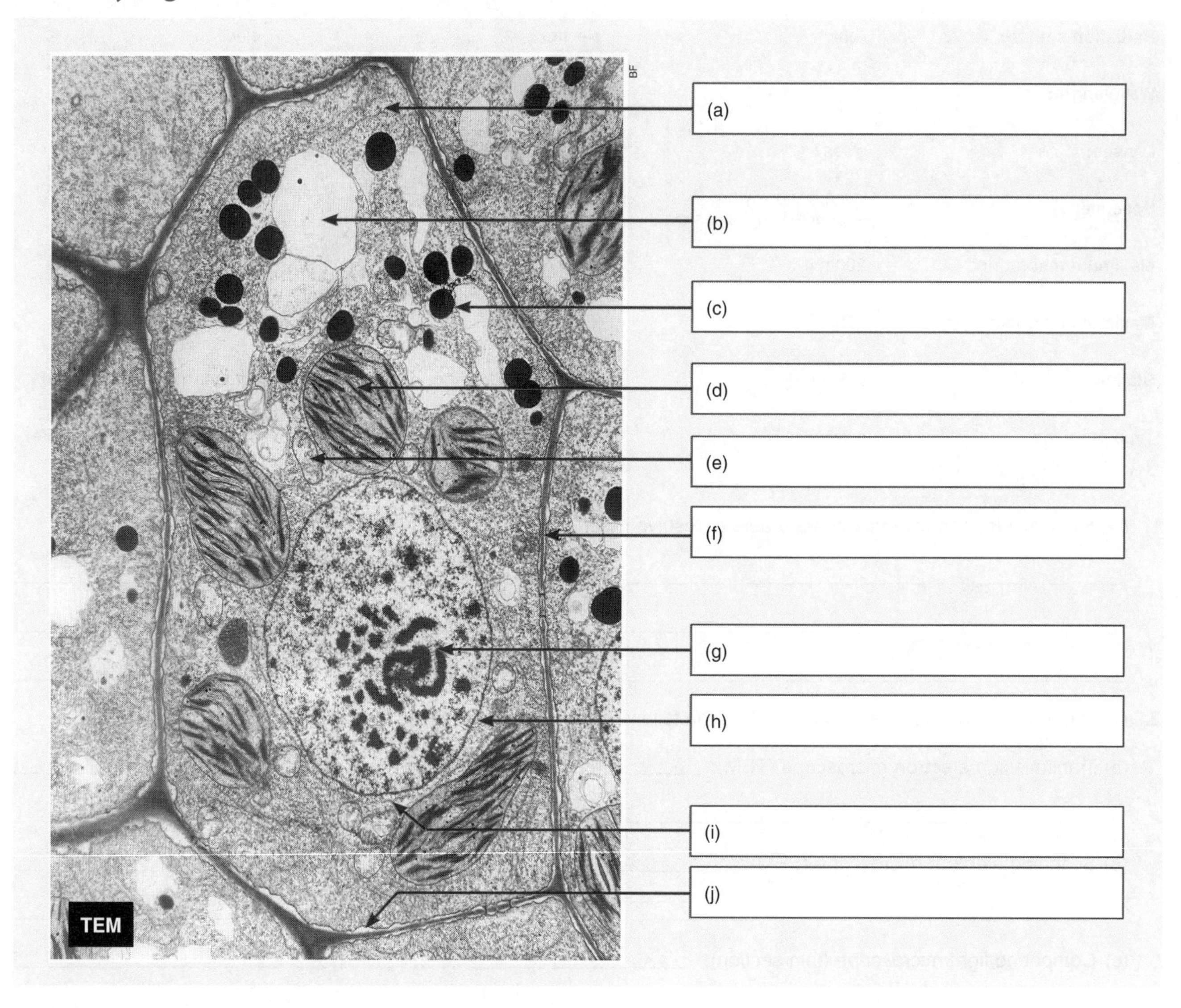

1. Identify and label the ten structures in the cell above using the following list of terms: *nuclear membrane, cytoplasm, endoplasmic reticulum, mitochondrion, starch granules, chromosome, vacuole, plasma membrane, cell wall, chloroplast*

2. State how many cells, or parts of cells, are visible in the electron micrograph above: __________

3. Describe the features that identify this as a plant cell: __________

4. (a) Explain where cytoplasm is found in the cell: __________

   (b) Describe what cytoplasm is made up of: __________

5. Describe two structures, pictured in the cell above, that are associated with storage:

   (a) __________

   (b) __________

ISBN: 978-1-877462-96-2

Related activities: *Interpreting Electron Micrographs*

Identifying Structures in an Animal Cell

Our current knowledge of cell ultrastructure has been made possible by the advent of electron microscopy. Transmission electron microscopy is the most frequently used technique for viewing cellular organelles. When viewing TEMs, the cellular organelles may appear to be quite different depending on whether they are in transverse or longitudinal section.

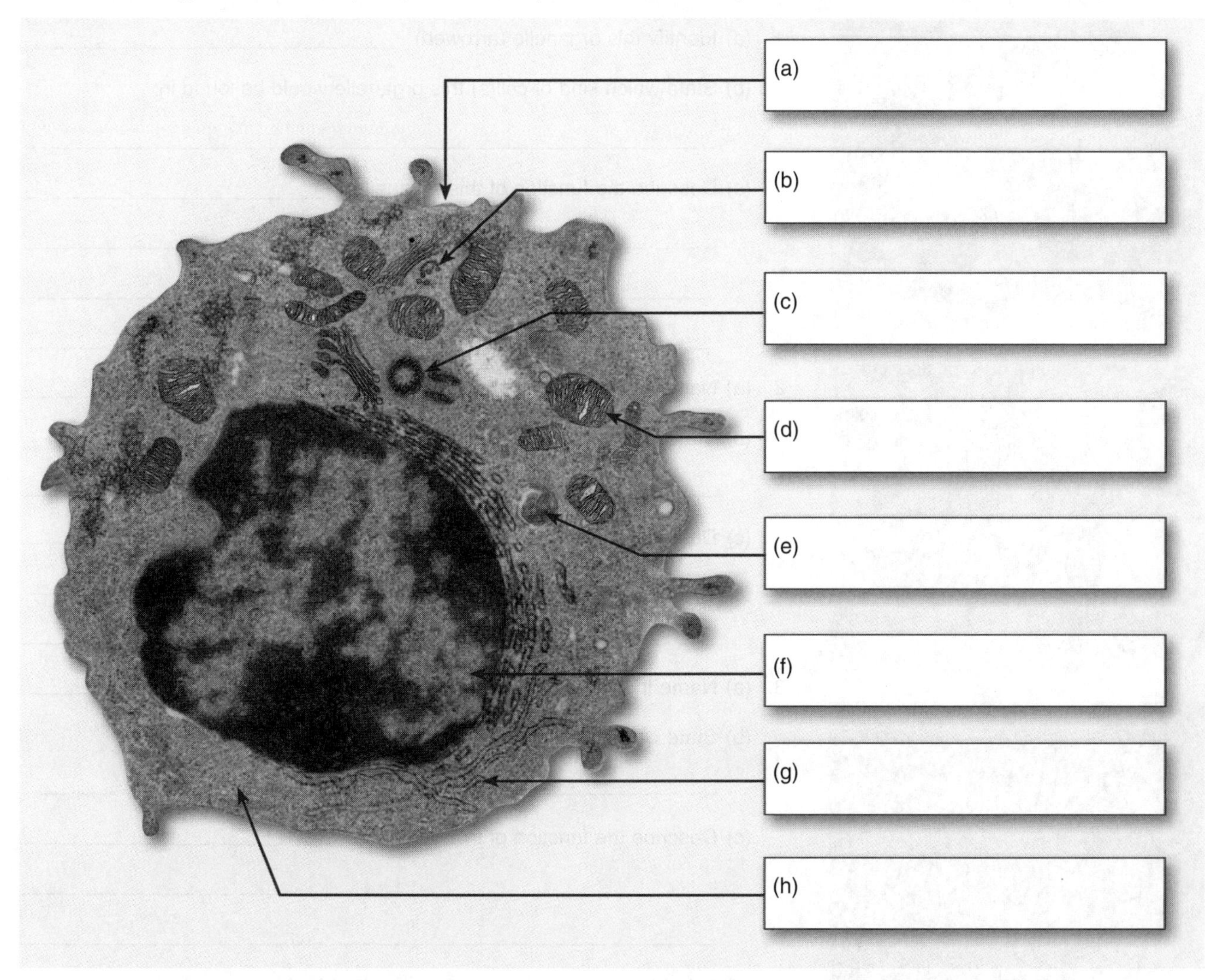

1. Identify and label the structures in the cell above using the following list of terms: *cytoplasm, plasma membrane, rough endoplasmic reticulum, mitochondrion, nucleus, centriole, Golgi apparatus, lysosome*

2. In the electron micrograph above, identify which of the organelles are shown in both transverse and longitudinal section:

3. Plants lack any of the mobile phagocytic cells typical of animals. Explain why this is the case:

4. The animal cell pictured above is a lymphocyte. Describe the features that suggest to you that:

   (a) It has a role in producing and secreting proteins:

   (b) It is metabolically very active:

5. Describe the features of the lymphocyte cell above that identify it as an eukaryotic cell:

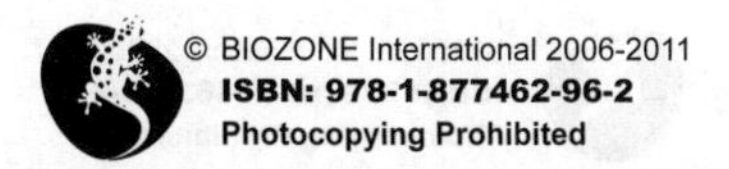

ISBN: 978-1-877462-96-2

Interpreting Electron Micrographs

The photographs below were taken using a **transmission electron microscope** (TEM). They show some of the cell organelles in great detail. Remember that these photos are showing only **parts of cells, not whole cells**. Some of the photographs show more than one type of organelle. The questions refer to the main organelle in the center of the photo.

EII

1. (a) Identify this organelle (arrowed): ______________________

   (b) State which kind of cell(s) this organelle would be found in:

   ____

   (c) Describe the function of this organelle: ______________________

   ____

   ____

   ____

WMU

2. (a) Name this organelle (arrowed): ______________________

   (b) State which kind of cell(s) this organelle would be found in:

   ____

   (c) Describe the function of this organelle: ______________________

   ____

   ____

WMU

3. (a) Name the large, circular organelle: ______________________

   (b) State which kind of cell(s) this organelle would be found in:

   ____

   (c) Describe the function of this organelle: ______________________

   ____

   ____

   (d) Label **two** regions that can be seen **inside** this organelle.

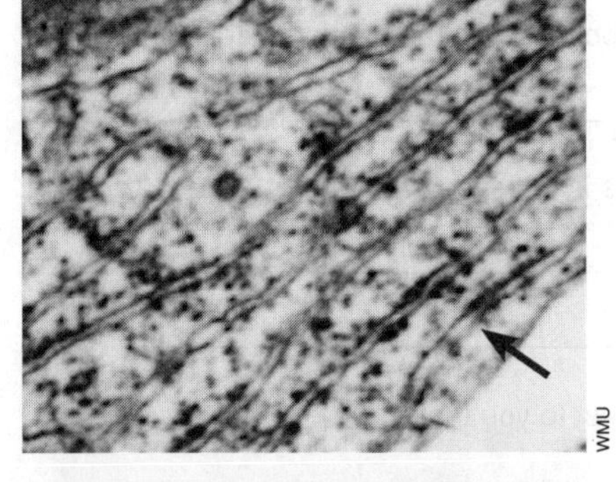

WMU

4. (a) Name and label the ribbon-like organelle in this photograph (arrowed):

   ____

   (b) State which kind of cell(s) this organelle is found in:

   ____

   (c) Describe the function of these organelles: ______________________

   ____

   (d) Name the dark 'blobs' attached to the organelle you have labelled:

   ____

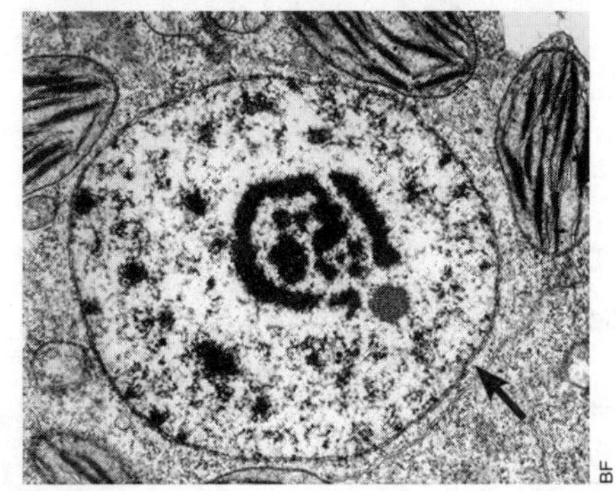

BF

5. (a) Name this large circular structure (arrowed): ______________________

   (b) State which kind of cell(s) this structure would be found in:

   ____

   (c) Describe the function of this structure: ______________________

   ____

   (d) Label three features relating to this structure in the photograph.

ISBN: 978-1-877462-96-2

Biochemical Tests

Biochemical tests are used to detect the presence of molecules such as lipids, proteins, and carbohydrates (sugars and starch). For tests where the presence of a substance is indicated by a color change, **colorimetric analysis** can be used to quantify the concentration of the substance present. To analyze a mix of substances, a technique such as **chromatography** is required. For example, a positive Benedict's test indicates the presence of reducing sugar(s), but chromatography will distinguish different sugars (e.g. fructose and glucose) and colorimetry can be used to estimate sugar concentration.

Simple Food Tests

Proteins: The Biuret Test

Reagent:	Biuret solution.
Procedure:	A sample is added to biuret solution and gently heated.
Positive result:	Solution turns from blue to lilac.

Starch: The Iodine Test

Reagent:	Iodine.
Procedure:	Iodine solution is added to the sample.
Positive result:	Blue-black staining occurs.

Lipids: The Emulsion Test

Reagent:	Ethanol.
Procedure:	The sample is shaken with ethanol. After settling, the liquid portion is distilled and mixed with water.
Positive result:	The solution turns into a cloudy-white emulsion of suspended lipid molecules.

Sugars: The Benedict's Test

Reagent:	Benedict's solution.
Procedure:	Non reducing sugars: The sample is boiled with dilute hydrochloric acid (acid hydrolysis), then cooled and neutralized. A test for reducing sugars is then performed. Reducing sugar: Benedict's solution is added, and the sample is placed in a water bath.
Positive result:	Solution turns from blue to orange to red-brown.

A Qualitative Test For Reducing Sugar

To determine whether this muffin contains any reducing sugars (e.g. glucose), the Benedict's test for reducing sugar is carried out.

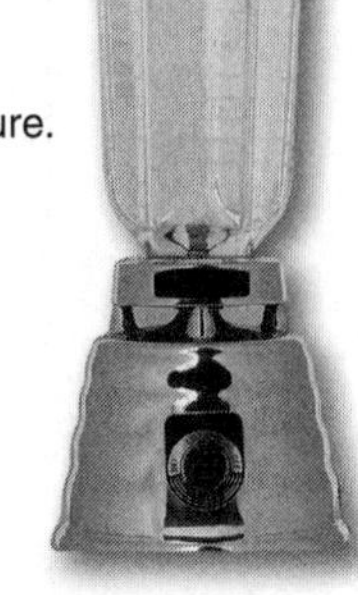

The muffin is placed in a blender with some water and mixed until it forms an homogenous (uniform) mixture.

2 -3 mL of the muffin mixture is placed into a test tube with 1 mL of Benedict's solution. The tubes are heated for 4 -10 minutes.

The intensity of the color depends on the concentration of glucose present in the sample. The darker the color, the more glucose is present. A **colorimetric analysis** enables the amount of glucose present to be quantified (see the following activity).

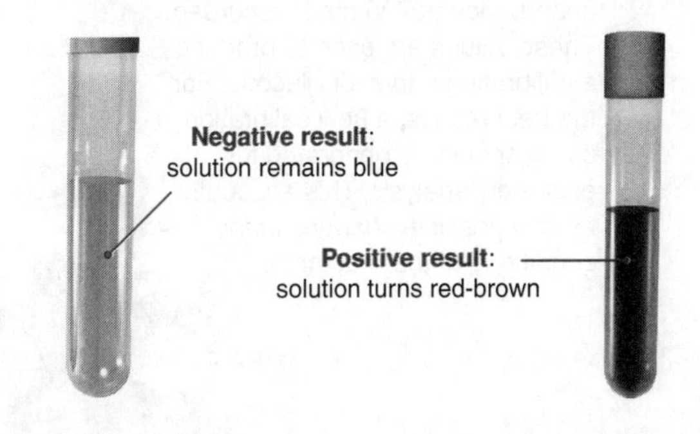

1. Explain why lipids must be mixed in ethanol before they will form an emulsion in water:

2. What is the purpose of the acid hydrolysis step when testing for non-reducing sugars with Benedict's reagent?

3. Explain why the emulsion of lipids, ethanol, and water appears cloudy:

ISBN: 978-1-877462-96-2

Related activities: *Colorimetry, Paper Chromatography*

Colorimetry

Colorimetric analysis is a simple quantitative technique used to determine the concentration of a specific substance in a solution. A specific reagent (e.g. Benedict's) is added to the test solution where it reacts with the substance of interest to produce a color. After an appropriate reaction time, the samples are placed in a **colorimeter**, which measures the solution's absorbance at a specific wavelength. A dilution series can be used to produce a **calibration curve**, which can then be used to quantify that substance in samples of unknown concentration. This is illustrated from glucose in the example below.

❶ Prepare glucose standards

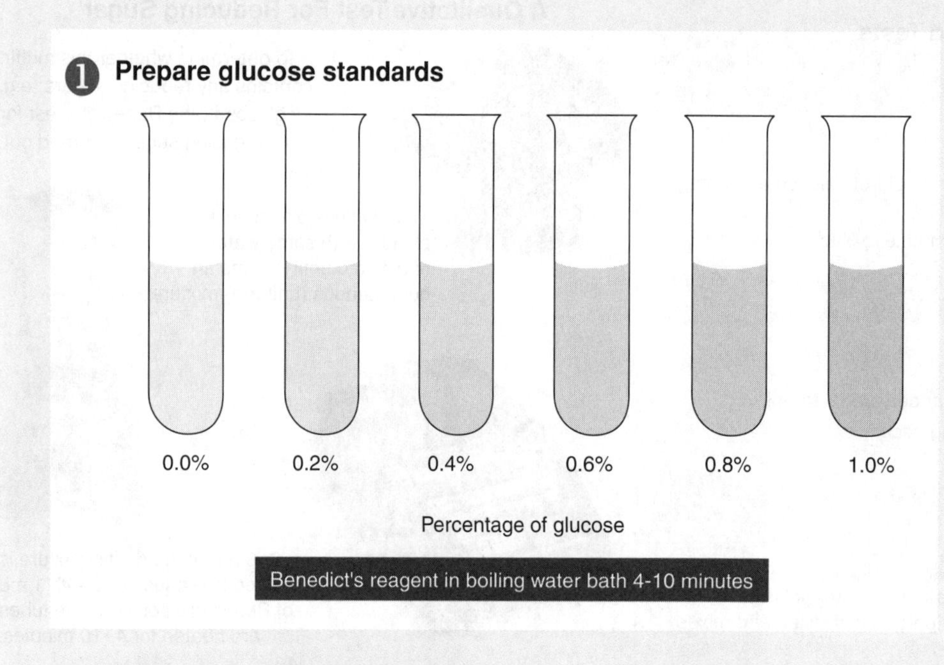

Solutions containing a range of known glucose concentrations are prepared in test tubes. Benedict's reagent is added, and the test tubes are heated in a boiling waterbath for 4-10 minutes. At the end of the reaction time, samples containing glucose will have undergone a color change. The samples are cooled, then filtered or centrifuged to remove suspended particles.

❷ Produce the calibration curve

To produce a calibration curve, the prepared glucose standards are placed in a colorimeter, and their absorbance at 735 nm is recorded. These values are used to produce a calibration curve for glucose. For the best results, a new calibration curve should be generated for each new analysis. This accounts for any possible changes in the conditions of the reactants.

Glucose

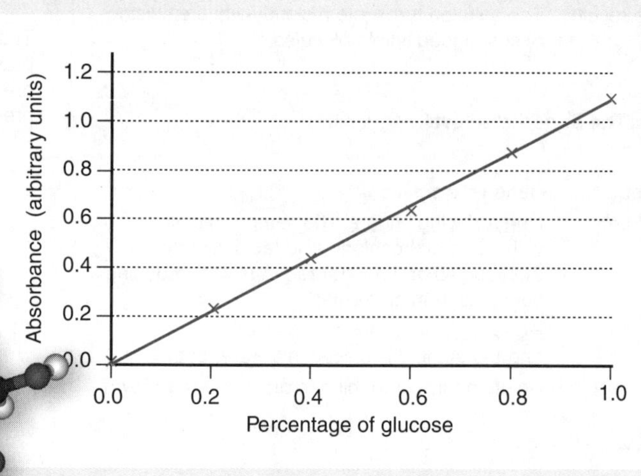

1. (a) How could you quantify the amount of glucose in a range of commercially available glucose drinks?

   (b) What would you do if the absorbance values you obtained for most of your 'unknowns' were outside the range of your calibration curve?

2. Why is it important to remove suspended solids from a sample before measuring its absorbance?

Related activities: *Biochemical Tests*

ISBN: 978-1-877462-96-2

Differential Centrifugation

Differential centrifugation (also called cell fractionation) is a technique used to extract organelles from cells so that they can be studied. The aim is to extract undamaged intact organelles. Samples must be kept very cool so that metabolism is slowed and self digestion of the organelles is prevented. The samples must also be kept in a buffered, isotonic solution so that the organelles do not change volume and the enzymes are not denatured by changes in pH.

Differential Centrifugation

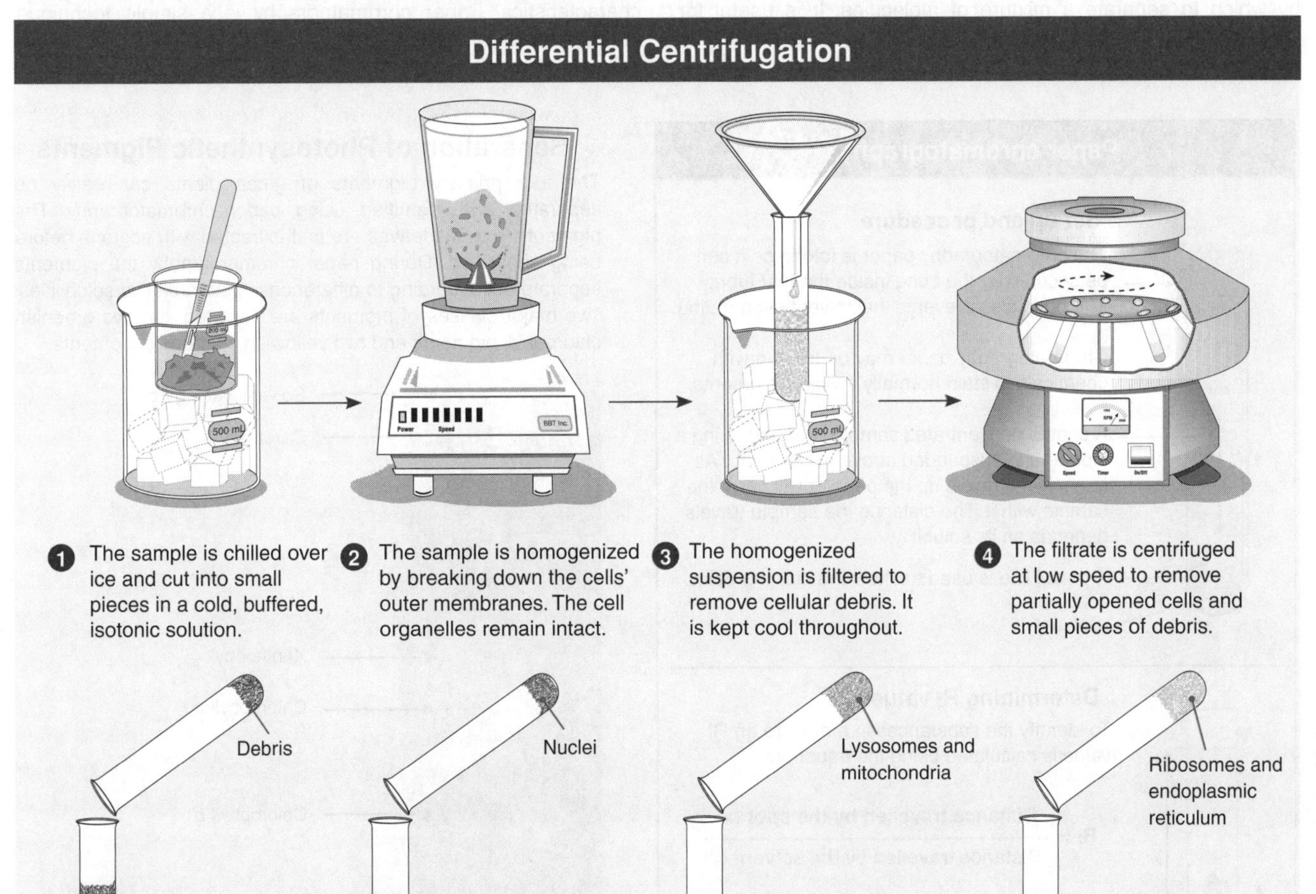

1. The sample is chilled over ice and cut into small pieces in a cold, buffered, isotonic solution.
2. The sample is homogenized by breaking down the cells' outer membranes. The cell organelles remain intact.
3. The homogenized suspension is filtered to remove cellular debris. It is kept cool throughout.
4. The filtrate is centrifuged at low speed to remove partially opened cells and small pieces of debris.

Debris — Supernatant used for the next round of centrifugation.

Nuclei — Supernatant used for the next round of centrifugation.

Lysosomes and mitochondria — Supernatant used for the next round of centrifugation.

Ribosomes and endoplasmic reticulum

5. The supernatant containing the organelles is carefully decanted off.
6. The sample is centrifuged at 500-600 *g* for 5-10 minutes then decanted.
7. The sample is centrifuged at 10 000-20 000 *g* for 15-20 minutes then decanted.
8. The sample is centrifuged at 100 000 *g* for 60 minutes then decanted.

NOTE: In centrifugation, the relative centrifugal force (RCF) is expressed as 'g', where g represents the gravitational field strength.

1. Explain why it is possible to separate cell organelles using centrifugation: ______

2. Suggest why the sample is homogenized before centrifugation: ______

3. Explain why the sample must be kept in a solution that is:

(a) Isotonic: ______

(b) Cool: ______

(c) Buffered: ______

4. **Density gradient centrifugation** is another method of cell fractionation. Sucrose is added to the sample, which is then centrifuged at high speed. The organelles will form layers according to their specific densities. Using the information above, label the centrifuge tube on the right with the organelles you would find in each layer.

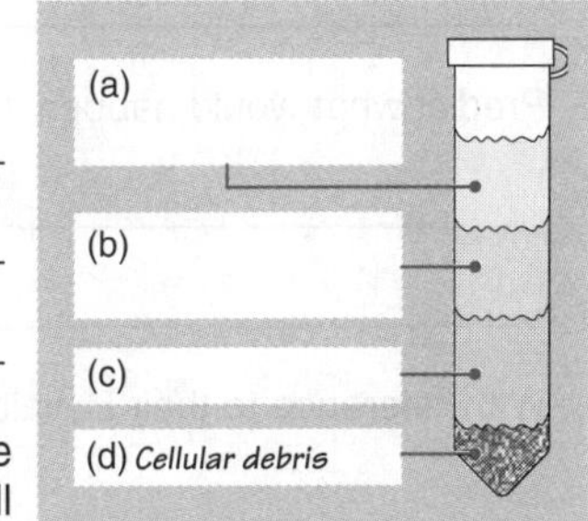

ISBN: 978-1-877462-96-2

Paper Chromatography

There are a number of simple biochemical (so-called food) tests used to detect the presence of certain molecules, but these are limited by being rather crude in terms of the information obtainable. **Chromatography** is a more accurate technique by which to separate a mixture of molecules. It is useful for small samples or to distinguish between specific molecules (e.g. between fructose or glucose). Chromatographic analysis is widely used in the pharmaceutical and food industries for both purification and analysis. It is based on passing a mixture dissolved in a mobile phase (a solvent) through a stationary phase, which separates the molecules according to their specific characteristics. Paper chromatography is a simple technique in which porous paper serves as the stationary phase, and a solvent, either water or ethanol, serves as the mobile phase.

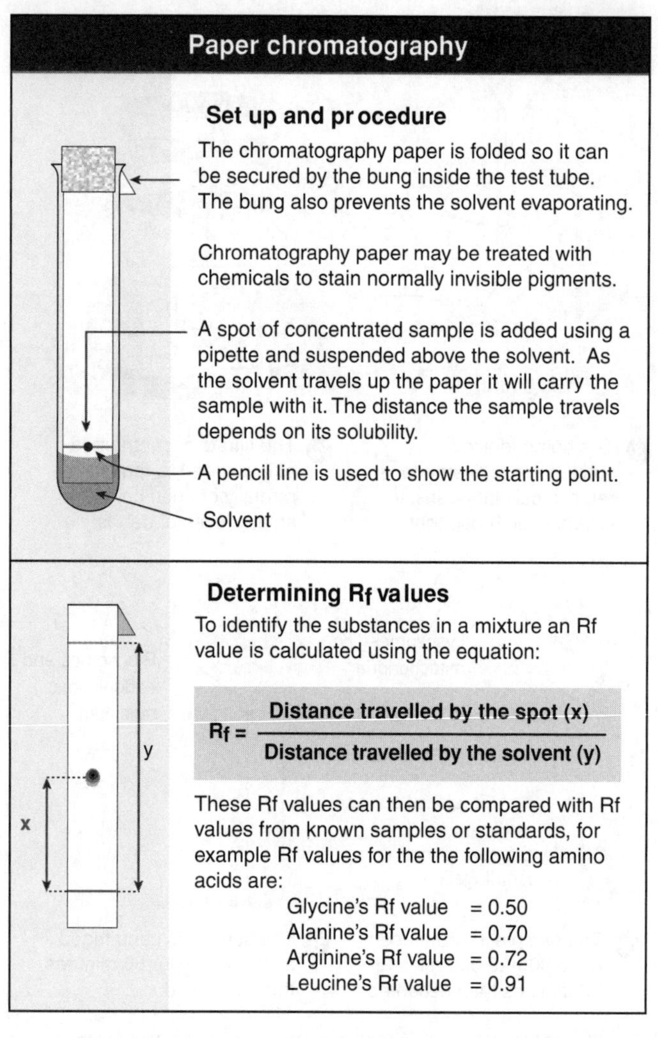

Separation of Photosynthetic Pigments

The four primary pigments of green plants can easily be separated and identified using paper chromatography. The pigments from the leaves are first extracted with acetone before being separated. During paper chromatography the pigments separate out according to differences in their relative solubilities. Two major classes of pigments are detected: the two greenish chlorophyll pigments and two yellowish carotenoid pigments.

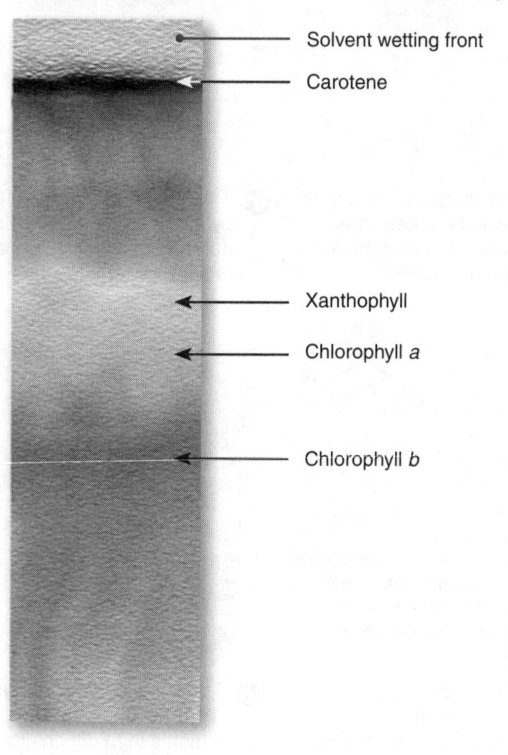

1. Calculate the R_f value for the example given above (show your working): ______

2. Explain why the R_f value of a substance is always less than 1: ______

3. Discuss when it is appropriate to use chromatography instead of a simple food test: ______

4. Predict what would happen if a sample was immersed in the chromatography solvent, instead of suspended above it: ______

5. With reference to their R_f values, rank the four amino acids (listed above) in terms of their solubility: ______

6. Outline why lipids must be mixed in ethanol before they will form an emulsion in water: ______

ISBN: 978-1-877462-96-2

Related activities: *Biochemical Tests*

Gel Electrophoresis

Gel electrophoresis is a method that separates large molecules (including nucleic acids or proteins) on the basis of size, electric charge, and other physical properties. Such molecules possess a slight electric charge (see DNA below). To prepare DNA for gel electrophoresis the DNA is often cut up into smaller pieces. This is done by mixing DNA with restriction enzymes in controlled conditions for about an hour. Called **restriction digestion**, it produces a range of DNA fragments of different lengths. During electrophoresis, molecules are forced to move through the pores of a **gel** (a jelly-like material), when the electrical current is applied. Active electrodes at each end of the gel provide the driving force. The electrical current from one electrode repels the molecules while the other electrode simultaneously attracts the molecules. The frictional force of the gel resists the flow of the molecules, separating them by size. Their rate of migration through the gel depends on the strength of the electric field, size and shape of the molecules, and on the ionic strength and temperature of the buffer in which the molecules are moving. After staining, the separated molecules in each lane can be seen as a series of bands spread from one end of the gel to the other.

Analyzing DNA using Gel Electrophoresis

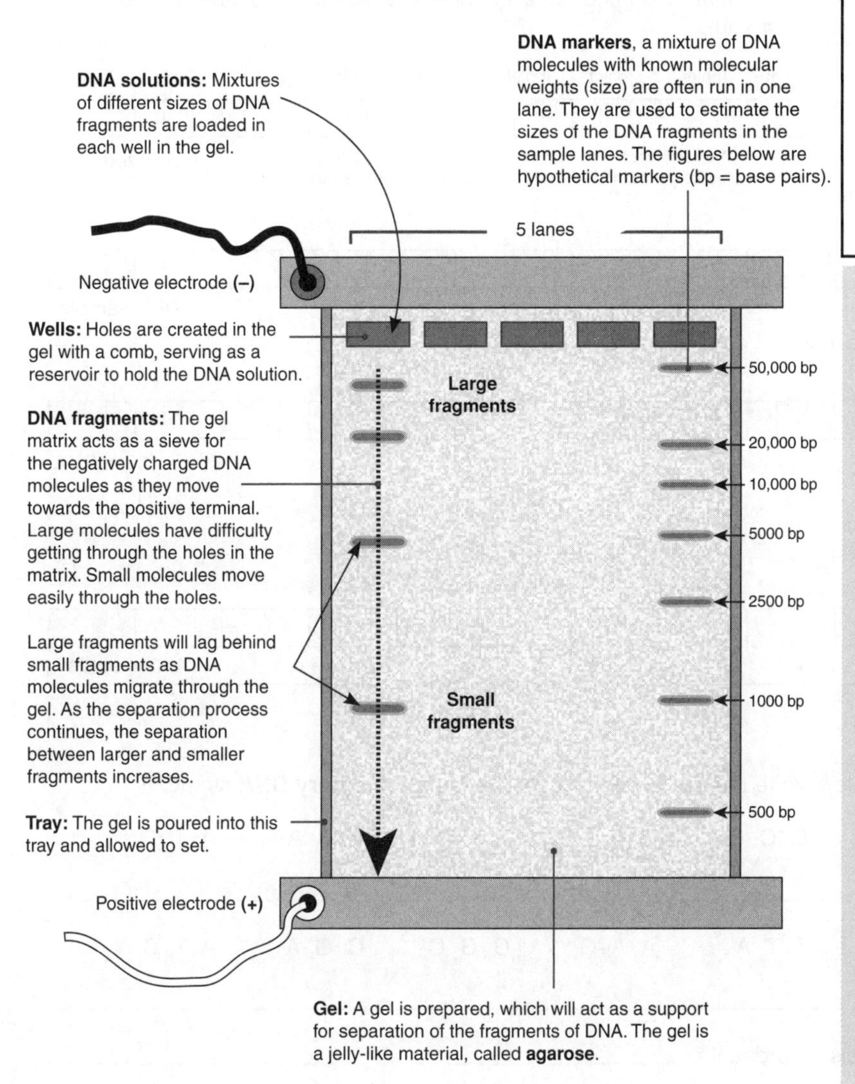

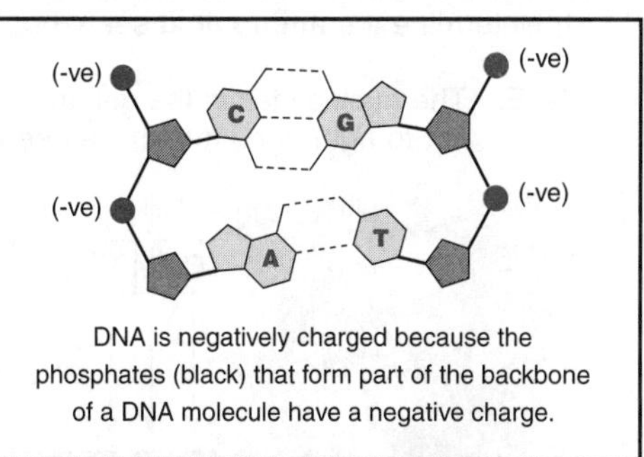

DNA is negatively charged because the phosphates (black) that form part of the backbone of a DNA molecule have a negative charge.

Steps in gel electrophoresis of DNA

1. A tray is prepared to hold the gel matrix.
2. A gel comb is used to create holes in the gel. The gel comb is placed in the tray.
3. Agarose gel powder is mixed with a buffer solution (the liquid used to carry the DNA in a stable form). The solution is heated until dissolved and poured into the tray and allowed to cool.
4. The gel tray is placed in an electrophoresis chamber and the chamber is filled with buffer, covering the gel. This allows the electric current from electrodes at either end of the gel to flow through the gel.
5. DNA samples are mixed with a "loading dye" to make the DNA sample visible. The dye also contains glycerol or sucrose to make the DNA sample heavy so that it will sink to the bottom of the well.
6. A safety cover is placed over the gel, electrodes are attached to a power supply and turned on.
7. When the dye marker has moved through the gel, the current is turned off and the gel is removed from the tray.
8. DNA molecules are made visible by staining the gel with ethidium bromide which binds to DNA and will fluoresce in UV light.

Laboratory Techniques

1. Explain the purpose of gel electrophoresis: ____________________

2. Describe the two forces that control the speed at which fragments pass through the gel:

   (a) ____________________

   (b) ____________________

3. Explain why the smallest fragments travel through the gel the fastest: ____________________

ISBN: 978-1-877462-96-2

Related activities: Analyzing a DNA Sample
Weblinks: DNA Extraction, Gel Electrophoresis

Analyzing a DNA Sample

The nucleotide (base sequence) of a section of DNA can be determined using DNA sequencing techniques (see the modular workbook called *Microbiology and Biotechnology* for a description of this technology). The base sequence determines the amino acid sequence of the resultant protein therefore the DNA tells us what type of protein that gene encodes. This exercise reviews the areas of DNA replication, transcription, and translation using an analysis of a gel electrophoresis column. Remember that the gel pattern represents the sequence in the synthesized strand.

1. Determine the amino acid sequence of a protein from the nucleotide sequence of its DNA, with the following steps:
   (a) Determine the sequence of **synthesized DNA** in the gel
   (b) Convert it to the complementary sequence of the **sample DNA**
   (c) Complete the **mRNA** sequence
   (d) Determine the **amino acid** sequence by using a 'mRNA amino acid table' (consult a reference source).

   NOTE: The nucleotides in the gel are read from bottom to top and the sequence is written in the spaces provided from left to right (the first 4 have been done for you).

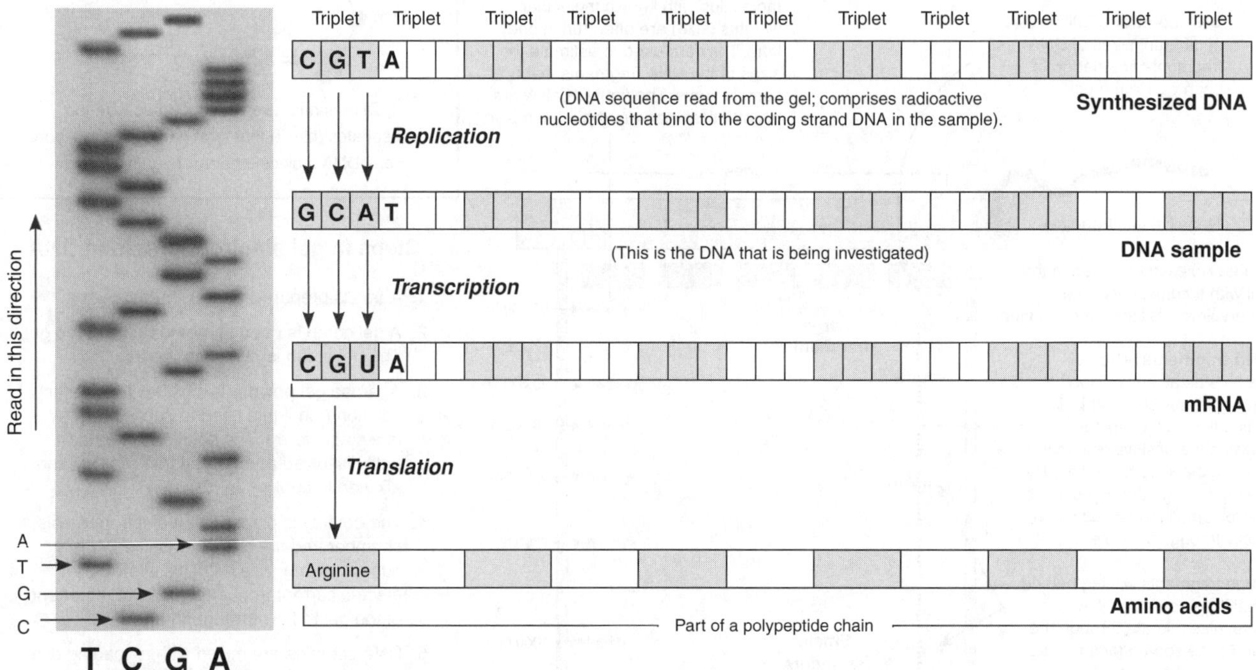

2. For each single strand DNA sequence below, write the base sequence for the **complementary DNA** strand:

   (a) DNA: TAC TAG CCG CGA TTT ACA ATT

   DNA: ______________________

   (b) DNA: TAC GCC TTA AAG GGC CGA ATC

   DNA: ______________________

   (c) Identify the cell process that this exercise represents: ______________________

3. For each single strand DNA sequence below, write the base sequence for the **mRNA** strand and the **amino acid** that it codes for (refer to a mRNA amino acid table to determine the amino acid sequence):

   (a) DNA: TAC TAG CCG CGA TTT ACA ATT

   mRNA: ______________________

   Amino acids: ______________________

   (b) DNA: TAC GCC TTA AAG GGC CGA ATC

   mRNA: ______________________

   Amino acids: ______________________

   (c) Identify the cell process that this exercise represents: ______________________

ISBN: 978-1-877462-96-2

Related activities: Gel Electrophoresis

Plant Tissue Culture

Plant tissue culture, or **micropropagation**, is a method used for cloning plants. It is used widely for the rapid multiplication of commercially important plant species with superior genotypes, as well as for the recovery of endangered plant species. Cloning can rapidly improve plant productivity and quality, and increase resistance to disease, pollutants, and insect pests. However, continued culture of a limited number of cloned varieties can lead to a loss of genetic variation. New genetic stock may be introduced into cloned lines periodically to prevent this happening. Micropropagation is possible because differentiated plant cells have the potential to give rise to all the cells of an adult plant. It has considerable advantages over traditional methods of plant propagation (see table below), but it is very labour intensive. In addition, the optimal conditions for growth and regeneration must be determined and plants propagated in this way may be genetically unstable or infertile, with chromosomes structurally altered or in unusual numbers. The success of tissue culture is affected by factors such as selection of **explant** material, the composition of the culturing media, plant hormone levels, lighting, and temperature.

Advantages of Tissue Culture

- Possible to create large numbers of clones from a single seed or explant.
- Selection of desirable traits is possible directly from the culturing setup (*in vitro*), decreasing the amount of space required for field trials.
- Reproduction of plants is possible without having to wait for the onset of seed production.
- Rapid propagation is possible for species that have long generation times, low levels of seed production, or seeds that do not readily germinate.
- Enables the preservation of pollen and cell collections from which plants may be propagated (like a seed bank).
- Allows the international exchange of sterilised plant materials (eliminating the need for quarantine).
- Helps to eliminate plant diseases through careful stock selection and sterile techniques during propagation.
- Overcomes seasonal restrictions for germination.
- Enables cold storage of large numbers of viable plants in a small space.

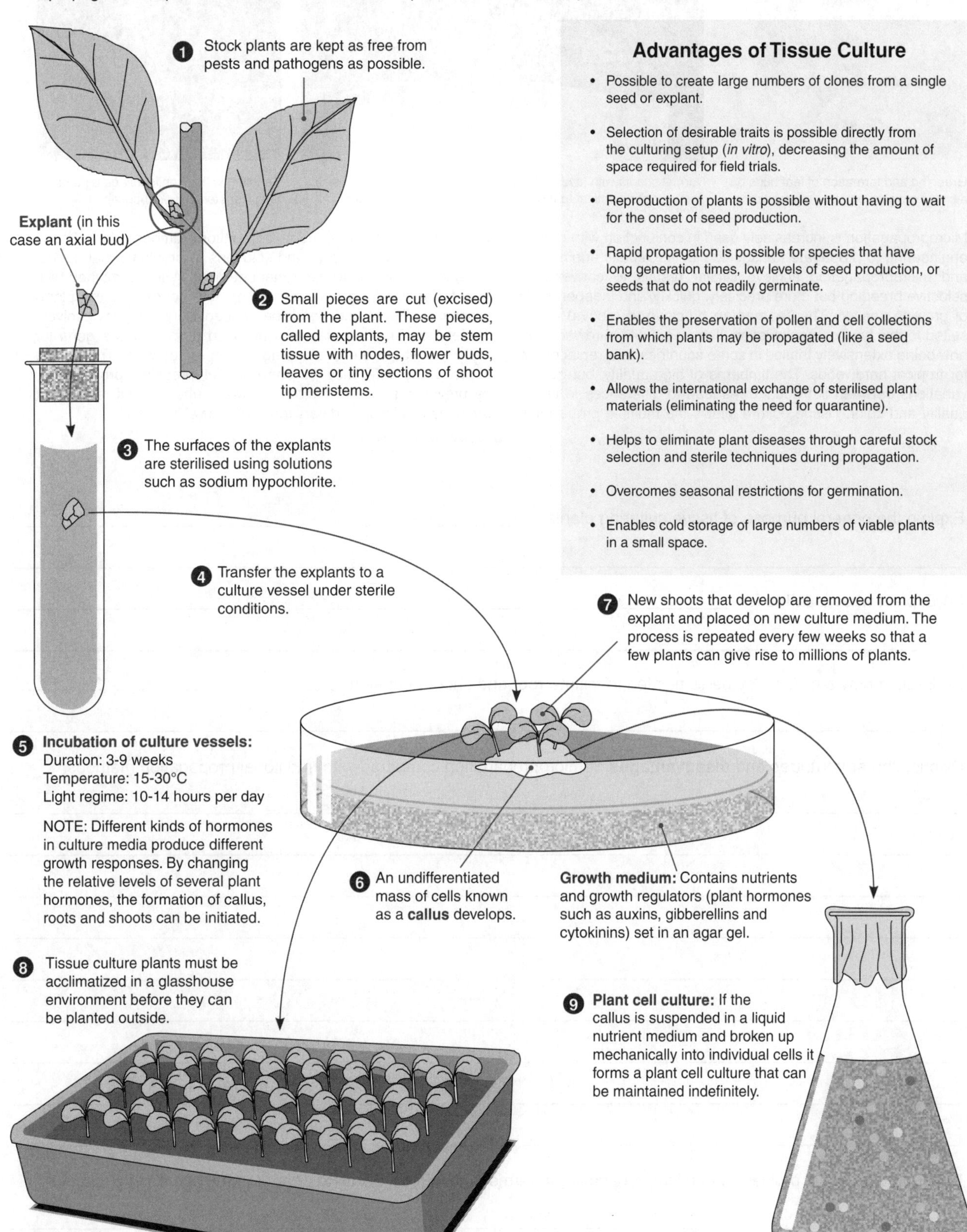

ISBN: 978-1-877462-96-2

Micropropagation of the Tasmanian blackwood tree (*Acacia melanoxylon*)

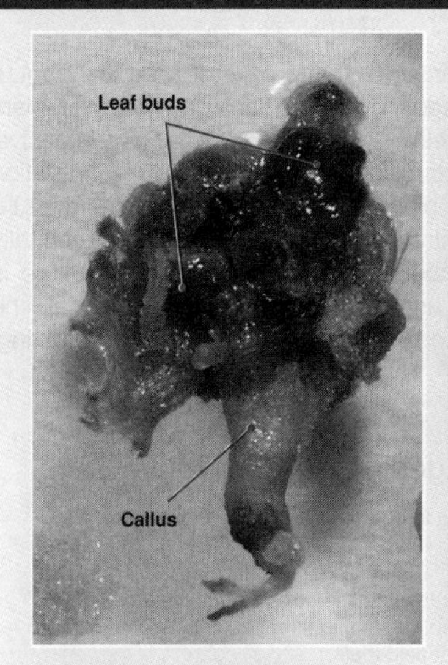

Greening and formation of leaf buds on a callus growing on culturing medium.

Normal shoots with juvenile leaves growing from a callus on media. They appear identical to those produced directly from seeds.

Seedling with juvenile foliage 6 months after transfer to greenhouse.

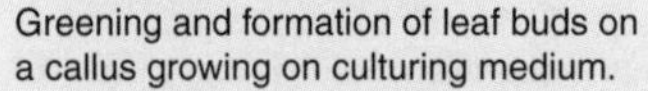

Micropropagation is increasingly used in conjunction with genetic engineering to propagate transgenic plants. Genetic engineering and micropropagation achieve similar results to conventional selective breeding but more precisely, quickly, and independently of growing season. The **Tasmanian blackwood** (above) is well suited to this type of manipulation. It is a versatile hardwood tree now being extensively trialled in some countries as a replacement for tropical hardwoods. The timber is of high quality, but genetic variations between individual trees lead to differences in timber quality and color. Tissue culture allows the multiple propagation of trees with desirable traits (e.g. uniform timber color). Tissue culture could also help to find solutions to problems that cannot be easily solved by forestry management. When combined with genetic engineering (introduction of new genes into the plant) problems of pest and herbicide susceptibility may be resolved. Genetic engineering may also be used to introduce a gene for male sterility, thereby stopping pollen production. This would improve the efficiency of conventional breeding programmes by preventing self-pollination of flowers (the manual removal of stamens is difficult and very labor intensive).

Information courtesy of Raewyn Poole, University of Waikato (Unpublished Msc. thesis).

1. Explain the general purpose of tissue culturing plants: ______________________________

____

2. (a) Explain what a **callus** is: ______________________________

____

(b) Explain how a callus may be stimulated to initiate root and shoot formation: ______________________________

____

3. Discuss the **advantages** and **disadvantages** of micropropagation compared with traditional propagation methods:

____

____

____

____

____

____

____

____

____

4. Describe a potential problem with micropropagation in terms of long term ability to adapt to environmental changes:

____

____

ISBN: 978-1-877462-96-2

Techniques in Microbial Culture

Bacteria and fungi may be cultured in liquid or solid media. These comprise a base of **agar** to which is added the nutrients required for microbial growth. Agar is a gelatinous colloidal extract of red algae, and can be used in solid or liquid form. It is used because of its two unique physical properties. Firstly, it melts at 100°C and remains liquid until cooled to 40°C, at which point it gels. Secondly, few microbes are capable of digesting agar so the medium is not used up during culture. The addition of microbes to an agar plate, or to liquid agar, is called **inoculation** and must be carried out under aseptic conditions. **Aseptic techniques** involve the **sterilization** of equipment and culture media to prevent cross contamination by unwanted microbes. Sterilization is a process by which all organisms and spores are destroyed, either by heat or by chemicals.

Conditions for the Culture of Bacteria and Fungi

Fungi

Temperature: Most fungi have an optimum temperature for growth of 25°C, but most are adapted to survive between 5 and 35°C.

pH: Fungi prefer a neutral (pH 7) growing environment, although most species can tolerate slightly acidic conditions.

Nutrients: Fungi require a source of carbon and nitrogen to produce protein. They also require trace elements such as potassium, phosphorus and magnesium. Growth factors can be added to increase the rate of fungal growth.

Water potential: Fungi are 85-90% water by mass. Water is constantly lost from the hyphae via evaporation and must be replaced through absorption from the media. To aid water uptake, media have a water potential that is less negative than that of the fungal tissue.

Gaseous environment: The majority of fungi are aerobic and very few species can tolerate anaerobic conditions. This is why fungi always grow on the surface of a culture medium, not inside it.

Bacteria

Temperature: Most bacteria cultured in the school laboratory are classified as mesophiles. Mesophiles prefer temperatures between 20 and 40°C.

pH: Most bacteria grow optimally in media with a pH between 6 and 8. Very few bacteria can grow in acidic conditions.

Nutrients: Bacteria need a source of carbon, nitrogen and mineral salts as raw ingredients for cellular growth.

Water potential: All bacteria require water for growth. To prevent cell lysis or dehydration, the water potential of the medium must be such that net water fluxes into and out of the bacterial cell are minimized.

Gaseous environment: Aerobic bacteria will grow only in oxygenated environments, whereas obligate anaerobes (e.g. Clostridium) do not tolerate oxygen. Facultative anaerobes grow under aerobic conditions, but are able to metabolize anaerobically when oxygen is unavailable. All bacterial cultures benefit from a low concentration of carbon dioxide.

Inoculating Solid Media

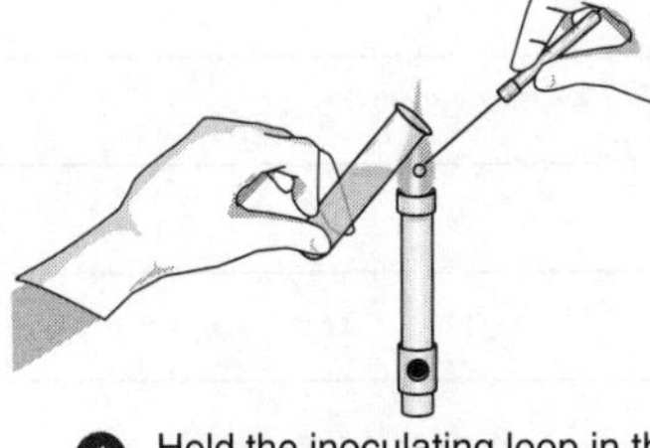

1. Hold the inoculating loop in the flame until it glows red hot. Remove the lid from the culture broth and pass the neck of the bottle through the flame.

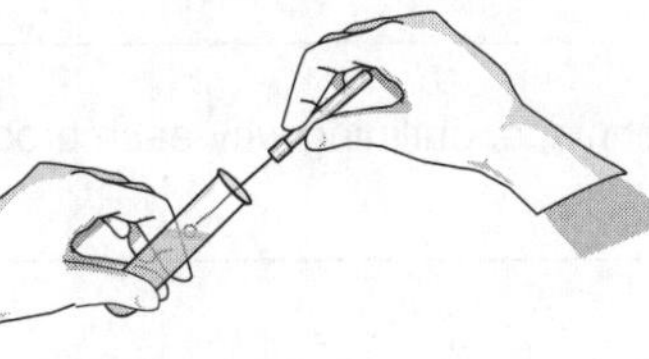

2. Dip the cool inoculating loop into the broth. Flame the neck of the bottle again and replace the lid.

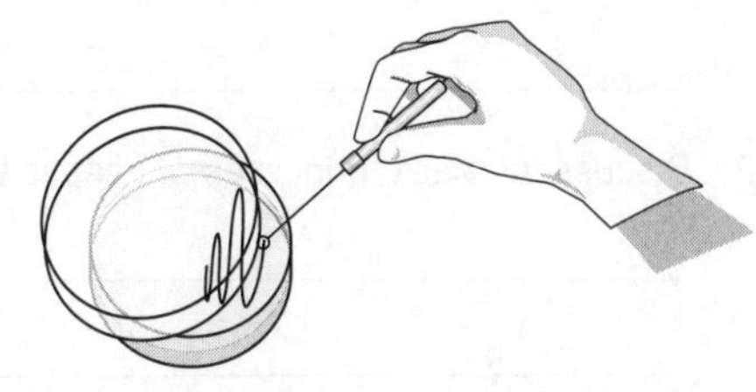

3. Raise the lid of the plate just enough to allow the loop to streak the plate. Streak the surface of the media. Seal the plate with tape and incubate upside down.

1. Explain why inoculated plates must be stored upside down in an incubator: ______

2. Outline the correct procedure for the disposal of microbial plates and cultures: ______

3. Suggest a general method by which you could separate microorganisms through culturing: ______

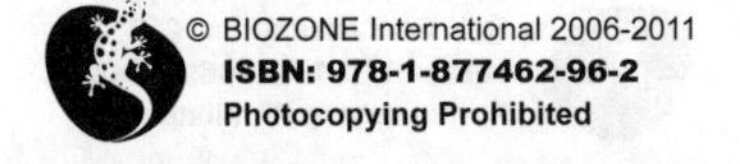

ISBN: 978-1-877462-96-2

Strain Isolation

In nature, bacteria exist as mixed populations. However, in order to study them in the laboratory they must exist as pure cultures (i.e. cultures in which all organisms are descendants of the same organism or clones). The most common way of separating bacterial cells on the agar surface is the **streak plate method**. This provides a simple and rapid method of diluting the sample by mechanical means. As the loop is streaked across the agar surface, more and more bacteria are rubbed off until individual separated organisms are deposited on the agar. After incubation, the area at the beginning of the streak pattern will show **confluent** growth (growth as a continuous sheet), while the area near the end of the pattern should show discrete colonies. Isolated colonies can then be removed from the streak plate using aseptic techniques, and transferred to new sterile medium. After incubation, all organisms in the new culture will be descendants of the same organism (i.e. a pure culture).

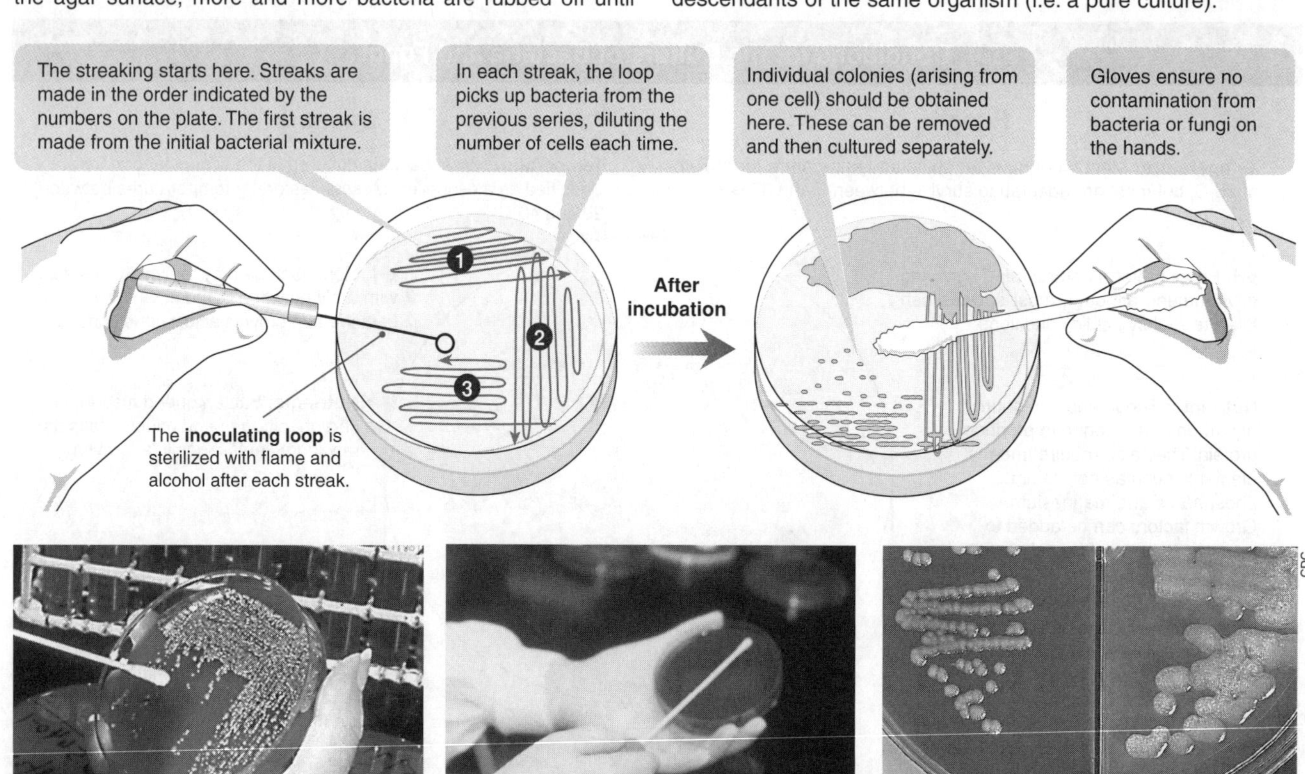

When approximately 10 to 100 million bacterial cells are present, colonies become visible. Note the well-isolated colonies in the photo above. A single colony may be removed for further investigation.

A swab containing a single strain of bacteria is used to inoculate additional nutrient plates to produce pure cultures of bacteria (clones

To test purity, a sample of a culture can be grown on a selective medium that promotes the growth of a single species. The photo above shows a positive encapsulation test for *Bacillus anthracis*.

1. Explain the basis by which bacteria are isolated using streak plating: ______________________________

____

2. Discuss the basic principles of aseptic technique, outlining why each procedure is necessary: ______________

____

____

____

____

3. Comment on the importance of aseptic (sterile) technique in streak plating: ______________________________

____

____

4. State how many bacterial cells must be present on the plate before the colony becomes visible to the naked eye:

____

5. Outline when it might be necessary to use **selective media** to culture bacteria: ______________________________

____

Related activities: *Techniques in Microbial Culture*
Weblinks: *Streak Plate Procedure*

Periodicals:
Haemocytometers and dilution plating

ISBN: 978-1-877462-96-2

Serial Dilution

The growth of microorganisms in culture can be measured in a number of ways. Some indirect methods measure culture dry weight or turbidity, both of which are often directly proportional to cell density. More commonly used are methods that directly or indirectly count the number of cells in a culture. Microbial populations are often very large, so most counting methods rely on counting a very small sample of the culture. A commonly used indirect method is serial dilution followed by plate counts (below). If care is taken with the serial dilution, this method can provide a relatively accurate estimate of culture density.

Measuring Microbial Growth Using Serial Dilution

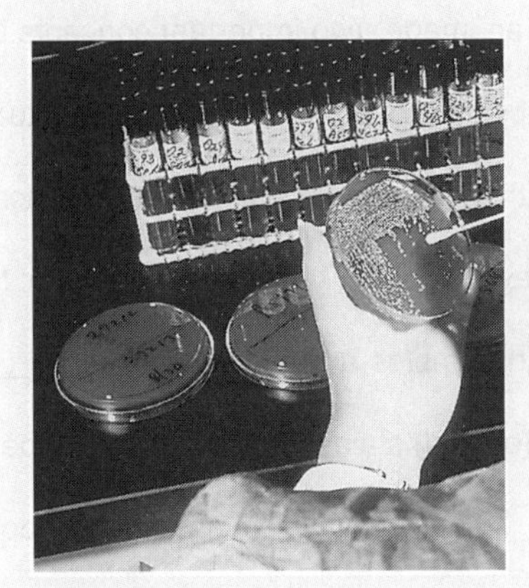

Serial dilution can be performed at different stages during the culture growth. By making a series of dilutions and then counting the colonies that arise after plating, the density of the original inoculum (starting culture) can be calculated. Colonies should be well separated and the number of colonies counted should ideally be neither too small nor too large (about 15-30 is good).

CALCULATION: No. of colonies on plate X reciprocal of sample dilution = no. of bacteria per cm^3.

EXAMPLE: *28 colonies on a plate of 1/1000 dilution, then the original culture contained:*
28 x 1000 = 28 x 103 cm^{-3} bacterial cells

Plate counts are widely used in microbiology. It is a useful technique because only the viable colonies are counted, but it requires some incubation time before colonies form. For quality control purposes in some food industries where the food product is perishable (e.g. milk processing) this time delay is unacceptable and direct methods (e.g. cell counts using oil immersion microscopy) are used.

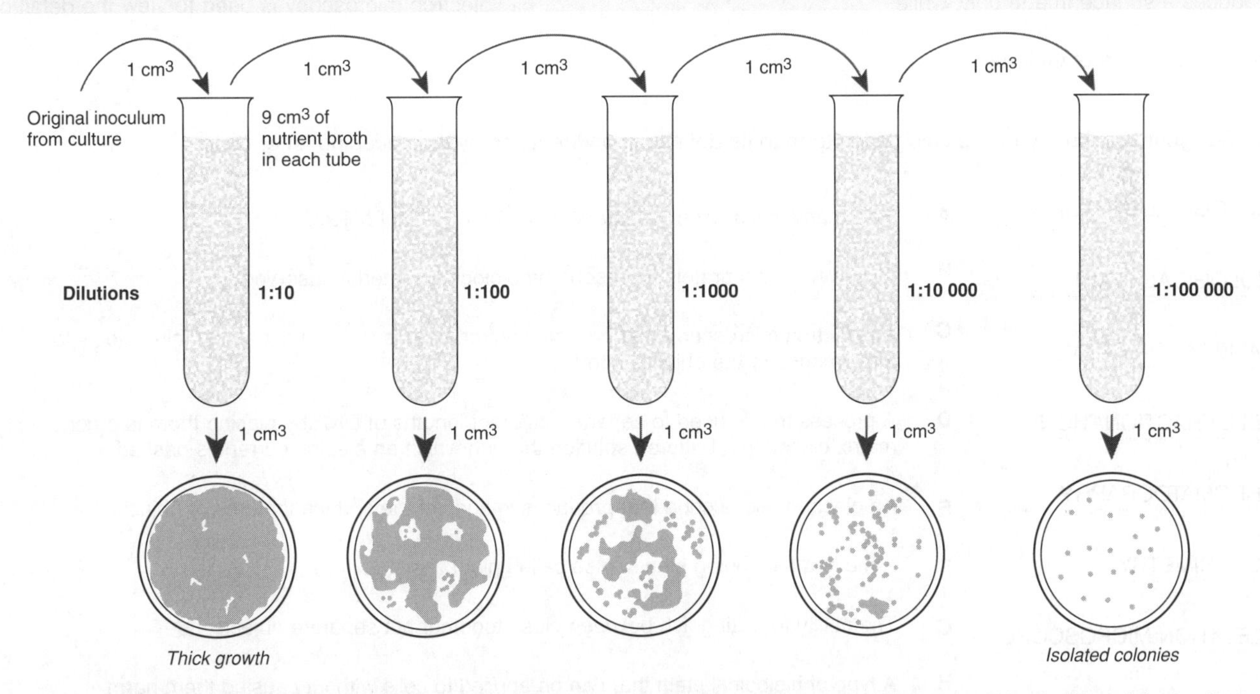

1. In the example of serial dilution above, use the equation provided to calculate the cell concentration in the original culture:

____

2. (a) Explain the term **viable count**: ____

____

(b) Explain why dilution plating is a useful technique for obtaining a viable count: ____

____

____

(c) Investigate an alternative technique, such as turbidimetry and identify how the technique differs from dilution plating:

____

____

____

____

ISBN: 978-1-877462-96-2

Periodicals: *Haemocytometers and dilution plating*

Related activities: *Techniques in Microbial Culture, Strain Isolation*

Comprehension and Vocabulary

1. The following paragraph summarizes some of the concepts about the techniques used in microscopy that have been discussed in this chapter. Use the key terms below to fill in the spaces to complete the paragraph.
(*light, scanning, stains, viable, transmission, visible, magnification, resolution, non-viable, electrons, microscopy)*

_ _ _ _ _ _ _ _ _ _ is the field of science that uses microscopes to view objects in greater detail than can be seen with the naked eye. Optical (_ _ _ _ _) microscopes use reflected light to produce an image. Two important concepts in microscopy are _ _ _ _ _ _ _ _ _ _ _ _ _ (how many times larger an object appears compared to its actual size), and _ _ _ _ _ _ _ _ _ _ (the ability to distinguish between close together but separate objects). Biological _ _ _ _ _ _ and dyes are often added to microscopy samples to enhance the level of detail that can be seen, or to make specific components more _ _ _ _ _ _ _ . Most stains are used on dead samples and are called _ _ _-_ _ _ _ _ _ stains. Stains that do not harm a sample are called _ _ _ _ _ _ (or vital) stains. Electron microscopes use a beam of _ _ _ _ _ _ _ _ _ to produce very high resolution images. _ _ _ _ _ _ _ _ electron microscopy produces a surface image only, while _ _ _ _ _ _ _ _ _ _ _ _ electron microscopy is used to view the detail of very thin sections of material.

2. Test your vocabulary by matching each term to its definition, as identified by its preceding letter code.

BIOLOGICAL DRAWING ....

BIOLOGICAL STAIN ....

CALIBRATION CURVE ....

CELL FRACTIONATION ....

CHROMATOGRAPHY ....

COLORIMETRY ....

ELECTRON MICROSCOPE ....

GEL ELECTROPHORESIS ....

MAGNIFICATION ....

MICROPROPAGATION ....

OPTICAL MICROSCOPE ....

RESOLUTION ....

SEM ....

SERIAL DILUTION ....

TEM ....

VIABLE STAIN ....

A How many times larger an image is than the original object.

B A drawing to accurately represent the biological material observed.

C An electron microscope that passes electron beams through extremely thin objects to form images of the object's interior.

D A process that is used to separate different lengths of DNA by placing them in a gel matrix placed in a buffered solution through which an electric current is passed.

E An electron microscope that produces images of the surface features of objects.

F A method for cloning plants. Also called plant tissue culture.

G The ability to distinguish between close together but separate objects.

H A type of biological stain that can be applied to cells without causing them harm.

I The separation of organelles in a solution using differential centrifugation.

J A method for determining concentration of a solution on the basis of the density of a color change.

K An advanced microscope that uses electron beams to produce high resolution images.

L A technique that separates the compounds in a mixture on the basis of their chemistry or physical characteristics.

M A type of microscope that uses lenses to focus light waves passing through an object into an image.

N A chemical that binds to specific parts of the cell to make them more visible.

O The stepwise dilution of a substance in solution.

P A curve produced using a set of standard samples of known concentrations, which is then used to determine the concentration of an unknown sample.

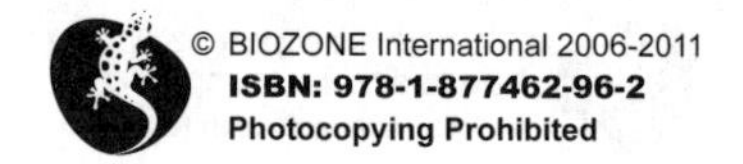

ISBN: 978-1-877462-96-2

Appendix A

PERIODICAL REFERENCES

ASKING QUESTIONS FINDING ANSWERS

► **The Truth Is Out There**
New Scientist, 26 February 2000 (Inside Science). *The philosophy of scientific method: starting with an idea, formulating a hypothesis, and following the process to theory.*

► **Descriptive Statistics**
Biol. Sci. Rev., 13(5) May 2001, pp. 36-37. *An account of descriptive statistics using text, tables and graphs.*

► **Experiments**
Biol. Sci. Rev., 14(3) February 2002, pp. 11-13. *The basics of experimental design and execution: determining variables, measuring them, and establishing a control.*

► **Be Confident with Calculations**
Biol. Sci. Rev., 23(2) Nov. 2010, pp. 13-15. *How to use some commonly used calculations in biology. Includes percentages, rates, and magnification.*

► **Dealing with Data**
Biol. Sci. Rev., 12 (4) March 2000, pp. 6-8. *A short account of the best ways in which to deal with the interpretation of graphically presented data in examinations.*

► **Estimating the Mean and Standard Deviation**
Biol. Sci. Rev., 13(3) January 2001, pp. 40-41. *Simple statistical analysis. Includes formulae for calculating sample mean and standard deviation.*

► **Percentages**
Biol. Sci. Rev., 17(2) November 2004, pp. 28-29. *The calculation of percentage and the appropriate uses of this important transformation.*

► **Drawing Graphs**
Biol. Sci. Rev., 19(3) February 2007, pp. 10-13. *A guide to creating graphs. The use of different graphs for different tasks is explained and there are a number of pertinent examples described to illustrate points.*

ANALYSIS AND REPORTING

► **Describing the Normal Distribution**
Biol. Sci. Rev., 13(2) November 2000, pp. 40-41. *The normal distribution: data spread, mean, median, variance, and standard deviation.*

► **Estimating the Mean and Standard Deviation**
Biol. Sci. Rev., 13(3) January 2001, pp. 40-41. *Simple statistical analysis. Includes formulae for calculating sample mean and standard deviation.*

► **The Variability of Samples**
Biol. Sci. Rev., 13(4) March 2001, pp. 34-35. *The variability of sample data and the use of sample statistics as estimators for population parameters.*

FIELD STUDIES

► **Fieldwork - Sampling Plants**
Biol. Sci. Rev., 10(5) May 1998, pp. 6-8. *Methodology for sampling plant communities. Includes thorough coverage of quadrat use.*

► **Fieldwork - Sampling Animals**
Biol. Sci. Rev., 10(4) March 1998, pp. 23-25. *Excellent article covering the appropriate methodology for collecting different types of animals in the field. Includes a synopsis of the mark and recapture technique.*

► **Bowels of the Beast**
New Scientist, 22 August 1998, pp. 36-39. *Analyses of the faeces of animals can reveal much about the make-up, size, and genetic diversity of a population.*

► **Bird Ringing**
Biol. Sci. Rev., 14(3), February 2002, pp. 14-19. *Techniques used in investigating populations of highly mobile organisms: mark and recapture, ringing, and using diversity indices.*

► **Drawing Graphs**
Biol. Sci. Rev., 19(3) February 2007, pp. 10-13. *A guide to creating graphs. The use of different graphs for different tasks is explained and there are a number of pertinent examples described to illustrate points.*

► **Descriptive Statistics**
Biol. Sci. Rev., 13(5) May 2001, pp. 36-37. *An account of descriptive statistics using text, tables and graphs.*

CLASSIFICATION OF ORGANISMS

► **What is a Species?**
Scientific American June 2008, pp. 48-55. *The science of classification; modern and traditional approaches, and the importance of taxonomy to identifying and recognising diversity.*

► **Uprooting the Tree of Life**
Scientific American Feb. 2000, pp. 72-77. *Using molecular techniques to redefine phylogeny and divulge the path of evolution.*

► **A Passion for Order**
National Geographic, 211(6) June 2007, pp. 73-87. *The history of Carl Linnaeus and the classification of plant species.*

► **The Loves of the Plants**
Scientific American, February 1996, pp. 98-103. *The classification of plants and the development of keys to plant identification.*

► **World Flowers Bloom after Recount**
New Scientist, 29 June 2002, p. 11. *A systematic study of flowering plants indicates more species than expected, especially in regions of high biodiversity such as South American and Asia.*

► **The Family Line - The Human-Cat Connection**
National Geographic, 191(6) June 1997, pp. 77-85. *An examination of the genetic diversity and lineages within the felidae. A good context within which to study classification.*

LABORATORY TECHNIQUES

► **Light Microscopy**
Biol. Sci. Rev., 13(1) September 2000, pp. 36-38. *An excellent account of the basis and various techniques of light microscopy.*

► **Size Does Matter!**
Biol. Sci. Rev., 17 (3) February 2005, pp. 10-13. *Measuring the size of organisms and calculating magnification and scale.*

► **Transmission Electron Microscopy**
Biol. Sci. Rev., 19(4) April 2007, pp. 6-9. *An account of the techniques and applications of TEM. Includes an excellent diagram comparing features of TEM and light microscopy.*

► **Scanning Electron Microscopy**
Biol. Sci. Rev., 13(3) January 2001, pp. 6-9. *An account of the techniques and applications of SEM. Includes details of specimen preparation and recent advancements in the technology.*

► **The Power Behind an Electron Microscopist**
Biol. Sci. Rev., 18(1) September 2005, pp. 16-20. *The use of TEMs to obtain greater resolution of finer details than is possible from optical microscopes.*

► **Haemocytometers and Dilution Plating**
Biol. Sci. Rev., 15(1) September 2002, pp. 14-17. *An article covering a number of fundamental microbiological techniques including serial dilution, dilution plating, aseptic technique, and viable counts.*

Appendix B

TERMS AND NOTATION

The definitions for some commonly encountered terms related to making biological investigations are provided below. Use these as you would use a biology dictionary when planning your investigation and writing up your report. It is important to be consistent with the use of terms i.e. use the same term for the same procedure or unit throughout your study. Be sure, when using a term with a specific statistical meaning, such as sample, that you are using the term correctly.

General Terms

Data: Facts collected for analysis.

Qualitative: Not quantitative. Described in words or terms rather than by numbers. Includes subjective descriptions in terms of variables such as color or shape.

Quantitative: Able to be expressed in numbers. Numerical values derived from counts or measurements.

The Design of Investigations

Hypothesis: A tentative explanation of an observation, capable of being tested by experimentation. Hypotheses are written as clear statements, not as questions.

Control treatment (control): A standard (reference) treatment that helps to ensure that responses to other treatments can be reliably interpreted. There may be more than one control in an investigation.

Dependent variable: A variable whose values are determined by another variable (the independent variable). In practice, the dependent variable is the variable representing the biological response.

Independent variable: A variable whose values are set, or systematically altered, by the investigator.

Controlled variables: Variables that may take on different values in different situations, but are controlled (fixed) as part of the design of the investigation.

Experiment: A contrived situation designed to test (one or more) hypotheses and their predictions. It is good practice to use sample sizes that are as large as possible for experiments.

Investigation: A very broad term applied to scientific studies; investigations may be controlled experiments or field based studies involving population sampling.

Parameter: A numerical value that describes a characteristic of a population (e.g. the mean height of all 17 year-old males).

Prediction: The prediction of the response (Y) variable on the basis of changes in the independent (X) variable.

Random sample: A method of choosing a sample from a population that avoids any subjective element. It is the equivalent to drawing numbers out of a hat, but using random number tables. For field based studies involving quadrats or transects, random numbers can be used to determine the positioning of the sampling unit.

Repeat / Trial: The entire investigation is carried out again at a different time. This ensures that the results are reproducible. Note that repeats or trials are not **replicates** in the true sense unless they are run at the same time.

Replicate: A duplication of the entire experimental design run at the same time.

Sample: A sub-set of a whole used to estimate the values that might have been obtained if every individual or response was measured. A sample is made up of **sampling units**, In lab based investigations, the sampling unit might be a test-tube, while in field based studies, the sampling unit might be an individual organism or a quadrat.

Sample size (*n*): The number of samples taken. In a field study, a typical sample size may involve 20-50 individuals or 20 quadrats. In a lab based investigation, a typical sample size may be two to three sampling units, e.g. two test-tubes held at 10°C.

Sampling unit: Sampling units make up the sample size. Examples of sampling units in different investigations are an individual organism, a test tube undergoing a particular treatment, an area (e.g. quadrat size), or a volume. The size of the sampling unit is an important consideration in studies where the area or volume of a habitat is being sampled.

Statistic: An estimate of a parameter obtained from a sample (e.g. the mean height of all 17 year-old males in your class). A precise (reliable) statistic will be close to the value of the parameter being estimated.

Treatments: Well defined conditions applied to the sample units. The response of sample units to a treatment is intended to shed light on the hypothesis under investigation. What is often of most interest is the comparison of the responses to different treatments.

Variable: A factor in an experiment that is subject to change. Variables may be controlled (fixed), manipulated (systematically altered), or represent a biological response.

Precision and Significance

Accuracy: The correctness of the measurement (the closeness of the measured value to the true value). Accuracy is often a function of the calibration of the instrument used for measuring.

Measurement errors: When measuring or setting the value of a variable, there may be some difference between your answer and the 'right' answer. These errors are often as a result of poor technique or poorly set up equipment.

Objective measurement: Measurement not significantly involving subjective (or personal) judgment. If a second person repeats the measurement they should get the same answer.

Precision (of a measurement): The repeatability of the measurement. As there is usually no reason to suspect that a piece of equipment is giving inaccurate measures, making precise measurements is usually the most important consideration. You can assess or quantify the precision of any measurement system by taking repeated measurements from individual samples.

Precision (of a statistic): How close the statistic is to the value of the parameter being estimated. Also called **reliability**.

The Expression of Units

The value of a variable must be written with its units where possible. Common ways of recording measurements in biology are: volume in liters, mass in grams, length in meters, time in seconds. The following example shows different ways to express the same term. Note that ml and cm^3 are equivalent.

Oxygen consumption (milliliters per gram per hour)
Oxygen consumption ($ml g^{-1} h^{-1}$) or ($mL g^{-1} h^{-1}$)
Oxygen consumption (ml/g/h) or (mL/g/h)
Oxygen consumption/$cm^3 g^{-1} h^{-1}$

Statistical significance: An assigned value that is used to establish the probability that an observed trend or difference represents a true difference that is not due to chance alone. If a level of significance is less than the chosen value (usually 1-10%), the difference is regarded as statistically significant. Remember that in rigorous science, it is the hypothesis of no difference or no effect (the null hypothesis, H_0) that is tested. The alternative hypothesis (your tentative explanation for an observation) can only be accepted through statistical rejection of H_0.

Validity: Whether or not you are truly measuring the right thing.

Appendix C

CALCULATIONS, CONVERSIONS, AND MULTIPLES

Carrying out calculations:

When answering computational questions, it is important to show all the working associated with calculating the answer. Some examples of the calculations and conversions you may encounter are described below.

1. Converting between multiples:

(a) Convert the following to kilometers:

(i) 5 millimeters: 5 mm = 0.000 005 km = 5×10^{-6} km.

(ii) 10 000 centimeters: 10 000 cm = 0.1 km.

(iii) 8000 meters: 8000 m = 8 km.

(b) Convert 12 ms^{-1} to $kmhr^{-1}$: $12 \times 60 \times 60$ = 43 200 mhr^{-1}. 43 200/1000 = 43.2 $kmhr^{-1}$.

2. Sampling:

(a) A study of a bear population discovers that there were 5 bears living within a 4 km^2 area of a forest:

(i) Calculate the total population if the forest is 100 km^2.
5/4 = 1.25 bears per 1 km^2. 1.25×100 = 125 bears.

(ii) It is estimated that the bear population may be 20% larger than the sample suggests. Calculate the new population: 125 + (125 × 0.20) = 150 bears.

(iii) It is estimated that the population has an annual growth rate of 1.3 percent. Calculate the bear population in a further five years:
$Pop_{future\ bears} = Pop_{present\ bears} \times (1 + 0.013)^5 = 150 \times (1.013)^5$ = 160 bears in 5 years time.

(b) A coal deposit is estimated at 2000 tonnes (t). If the coal is extracted at a rate of 30 thr^{-1} calculate how long the deposit will last: 2000/30 = 66.67 hours.

3. Reading off a graph:

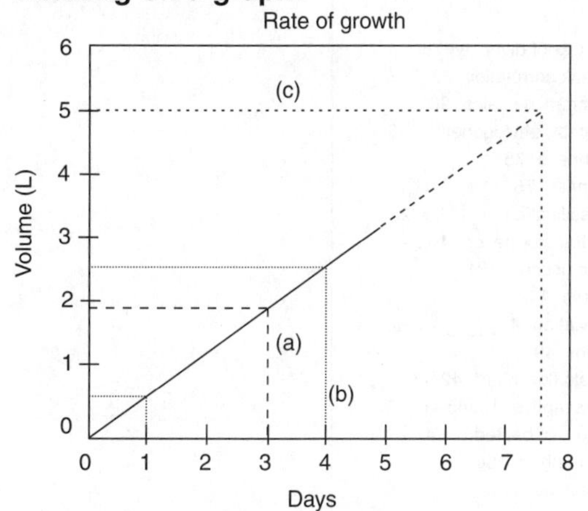

(a) State the volume after 3 days: 1.95 L

(b) Calculate the rate of growth per day:
Day 1 = 0.5 L. Day 4 = 2.5 L. Change = 2.5-0.5 = 2.0 over 3 days. 2.0/3 = 0.667 L per day.

(c) Extrapolate the graph to determine how long it will take to reach a volume of 5 L: 7.55-7.65 days. (confirm from calculation 5/0.667 = 7.5).

INTERNATIONAL SYSTEM OF UNITS (SI)

Examples of SI derived units

DERIVED QUANTITY	NAME	SYMBOL
area	square meter	m^2
volume	cubic meter	m^3
speed, velocity	meter per second	ms^{-1}
acceleration	meter per second squared	ms^{-2}
mass density	kilogram per cubic meter	kgm^{-3}
specific volume	cubic meter per kilogram	m^3kg^{-1}
amount-of-substance/ concentration	mole per cubic meter mole per liter	$molm^{-3}$ $molL^{-1}$
luminance	candela per square meter	cdm^{-2}

MULTIPLES

MULTIPLE	PREFIX	SYMBOL	EXAMPLE
10^9	giga	G	gigawatt (GW)
10^6	mega	M	megawatt (MW)
10^3	kilo	k	kilogram (kg)
10^2	hecto	h	hectare (ha)
10^{-1}	deci	d	decimeter (dm)
10^{-2}	centi	c	centimeter (cm)
10^{-3}	milli	m	milliimeter (mm)
10^{-6}	micro	µ	microsecond (µs)
10^{-9}	nano	n	nanometer (nm)
10^{-12}	pico	p	picosecond (ps)

CONVERSION FACTORS FOR COMMON UNITS OF MEASURE

For all conversions multiply by the factor shown

LENGTH	
Centimeters to inches:	0.393
Meters to feet:	3.280
Kilometers to miles:	0.621
VOLUME	
Milliliters to fluid ounces:	0.034
Liters to gallons:	0.264
Cubic meters to gallons:	264.1
AREA	
Square meters to square feet:	10.76
Hectares to acres:	2.471
Square kilometers to square miles	0.386
TEMPERATURE	
°C to °F:	0 °C = 32 °F 100 °C = 212 °F
Formula °C to °F:	°F = °C x 1.8 + 32

Index